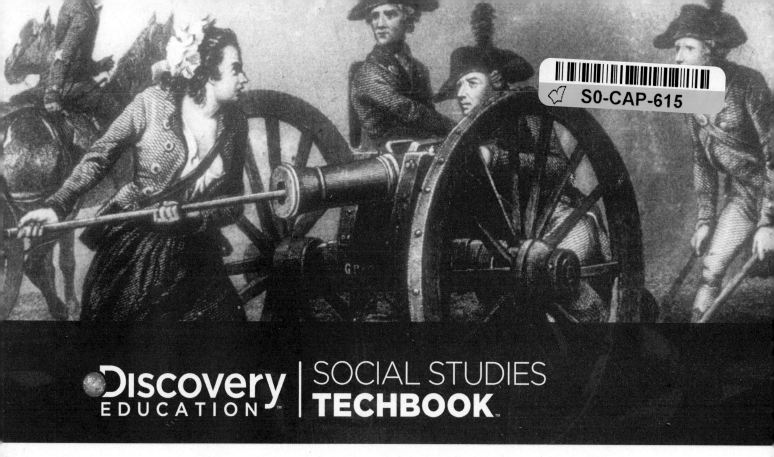

Discovery EDUCATION™ | SOCIAL STUDIES **TECHBOOK**™

UNITED STATES HISTORY

CALIFORNIA EDITION

Log in to Discovery Education
Social Studies Techbook
at DiscoveryEducation.com

ISBN 13: 978-1-68220-237-1

Printed in the United States of America.

8 9 CWR 23 22　　B

800-323-9084
4350 Congress Street, Suite 700, Charlotte, NC 28209
©2017 Discovery Education. All rights reserved.

Table of Contents

UNIT 2 | Becoming an Independent Nation (1776 to 1800)

Chapter 4 | *Establishing a New Government*

CONCEPTS

Chapter 5 | *Leaders and Challenges of a New Nation*

CONCEPTS

UNIT 3 | A Nation Expands (1790 to 1860)

Chapter 6 | *Building a New National Identity*

CONCEPTS

Chapter 7 | *New Horizons*

CONCEPTS

Chapter 8 | *Industrial Expansion and Reform*

CONCEPTS

UNIT 4 | A Nation Divided (1820 to 1877)

Chapter 9 | *Slavery and the Civil War*

CONCEPTS

Chapter 10 | *Reconstruction*

CONCEPTS

UNIT 5 | Dawn of the American Century (1878 to 1913)

Chapter 11 | *A Country Transformed*

CONCEPTS

Chapter 12 | *Conflict in the Gilded Age*

CONCEPTS

Letter to the Student

Dear Student,

Welcome to United States History! You're about to begin an exciting journey into the world of Social Studies. There's more to U.S. history than you might think. You will learn about colonial America, the American Revolution, the government of the early United States, the Civil War, Reconstruction, and the Progressive Era from many perspectives. Then, you will use what you have learned to analyze and understand historical issues and propose solutions.

This resource is designed to draw on your reading and writing skills and to prepare you for college, a career, and civic life.

Each lesson in this course is called a concept. Each concept has an Essential Question to guide your investigation of the main topic. The different tabs guide you through the lesson.

- ENGAGE: What do I know about this topic? What do I want to learn? Make connections between past and present learning as you dive into the concept.

- EXPLORE: Interact with text and multimedia as you explore key people, places, and events.

- EXPLAIN: Describe what you learned about the concept's topics and submit your answers online.

- ELABORATE: Examine primary sources, analyze complex problems, and complete activities to go deeper into the concept.

- EVALUATE: Review the concept's information with flashcards, quizzes, and writing assignments that help you express your position on critical topics.

Get ready to learn about the people, places, and ideas that have built and shaped the United States!

The Discovery Education Team

Keep this workbook handy as you explore the digital Techbook:
- **FLASHCARDS** for reviewing each concept's essential information
- **GRAPHIC ORGANIZERS** for taking notes on the Core Interactive Text
- **FOCUS QUESTIONS** for working through each concept
- **QR CODES** for connecting to Techbook pages and activities

Discovery Education
Digital Connections

 Core Interactive Text: Explore an exciting combination of videos, photographs, audio recordings, interactive maps, and activities. A variety of reading tools, including highlighting, taking notes, two different text levels, text-to-speech, and Spanish translations will help you understand the text.

 Techbook Atlas: Use this interactive map to explore the human and physical geography of Earth with different overlays and base maps.

 Reference: View the definition and related media for key words and phrases.

 Global News: Watch exclusive videos that summarize the week's most pressing global news, through a Discovery Education partnership with trusted news leader MacNeil/Lehrer Productions.

 Online Entry: Submit your answers online for EXPLAIN activities, and be sure to check the evaluation criteria or rubric before you do.

 Interactive Investigations: Found on the ELABORATE tab and other places, these activities challenge you to make critical decisions and study change over time through analyzing people, data, and places.

 Board Builder: Use images and text to create presentations with this handy tool.

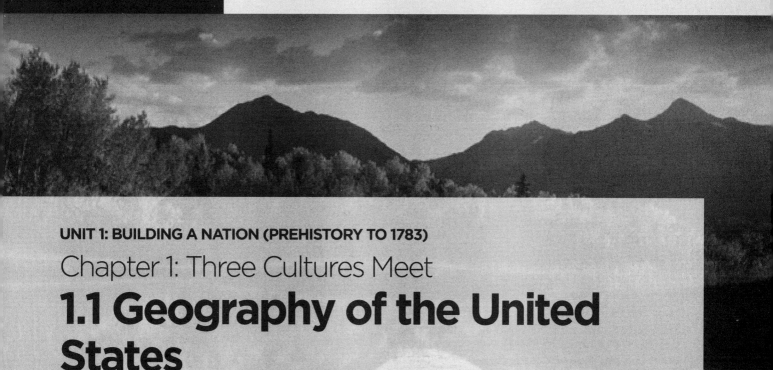

photo: Getty Images

UNIT 1: BUILDING A NATION (PREHISTORY TO 1783)

Chapter 1: Three Cultures Meet

1.1 Geography of the United States

LESSON OVERVIEW

Lesson Objectives:

By the end of this lesson, you should be able to:

- Analyze and compare contemporary and historical regions of the United States on the basis of physical characteristics, such as landforms, bodies of water, climate, and vegetation; and human characteristics, such as language, religion, economic activities, and political system.

Lesson Essential Question:

What are the most important geographic characteristics of the United States?

Key Vocabulary

Appalachian Mountains, Arctic, arid, Basin and Range, biome, Canadian Shield, Central Plains, climate, climate region, Coastal Range, cultural region, culture, deciduous forest, desert, East, ecosystem, elevation, grasslands, Great Lakes, Great Plains, Gulf and Atlantic Coastal Plains, habitat, highland, humid continental, humid subtropical, Kansas, landform, Louisiana Territory, Maine, marine west coast, Mediterranean Sea, Mexico, Nebraska, New Mexico, nomadic, Northwest, Oklahoma (Indian Territory), Oregon Territory, Oregon Trail, Ozark Plateau, Pacific Northwest, plain, plateau, prairie, precipitation, region, Rocky Mountains, Santa Fe Trail, semiarid, Southwest, temperate zone, Texas, Washington, DC

FLASHCARDS

1 ▸ Climate, Landforms, and Biomes

A region is an area that shares certain characteristics that distinguish it from other areas. Humans organize places into regions to categorize places and generalize about them.

- **The United States can be divided into different regions based on climate. The major climate regions are**
  - **Humid continental**
  - **Humid subtropical**
  - **Arid**
  - **Semiarid**
  - **Highland**
  - **Mediterranean**
  - **Marine west coast**
- **The United States can be divided into different regions based on landforms. The major landform regions are**
  - **Gulf and Atlantic Coastal Plains**
  - **Appalachian Mountains**
  - **Central Plains**
  - **Ozark Plateau**
  - **Canadian Shield**
  - **Great Plains**
  - **Rocky Mountains**
  - **Basin and Range**
  - **Coastal Range**
- **The ecosystems of North America can be used to divide the United States into biomes. Important biomes in North America include**
  - **Rain forest**
  - **Deciduous forest**
  - **Grassland or prairie**
  - **Desert**

Why Does It Matter?

Climate, landforms, and ecosystems in a region affect the ways of life there.

photo: IRC

Most of North America experiences a distinct change of seasons. Its landforms support varied vegetation and wildlife.

2 ▸ Characteristics of Cultural Regions

A cultural region is an area where people share cultural characteristics.

- **Language, religion, music, and food are all examples of cultural characteristics.**
- **Cultural regions in the United States reflect climate, landforms, and ecosystems, as well as historical immigration patterns.**
- **One cultural region in the United States is Pennsylvania Dutch Country, in and around Lancaster County, Pennsylvania, where people commonly speak Pennsylvania Dutch and practice Amish or Mennonite religions.**

Why Does It Matter?

Defining cultural regions helps us better understand human geography, history, and patterns of migration.

photo: Paul Fuqua

Regions can be defined by human cultural characteristics such as language and religion.

Name _____ **Date** _____

GRAPHIC ORGANIZER: Climate and Landform Regions of the United States

Use this Outline Map to mark and label significant landforms, climate regions, and eco-regions. For supporting resources, go to Building a Nation > Three Cultures Meet > Geography of the United States > Explore > Climate Regions.

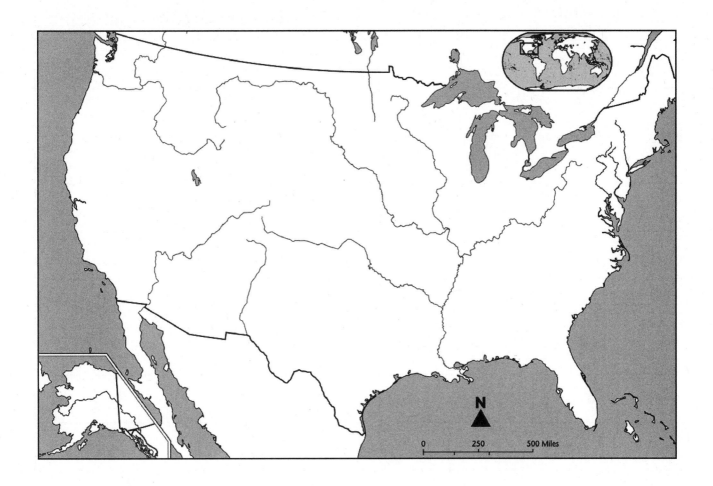

Name _____ Date _____

GRAPHIC ORGANIZER: Climate and Landform Regions of the United States *(continued)*

Map Key		
Climate/Landform Region	**Map Symbol/ Color**	**Definition/Description**
Humid Continental		
Humid Subtropical		
Arid		
Semiarid		
Highland		
Mediterranean		
Marine West Coast		
Appalachian Mountains		
Coastal Plains		
Ozark Plateau		
Canadian Shield		
Great Plains		
Rocky Mountains		
Basin and Range		
Coastal Range		

Name _____ **Date** _____

GRAPHIC ORGANIZER: Types of Regions

Use this Comparison Chart to define and identify examples of biomes, economic regions, and cultural regions. Be sure to describe the locations of each example you provide. For supporting resources, go to Building a Nation > Three Cultures Meet > Geography of the United States > Explore > Creating Biomes.

Region Type/Definition	Examples/Locations
Biomes	
Economic Regions	
Cultural Regions	

Name _____ Date _____

EXPLORE: FOCUS QUESTIONS

Using what you learned from the Core Interactive Text, answer each page's focus question:

The Characteristics of Place

What is a region?

_____
_____
_____

Climate Regions

What climate regions are found in the United States?

_____
_____
_____

Landform Regions—Eastern and Central United States

What landform regions are in the eastern United States?

_____
_____
_____

Landform Regions—Western United States

What landform regions are in the western United States?

_____
_____
_____

Creating Biomes

How do ecosystems help define regions in the United States?

_____
_____
_____

Name _____ Date _____

EXPLORE: FOCUS QUESTIONS *(continued)*

Examples of Biomes

What are some examples of biomes in the United States?

_____

_____

_____

Economic Regions

How can the United States be divided into economic regions?

_____

_____

_____

Cultural Regions

What are some cultural regions in the United States?

_____

_____

_____

PROJECTS AND ASSESSMENTS

Explain Activities

ACTIVITY TYPE: VISUALIZATION

Regions of the United States

Select one of the following region categories: climate regions, landform regions, cultural regions. Now, think about examples of the region category you have selected. Collect pictures that represent these examples and paste them in the blank frames. On the lines below the frames, define and describe the location of each region type in the United States.

ACTIVITY TYPE: DIAGRAM

Venn Diagram

Geographers have divided the United States and parts of Canada into nine landform regions. Choose two landform regions and use the Venn Diagram to compare and contrast their characteristics.

ACTIVITY TYPE: DIAGRAM

Economic Regions of the United States

In this activity, you will compare the different economic regions of the United States.

ACTIVITY TYPE: SOCIAL STUDIES EXPLANATION

Geography of the United States

In this activity, you will use the template to assemble evidence from the sources you have explored. Then, you will write an answer to the Essential Question and defend your answer with supporting evidence.

Elaborate Activities

photo: Getty Images

Diving into Data

In this activity, you will interpret and organize statistics in the Database of United States History to begin to examine the impact geography has had on the history of the United States. Then, using data from the Database as a starting point, you will select a question on this topic for further study.

PROJECTS AND ASSESSMENTS *(continued)*

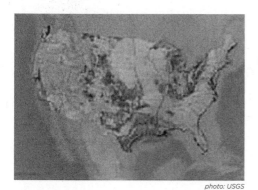

photo: USGS

ACTIVITY TYPE: DOCUMENT-BASED INVESTIGATION

Energy Production in the Ocean

As one of the largest energy consumers in the world, the United States is constantly searching for new sources of energy. One area of increased production in recent years has been drilling for oil in ocean waters. What are the risks associated with oil drilling?

photo: Getty Images

ACTIVITY TYPE: EXPRESS YOUR OPINION

Geography of the United States

In this activity, you will write an op-ed article describing the best region in the United States in which to hold the Winter Olympics.

photo: Getty Images

ACTIVITY TYPE: DOCUMENT-BASED INVESTIGATION

Relocating the Capital City

Imagine you are an expert urban planner who has been given the chance to travel back in time to the 1790s, when the Framers of the Constitution were deciding where to locate the capital city of the United States. You will use your knowledge of the United States today to provide the Founders with advice on where to locate the nation's capital. You will present your argument in either a formal presentation or a written letter to the editor of an early U.S. newspaper.

PROJECTS AND ASSESSMENTS *(continued)*

photo: Dreamstime

ACTIVITY TYPE: CURRENT EVENTS CONNECTION

The Impact of Human Development

In this activity, you will research how human development has affected and changed a specific biome in the United States. You will then create a "before and after" slide show that presents the effects of people on the biome's geography.

photo: Paul Fuqua

ACTIVITY TYPE: STUDENT SLEUTH

Where Are We?

In this Student Sleuth activity, you will examine a collection of uncaptioned postcard images of places in the United States. Then, by analyzing EXPLORE maps or the Techbook Interactive Atlas, you will make educated predictions about where each photo was taken.

Evaluate Activities

BRIEF-CONSTRUCTED RESPONSE (BCR)

Geography of the United States

EXTENDED-CONSTRUCTED RESPONSE (ECR)

Geography of the United States

UNIT 1: BUILDING A NATION (PREHISTORY TO 1783)

Chapter 1: Three Cultures Meet

1.2 Cultures Meet in America

photo: Getty Images

LESSON OVERVIEW

Lesson Objectives:

By the end of this lesson, you should be able to:

- Summarize theories regarding the arrival of the first human inhabitants of the Americas.
- Compare and contrast cultural characteristics of civilizations that lived in the Western Hemisphere.
- Explain how various Native American cultures, including the Arctic (Inuit), Plains (Lakota), and Eastern Woodlands (Iroquois), adapted to their surroundings.
- Connect social, political, and technological developments in Europe to the emergence of the Age of Exploration.
- Compare the roles, motivations, and accomplishments of the English, French, Portuguese, and Spanish exploration of North America.
- Describe characteristics of the Dahomey and Asante cultures of West Africa.
- Analyze causes and consequences of trade between West Africa and Europe, including the establishment of the slave trade.

Lesson Essential Question:

In what ways were the cultural traditions of Native Americans, Europeans, and West Africans alike and different?

Key Vocabulary

Adena, Algonquian, Anasazi, Asante, Aztec, Beringia, Calvinism, Catholic Church, Cherokee, Creek, Dahomey, drought, empire, England, France, Hopewell, Hopi, hunter-gatherer, igloos, Inca, Inuit, Iroquois, Iroquois League, irrigation, Johannes Gutenberg, Kwakiutl, Leonardo da Vinci, longhouse, maize, matrilineal, Maya, Michelangelo, migration, Mohawks, Muslims, natural resource, Navajo, Oneidas, Onondagas, Paleo-Indians, Portugal, Protestant Reformation, pueblos, Renaissance, Senecas, Spain, Spanish Inquisition, tepee, Tlingit, Tomás de Torquemada, totem, translatlantic slave trade, Triangular Trade, Yupik

FLASHCARDS

1 By Land or by Sea?

There are two main theories about how the first humans arrived in North America.

- **Many believe that the first Paleo-Indians walked across the Beringia land bridge between Asia and North America 13,000 years ago.**
- **Others believe the first Paleo-Indians sailed to North America from Asia by boat 15,000 years ago.**

Why Does It Matter?

However the first humans in North America arrived, they did so with the help of—and in spite of—the environment. The people who arrived by land could not have done so if it weren't for the glaciers that created that temporary land bridge. The people who arrived by sea had to build boats that could survive such a long voyage. Whether dealing with energy, climate change, or space exploration, we face these same types of challenges today.

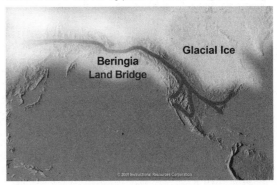

photo: IRC

The first groups who came to North America were primitive hunter-gatherers—people who lived by hunting game and gathering fruits, nuts, and other plants.

2 Hundreds of Cultures

As human life spread across the North American continent, each group of people defined themselves partly according to the areas in which they settled.

- **The Ancestral Pueblo built aqueducts and dams to irrigate their land. They used adobe and stone masonry to build their homes. They built them in the sides of cliffs and in canyon walls to help keep cool in the desert heat.**
- **The Hopewell and the Adena shaped the land.**

Why Does It Matter?

Throughout history, humans have had to adapt to their environment. Irrigation skills, such as those of the Ancestral Pueblo, were essential to making certain parts of the world livable. People have always turned to their environment to create works of art. We can trace the connection from the Hopewell and Adena mounds to modern monuments like Mount Rushmore.

photo: National Park Service

These ruins at Gran Quivira in New Mexico were once home to the Pueblo people.

FLASHCARDS *(continued)*

3 ▸ Three Ways of Life

Depending on where they settled on the continent, the people of the Western Hemisphere had very different lives.

- The Arctic peoples hunted whales and seals for food, clothing, and tools. They built homes of ice and snow.
- People of the Plains hunted buffalo, deer, and elk for food and used their hides as clothing and building materials.
- People of the Eastern Woodlands built homes, tools, and canoes from trees. They hunted and fished and used animal skins for clothing.
- The people of the Northwest carved wooden totems of animals and spirits. They also built homes and tools from trees and hunted, fished, and trapped animals for food and other materials.

Why Does It Matter?

The central location of the Mayan people, along with the warm and fertile climate, allowed them to share both goods and ideas with neighboring peoples. This also allowed their innovations to survive.

photo: Bigstock
Two tepees on the plains of Montana show how people lived on this vast, flat landscape.

4 ▸ Renaissance Innovation

In Renaissance Europe, the rediscovery of classical Greek and Roman culture led to art, literature, architecture, and science focusing on human values.

- Depth, perspective, realism, and symmetry were features of Renaissance art and architecture.
- Literature focused on human stories.
- The invention of movable type allowed new ideas to spread quickly and far.
- Scientific thought and religious reformers challenged the power of the Catholic Church.
- New scientific discoveries made voyages of exploration possible.

Why Does It Matter?

The inquisitive spirit of Renaissance culture, along with a new willingness to challenge the authority of the Church, created an atmosphere that inspired the Age of Exploration.

photo: Pixabay
Raphael's School of Athens *celebrates the Renaissance ideals and demonstrates the influence of classical Greek culture.*

FLASHCARDS (continued)

5 ▶ The Dahomey and the Asante

The Dahomey and the Asante were two powerful kingdoms in West Africa before Europeans arrived.

- The Dahomey expanded their territory through warfare. Military life and the power of the king were important to their society.
- Dahomey culture was focused on their religious beliefs, known as vodu. Dahomey art and music had symbolic meaning to honor the king or the gods.
- The Asante were rich in gold. They had a matrilineal society with a powerful king and many lesser clan chiefs.
- Asante politics and religion were both centered on a symbolic item called the Golden Stool. The Asante honored their king, their ancestors, and a supreme creator god.
- Both kingdoms were parts of trade networks that crossed the Sahara and the Mediterranean Sea.
- Enslaved people were commonly bought and sold through African trade networks.

Why Does It Matter?

For centuries, these and other kingdoms had healthy trade systems. When Europeans arrived and greatly increased trade, it may have seemed like Africa would profit. However, while some kings and merchants did become wealthy, many more Africans suffered, and some once-great kingdoms declined.

photo: IRC

This print depicts Kumasi, the capital city of Asante, as seen by a European in the 1800s.

Name _____ Date _____

GRAPHIC ORGANIZER: Main Idea Web

Use this Main Idea Web to record ideas about two theories to explain the arrival of the first Americans. For supporting resources, go to Building a Nation > Three Cultures Meet > Cultures Meet in America > Explore > The First Americans.

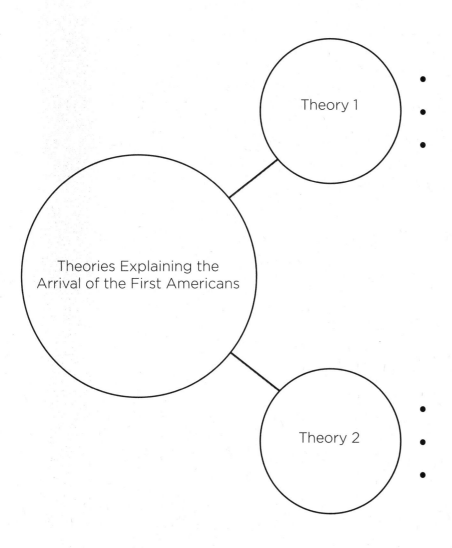

Name _____ **Date** _____

GRAPHIC ORGANIZER: Main Idea Web

Use this Main Idea Web to record information about the Paleo-Indians of North America. Describe the locations where they were found, the natural resources to which they had access, and the ways in which they adapted to the environment. For supporting resources, go to Building a Nation > Three Cultures Meet > Cultures Meet in America > Explore > Earth Artists.

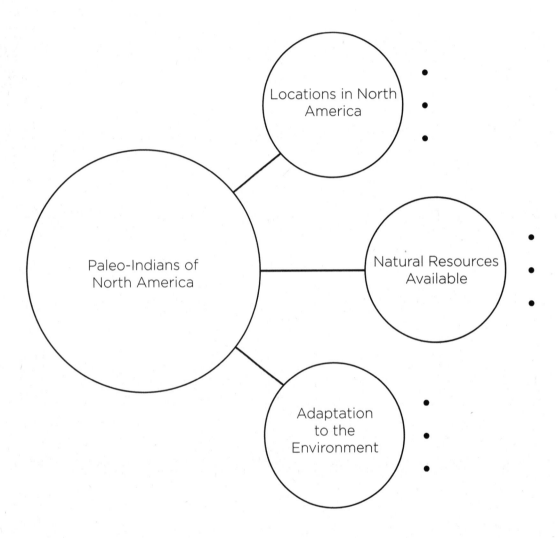

© Discovery Education | www.DiscoveryEducation.com

Name _____ **Date** _____

GRAPHIC ORGANIZER: Sequencing Chart

Use this Sequencing Chart to list in chronological order the major innovations that allowed the Ancestral Pueblo civilization to become more advanced. Then, explain how each advancement led to the development of cities. For supporting resources, go to Building a Nation > Three Cultures Meet > Cultures Meet in America > Explore > The Southwest.

Innovation	Date	Describe the Innovation. How Did It Lead to the Development of Cities?

Name _____ **Date** _____

GRAPHIC ORGANIZER: GREASES Chart

Use this GREASES Chart to record information about one Latin American empire's government, religion, economics, art and architecture, science and technology, environment, and social and cultural values. For supporting resources, go to Building a Nation > Three Cultures Meet > Cultures Meet in America > Explore > Three Latin American Empires.

Empire _____

Government	
Religion	
Economic	
Art & Architecture	
Science & Technology	
Environment	
Social & Cultural Values	

© Discovery Education | www.DiscoveryEducation.com

Name _____ **Date** _____

GRAPHIC ORGANIZER: GREASES Chart

Use this GREASES Chart to record information about one Native American culture's government, religion, economics, art and architecture, science and technology, environment, and social and cultural values. For supporting resources, go to Building a Nation > Three Cultures Meet > Cultures Meet in America > Explore > Peoples of the Arctic.

Culture _____

Government	
Religion	
Economic	
Art & Architecture	
Science & Technology	
Environment	
Social & Cultural Values	

Name _____ Date _____

GRAPHIC ORGANIZER: GREASES Chart

Use this GREASES chart to record information about European culture before the Age of Exploration. For supporting resources, go to Building a Nation > Three Cultures Meet > Cultures Meet in America > Explore > An Age of Ideas.

Government	
Religion	
Economic	
Art & Architecture	
Science & Technology	
Environment	
Social & Cultural Values	

Name _____ **Date** _____

GRAPHIC ORGANIZER: Venn Diagram

Use this Venn Diagram to compare and contrast the Protestant and Catholic Churches in Europe. For supporting resources, go to Building a Nation > Three Cultures Meet > Cultures Meet in America > Explore > The Reformation and the Counter-Reformation.

Protestant   Catholic

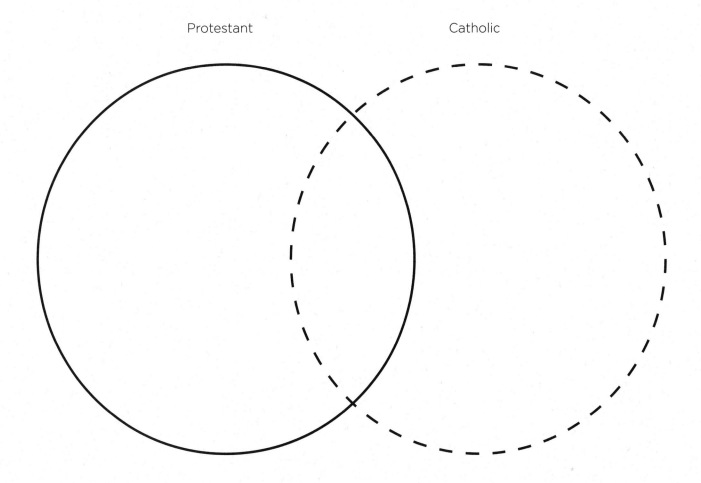

Name _____ **Date** _____

GRAPHIC ORGANIZER: Venn Diagram

Use this Venn Diagram to record similarities and differences between the Dahomey and Asante kingdoms in West Africa. For supporting resources, go to Building a Nation > Three Cultures Meet > Cultures Meet in America > Explore > Two African Kingdoms.

Dahomey   Asante

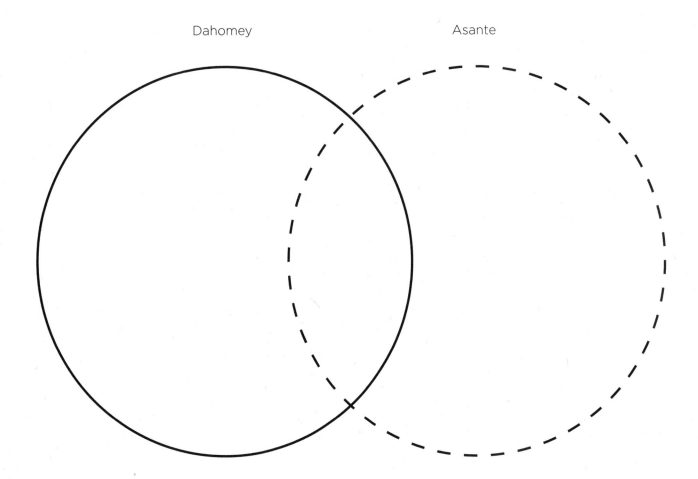

Name _____ Date _____

EXPLORE: FOCUS QUESTIONS

Using what you learned from the Core Interactive Text, answer each page's focus question:

The First Americans

How did human life first arrive in the Americas?

_____

_____

_____

Earth Artists

Who were the earliest people to settle in the Americas?

_____

_____

_____

The Southwest

How did the people of the Southwest form the first cities?

_____

_____

_____

Three Latin American Empires

How did the powerful empires of Central and South America transform the land?

_____

_____

_____

Peoples of the Arctic

How did the environment shape the lives of Paleo-Indians in the Arctic?

_____

_____

_____

Forest Peoples

How did the forests shape the lives of people in the Northwest and in the Eastern Woodlands?

_____

_____

_____

Name _____ Date _____

EXPLORE: FOCUS QUESTIONS *(continued)*

The Great Plains
How did people adapt to life on the open, mostly treeless Plains?

_____

_____

_____

An Age of Ideas
What changes in art and literature took place in Renaissance Europe?

_____

_____

_____

The Reformation and the Counter-Reformation
What new challenges did the Catholic Church face?

_____

_____

_____

Two African Kingdoms
Who controlled West African trade before the arrival of Europeans?

_____

_____

_____

Dahomey Society and Culture
What cultural practices did the Dahomey follow?

_____

_____

_____

Asante Society and Culture
How was Asante society structured? What cultural practices did they follow?

_____

_____

_____

PROJECTS AND ASSESSMENTS

Explain Activities

ACTIVITY TYPE: VISUALIZATION

Native Americans of North America

In this Visualization activity, you will explore the lives of Native American groups from one of the regions studied in this concept—Arctic, Eastern Woodlands, Great Plains, or Northwest. Create a slide show of illustrations or photographs showing aspects of life from the people in the region you chose. Then, write a caption for each image.

ACTIVITY TYPE: YOU AS JOURNALIST

Renaissance Review

You are a historian living in Europe during the Renaissance. You have the chance to see an amazing new creation or discovery for the first time and write about it for future generations. Write a review of this innovation. Be sure to point out why the innovation is important and what part it plays in bringing Europe into the Age of Exploration.

ACTIVITY TYPE: SOCIAL STUDIES EXPLANATION

Cultures Meet in America

In this activity, you will use the template to assemble evidence from the sources you have explored. Then, you will write an answer to the Essential Question and defend your answer with supporting evidence.

ACTIVITY TYPE: DIAGRAM

West African Cultures

In this activity, you will use a comparison chart to compare and contrast one West African culture (Dahomey or Asante) with European (British) and Native American (Eastern Woodlands) cultures.

Elaborate Activities

photo: Getty Images

INVESTIGATION TYPE: SOURCE ANALYSIS

Dogon Masks from West Africa

The art and religious artifacts people create can tell us a lot about their cultures. In this activity, you will use the Source Analysis interactive tool to study the culture of the Dogon people of West Africa.

PROJECTS AND ASSESSMENTS *(continued)*

photo: Getty Images

INVESTIGATION TYPE: MAP-GUIDED INQUIRY

Native American Cultures

How did geography shape the diverse cultures that developed in North America before the coming of European settlers? In this investigation, you will use the Map-Guided Inquiry tool to examine three maps of North America to determine how the cultures of the Native American nations were shaped by the places they lived.

photo: Library of Congress

ACTIVITY TYPE: CURRENT EVENTS CONNECTION

Adapting in the Past and Present

In this activity, you will explore the ways in which early Native American peoples adapted to and modified their environment. Then, you will learn more about the ways in which modern-day people shape and are shaped by their environment. Finally, you will create the transcript of an interview between a reporter, an early Native American, and a modern-day citizen discussing how they have interacted with their environment.

© 2015 Instructional Resource Corporation

photo: IRC

ACTIVITY TYPE: DOCUMENT-BASED INVESTIGATION

Adapting to the Environment

In this Document-Based Investigation, you will use a primary source document to prepare an argument on how a Native American culture adapted to its environment. You will present the argument by writing either a magazine article or a script for a lecture.

PROJECTS AND ASSESSMENTS *(continued)*

photo: Pixabay

ACTIVITY TYPE: EXPRESS YOUR
OPINION

From Medieval to Renaissance

How did ideas about art change during the
Renaissance? In this activity, you will look at a
pair of images—one from the Middle Ages and
one from the Renaissance—analyze the two
images, and write an article comparing the two
art styles.

Evaluate Activities

BRIEF-CONSTRUCTED RESPONSE (BCR)

Cultures Meet in America

EXTENDED-CONSTRUCTED RESPONSE (ECR)

Cultures Meet in America

photo: IRC

UNIT 1: BUILDING A NATION (PREHISTORY TO 1783)

Chapter 1: Three Cultures Meet

1.3 Contact and Exchange

LESSON OVERVIEW

Lesson Objectives:

By the end of this lesson, you should be able to:

- Identify key figures and exploration routes in the European exploration of North America, such as Prince Henry the Navigator, Vasco da Gama, Bartolomeu Dias, and Christopher Columbus.

- Assess the consequences of cultural exchanges among Europeans, Africans, and early Americans fostered by European exploration and colonization in the Americas.

- Explain factors and events that led to the growth of the slave trade in North America.

- Analyze religious, economic, and cultural factors that led to European colonization in North America.

Lesson Essential Question:

How did interaction among European, African, and Native American cultures shape early American history?

Key Vocabulary

Africa, Age of Exploration, Amerigo Vespucci, astrolabe, Atahualpa, Aztec, Aztec Empire, Bartolomeu Dias, Cape of Good Hope, caravel, Christopher Columbus, colony, Columbian Exchange, compass, conquistador, Dutch West India Company, encomienda, epidemic, expedition, Ferdinand Magellan, Francisco Pizarro, goods, Henry Hudson, Hernando de Soto, Hernán Cortés, Iberian Peninsula, Inca, Inca Empire, indentured servant, Jamestown, John Cabot, joint-stock company, Juan Ponce de León, lateen sail, line of demarcation, mercantilism, Middle Passage, mission, New Amsterdam, New Spain, Northwest Passage, Ottoman Empire, patron, Pocahontas, Prince Henry the Navigator, quadrant, Queen Isabella, Renaissance, Roanoke, Samuel de Champlain, Spain, Strait of Magellan, Tenochtitlán, transatlantic slave trade, Treaty of Tordesillas, Triangular Trade, Vasco da Gama, Vasco Núñez de Balboa, Virginia Company

© Discovery Education | www.DiscoveryEducation.com

FLASHCARDS

1 ▸ First Explorers

Portugal and Spain were the first countries to sponsor expeditions to India by sea to discover new trade routes.

- Sailing technology improved with a new type of sail and new navigational tools based on Muslim astronomy and mathematics.
- Bartolomeu Dias sailed south along the African coast and rounded the Cape of Good Hope.
- Vasco da Gama sailed past the Cape of Good Hope and reached India by ocean.
- Christopher Columbus sailed west across the Atlantic expecting to reach India, but instead landed on a "new" continent.

Why Does It Matter?

The European search for a new trade route to India was the result of Europe's reliance on foreign goods. Exploration resulted in European expansion and colonialism in the 1500s and beyond.

photo: Library of Congress
The Age of Exploration began in the Renaissance period and led to a race for the Americas.

2 ▸ Charting the Americas

Once it was determined that new continents had been discovered, European countries began to claim land in the Americas. The more land a country could claim, the more it extended its power.

- England's explorations focused on northern areas to avoid conflicts with Spain and Portugal.
- At first, the search for a passage to the Pacific Ocean was more important than expansion to the New World.
- Maps became more developed with the reports of explorers like Magellan, de Soto, and Hudson.

Why Does It Matter?

As cartographers mapped shorelines, it became apparent there was no quick and easy way to Asia. The territory claimed in the new land laid the foundation for later settlements.

photo: IRC
Columbus was the first person to establish European colonies in the Americas. This paved the way for the English and Spanish colonies.

FLASHCARDS *(continued)*

3 ▸ Cultures Collide

During the first centuries following Columbus's voyage to the Americas, Europeans invaded the Native Americans' lands.

- Hernán Cortés and Francisco Pizarro were able to conquer the powerful Aztec and Inca empires easily because of European diseases and civil war, which had ravaged the empires.
- Europeans viewed the Native Americans as a source of labor and as potential converts to Christianity. Some treated the Native Americans well, and others treated them very harshly.
- The Columbian Exchange was the movement of plants, animals, and diseases between the Eastern and Western hemispheres.
- The Columbian Exchange had positive effects, such as the introduction of new foods to European cuisine, and negative effects, such as the spread of new diseases among the Native Americans.

Why Does It Matter?

Early interactions between Europeans and Native Americans shaped and developed the growing population and culture in the Americas, helping mold these regions into the colonies and countries of later history.

photo: IRC

Spanish explorers, such as Francisco Coronado, led the way for Spanish colonial conquest of Native Americans and their lands.

4 ▸ The Development of Slavery in the Americas

The slave trade in the Americas grew and evolved from existing African slave customs. A variety of factors, including preexisting trade between Europe and West Africa and a European market hungry for Western Hemisphere products, combined to create a race-based slavery system.

- The Spanish and Portuguese were the first to bring Africans to the Americas as enslaved laborers.
- The early English colonies met their labor needs with indentured servants. As the price of indentured servants increased, colonists began to buy enslaved Africans.
- African slave traders sold prisoners of war to European slave traders.
- The pattern of trade among Europe, Africa, and the Americas was called the triangular trade. One leg of that triangle was the Middle Passage—the transatlantic shipment of enslaved Africans to the Americas.
- Once the pattern of trade was established, slave traders saw an increase in profits, and they began to capture people from the African interior.

Why Does It Matter?

Slavery enabled the colonies and nations of the Americas to make tremendous profits and develop into economic powerhouses. The slave trade decimated Africa of its working population and created an economy and culture revolving around the slave trade.

photo: IRC

A group of enslaved Africans are being bought and sold in the British colony of Jamaica.

Name _____ Date _____

GRAPHIC ORGANIZER: Comparison Chart

Use this Comparison Chart to record information about the journeys of 10 different European explorers. For supporting resources, go to Building a Nation > Three Cultures Meet > Contact and Exchange > Explore > Reaching the Ends of Earth.

Explorer	Date(s) of Voyage	Country Funding Voyage	Motives for Exploration	Lands Discovered	Significance of Voyage
Bartolomeu Dias					
Vasco da Gama					
Christopher Columbus					
Vasco Núñez de Balboa					
John Cabot					

Name _____ Date _____

GRAPHIC ORGANIZER: Comparison Chart *(continued)*

Explorer	Date(s) of Voyage	Country Funding Voyage	Motives for Exploration	Lands Discovered	Significance of Voyage
Amerigo Vespucci					
Ponce de León					
Hernando de Soto					
Ferdinand Magellan					
Henry Hudson					

Name _____ **Date** _____

GRAPHIC ORGANIZER: Main Idea Web

Use this Main Idea Web to record important details about Hernán Cortés and Francisco Pizarro and their conquest of the Americas. For supporting resources, go to Building a Nation > Three Cultures Meet > Contact and Exchange > Explore > Conquering the American Empires.

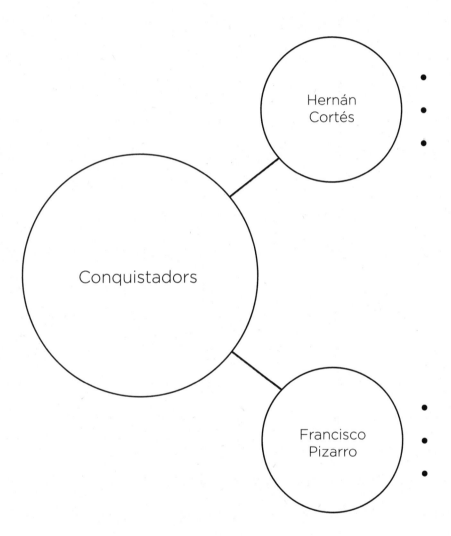

Name _____ **Date** _____

GRAPHIC ORGANIZER: Change Over Time Chart

Use this Change Over Time Chart to describe how the Americas changed before and after European conquest. For supporting resources, go to Building a Nation > Three Cultures Meet > Contact and Exchange > Explore > Native American and European Interactions.

Before:	After:

Changes:

Name _____ Date _____

GRAPHIC ORGANIZER: Summary Frames

Use these Summary Frames to show the sequence of events in the development of the slave trade in the Americas. For supporting resources, go to Building a Nation > Three Cultures Meet > Contact and Exchange > Explore > The Beginning of the Slave Trade.

Name _____ Date _____

EXPLORE: FOCUS QUESTIONS

Using what you learned from the Core Interactive Text, answer each page's focus question:

Reaching the Ends of Earth

How did ocean exploration start in the 1400s and 1500s?

_____
_____
_____

Tools of Travel

What technical innovations led to an increase in exploration?

_____
_____
_____

Finding the Americas

How did European explorers find the Americas?

_____
_____
_____

The Americas and Beyond

What early expeditions explored the Americas?

_____
_____
_____

Henry Hudson and the Northwest Passage

How did the English get more involved in exploration of the "New World"?

_____
_____
_____

Conquering the American Empires

How did the Spanish take control of land in the Americas?

_____
_____
_____

Name _____ Date _____

EXPLORE: FOCUS QUESTIONS *(continued)*

Native American and European Interactions
How did the Europeans and the conquered Native Americans treat each other?

_____

_____

_____

The Columbian Exchange
How did the Columbian Exchange affect life for Europeans, Africans, and Native Americans?

_____

_____

_____

Competing for Land: Spain and Portugal
How did the Spain and Portugal divide the "New World" that they found?

_____

_____

_____

Competing for Land: Holland and England
How did Holland and England divide the "New World" that they found?

_____

_____

_____

The Beginning of the Slave Trade
How did European colonists meet the need for labor?

_____

_____

_____

Triangular Trade and the Slave Trade
How did the slave trade function?

_____

_____

_____

PROJECTS AND ASSESSMENTS

Explain Activities

ACTIVITY TYPE: VISUALIZATION

Cultural Exchange

In this activity, you will create a slide show showing the steps involved in the development of slavery in the Americas. Before you create the slide show, answer the questions in the graphic organizer to help you plan your slide show.

ACTIVITY TYPE: DIAGRAM

Cultural Exchange

Use at least 12 words from the word bank to create a mind map that provides a graphic response to the Essential Question. You may add any other words or symbols, but you must use all of the starred words. Then, write a paragraph to summarize your mind map and be prepared to present your thinking.

ACTIVITY TYPE: VISUALIZATION

Events in European Exploration

Complete this timeline to track the most important advances made by European explorers.

ACTIVITY TYPE: SOCIAL STUDIES EXPLANATION

Contact and Exchange

In this activity, you will use the template to assemble evidence from the sources you have explored. Then, you will write an answer to the Essential Question and defend your answer with supporting evidence.

Elaborate Activities

photo: Library of Congress

INVESTIGATION TYPE: MAP-GUIDED INQUIRY

Exploration and Discovery

How did the Age of Exploration change Europe's understanding of the region that became the United States? In this investigation, you will use the Map-Guided Inquiry interactive tool to examine how the area of North America explored by the Europeans compares to the present-day United States on a map.

PROJECTS AND ASSESSMENTS *(continued)*

photo: Library of Congress

ACTIVITY TYPE: PITCH YOUR IDEA

Creating a Museum Exhibit on the Slave Trade

In this activity, you will create a museum exhibit documenting the roles played by individuals from a variety of perspectives in the slave trade.

photo: IRC

ACTIVITY TYPE: DOCUMENT-BASED INVESTIGATION

European Reasons for Colonization

Were European settlers in America primarily motivated by "push" factors or "pull" factors?

photo: Library of Congress

ACTIVITY TYPE: EXPRESS YOUR OPINION

The Colonists of Roanoke Island

In this activity, you will write an op-ed responding to some of the questions raised by the fate of the colonists at Roanoke. You may either blame the failure of Roanoke on England or defend the Crown and suggest other factors that led to the failure of the settlement. You will examine primary and secondary source documents to help form your opinion.

Evaluate Activities

BRIEF-CONSTRUCTED RESPONSE (BCR)

Cultural Exchange

EXTENDED-CONSTRUCTED RESPONSE (ECR)

Cultural Exchange

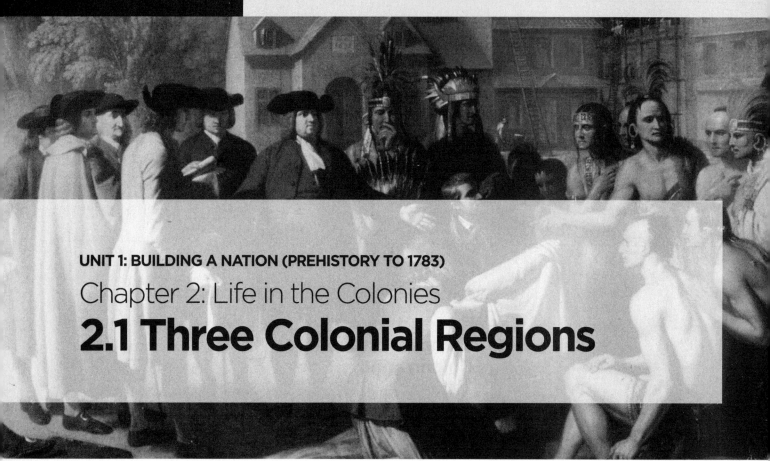

photo: Getty Images

UNIT 1: BUILDING A NATION (PREHISTORY TO 1783)

Chapter 2: Life in the Colonies

2.1 Three Colonial Regions

LESSON OVERVIEW

Lesson Objectives:

By the end of this lesson, you should be able to:

- Describe the motives and circumstances of the colonists who settled in each of the three colonial regions.
- Describe how the physical geography of the New England, Middle, and Southern colonies influenced trade in each region.
- Assess the interactions of European settlers in each colonial region with Native Americans.
- Describe the prominent political and cultural characteristics of the New England, Middle, and Southern colonies.

Lesson Essential Question:

How did location affect daily life in the New England, Middle, and Southern colonies?

Key Vocabulary

agriculture, Anne Hutchinson, assembly, Bacon's Rebellion, Boston, cash crop, corporate colony, cultural region, democracy, House of Burgesses, indentured servant, James Oglethorpe, Jamestown, John Winthrop, King Philip's War, Lenni Lenape, Lord Baltimore, Maine, Massachusetts Bay Colony, Massasoit, Mayflower Compact, Metacom, Middle Colonies, New England Colonies, Pennsylvania, Pequot War, Peter Stuyvesant, Philadelphia, Pilgrim, plantation, Plymouth Bay Colony, Powhatan Indian Confederacy, Powhatan War, proprietary colony, proprietor, Puritan, Quakers / Religious Society of Friends, reservation, Roger Williams, self-government, slavery, Southern Colonies, subsistence farming, Thomas Hooker, town meeting, treaty, William Penn

FLASHCARDS

1 ▶ Life in the New England Colonies

Colonists had to adapt to New England's harsh climate and thin, rocky soil. Many of the colonists came to escape religious persecution.

- Massachusetts was founded by Pilgrims and Puritans who had broken away from the Church of England.
- The Massachusetts Puritans enforced religious conformity.
- Connecticut and Rhode Island were founded by men who disagreed with the strict religious codes of Massachusetts.
- New Hampshire and Maine were founded for economic reasons.
- Farming was difficult because of the soil, the terrain, and the short growing season. Farms remained small, single-family businesses.
- Thick forests provided important resources but made the land difficult to clear for farming.
- Coastal towns developed around the fishing, whaling, and shipbuilding industries.

Why Does It Matter?

Religious devotion brought the Puritans from England to settle the New England Colonies. Their religious beliefs shaped the values and laws of the colonies. New England's geography and climate shaped how people lived and earned a living.

photo: IRC

The North Meeting House in Salem, Massachusetts, was the focus of this New England town.

2 ▶ Government and Diplomacy in New England

From the beginning, New England colonists took steps toward limited self-government, establishing a tradition of democratic practices. Their interactions with Native Americans deteriorated as they began fighting over land.

- The Wampanoag and the Plymouth Bay colonists celebrated what became known as the first Thanksgiving.
- Roger Williams befriended Native Americans of Rhode Island and bought land from them.
- The Pequot War nearly wiped out the Pequot people.
- King Philip's War united many Native American nations against the English settlers. Harsh attacks on civilians by both sides bred lasting hostility.
- The Pilgrims drew up the Mayflower Compact to ensure civil order in Plymouth.
- The Fundamental Orders of Connecticut was the first written constitution in America.
- Government in early New England was conducted mostly by town meeting.
- In Massachusetts, all male members of the established church could vote. In Connecticut, all male landowners could vote.

Why Does It Matter?

Success in warfare against Native Americans enabled the New England Colonies to survive and grow. This angered Native Americans who lost their homelands, and their relationship with the colonists deteriorated. New England's democratic traditions helped the New England Colonies resist later attempts by the British government to limit their freedoms. They had democratic practices, such as town hall meetings, which continue to this day.

photo: Library of Congress

Roger Williams of Rhode Island acted as a diplomat during the Pequot War.

FLASHCARDS (continued)

3 Life in the Middle Colonies

The Middle Colonies included the colonies of New York, New Jersey, Pennsylvania, and Delaware. The Middle Colonies were ideal for agriculture, which made them great proprietary colonies.

- The Duke of York, brother of King Charles II of England, was the proprietor of New York. George Berkeley and John Carteret were the proprietors of New Jersey. William Penn was the proprietor of Pennsylvania and the territory that later became Delaware.
- The proprietors of New York and New Jersey wanted to attract settlers to their territory, so they enacted policies of religious freedom and political freedom and granted inexpensive land.
- Penn was a Quaker, a member of a persecuted group of Christians. For that reason, he established a policy of religious freedom and allowed for some self-government in the colony.
- The Middle Colonies had fertile soil that enabled farming.
- The climate of the region was cool in winter but hot and wet in the summer, which was good for growing grains, fruits, and vegetables.
- The region's wide rivers, such as the Hudson and the Delaware, allowed farmers to ship their surplus goods to port cities.

Why Does It Matter?

The location and geography of the Middle Colonies made the region a good place for farmers in rural areas and for merchants and other business owners in the cities to earn a living. The proprietors who owned the colonies enacted polices of political and religious freedom that helped shape American values and government.

In the Middle Colonies, many people became farmers because of the geography of the region.

4 Government and Diplomacy in the Middle Colonies

The Lenni Lenape traded with William Penn and other Middle Colony proprietors. The proprietors established some democratic polices for their governments.

- In Pennsylvania, William Penn originally treated Native Americans fairly and had good relations with them.
- In the other Middle Colonies, Europeans seized land from Native Americans through misleading treaties.
- The proprietors of the colonies chose the governors of the colonies, but they allowed the male citizens to elect representatives to the colonial assemblies, which were the lawmaking bodies.
- All of the Middle Colonies had policies of religious tolerance that did not exist in England, in the New England Colonies, and in some Southern Colonies.

Why Does It Matter?

The policies of the Europeans in the Middle Colonies did not lead to significant warfare with the Native Americans who lived there. The European colonists eventually forced most of the native peoples to leave the region and move farther west.

photo: Getty Images

Although William Penn treated the Lenni Lenape fairly, the European colonists took over most Native American land as they settled in the region.

FLASHCARDS *(continued)*

5 ▸ Life in the Southern Colonies

The Southern Colonies had distinct cultural, political, and economic characteristics. One characteristic was a humid climate that suited large-scale tobacco farming.

- The colonists in the Southern Colonies developed a culture that strongly reflected their European heritage through the governments they set up, the types of homes they constructed, the religion they practiced, and the way they viewed land ownership.
- In Virginia, the colonists established representative government for themselves. However, throughout the Southern Colonies, enslaved laborers and other groups had few, if any, political rights.
- James Oglethorpe founded Georgia as a refuge for debtors and others in poverty.
- Lord Baltimore founded Maryland as a colony where Catholics could worship freely.
- Most Southern colonists practiced a form of Protestantism. The Anglican Church became the official church of Virginia.
- The Southern Colonies had a long growing season, good soil, and a warm, humid climate.
- The geographic conditions of the Southern Colonies were ideal for agriculture, and most Southern colonists earned their living by farming.
- Successful landowners began to establish plantations that grew cash crops, such as tobacco and rice.

Why Does It Matter?

In many parts of the Southern Colonies, settlement was centered on the development of plantations. However, plantations relied on the enslavement and oppression of African Americans. Because plantations grew cash crops, many basic goods had to be imported. Life in the region became dependent on trade.

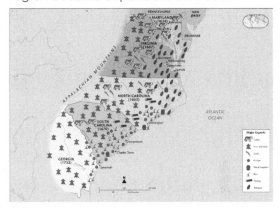

The people of the Southern Colonies developed a way of life that was in some ways similar to the lives of people in the other British colonies and in some ways different.

6 ▸ Government and Diplomacy in the Southern Colonies

In the Southern Colonies, settlers began to adopt aspects of a democratic government. However, the colonists also came into conflict with Native American groups.

- In Virginia, settlers fought the Powhatan Confederacy for land in the Powhatan Wars. The settlers eventually defeated the Powhatan Confederacy and gained control of the region.
- In Georgia, the Creek allowed colonists to settle in the region.
- In the late 1600s, Native American nations began to get involved in the struggle between European powers for control of southeastern North America.
- In 1619 in Virginia, colonists established the House of Burgesses—the first representative legislative body in colonial America.
- The General Assembly in Maryland passed the Act of Religious Toleration in 1649. This document allowed for religious freedom for all Christians living in the colony.
- In some ways, the Southern Colonies remained undemocratic: non-Christian religions were not tolerated, slavery was common, and only landowning white men were permitted to vote.

Why Does It Matter?

European settlers seized land from Native American nations and changed the culture, politics, and economy of the region. Through the Act of Religious Toleration and the House of Burgesses, colonists exercised two basic principles of democratic government—freedom of religion and representative government. However, these democratic practices would not be extended to African Americans and other minorities for centuries to come.

photo: IRC

One of the first actions of the House of Burgesses was to claim the authority to enact tax laws.

Name _____ **Date** _____

 ## GRAPHIC ORGANIZER: Outline Map

Use this Outline Map to color and label the New England Colonies. Then, identify and label their founding dates, founders, reason for founding, key rivers and bays, and key towns. For supporting resources, go to Building a Nation > Life in the Colonies > Three Colonial Regions > Explore > New England Colonies: Settlement.

Name _____ Date _____

GRAPHIC ORGANIZER: Cause/Effect Chart

Use this Cause/Effect Chart to record information about the effects of each cause listed. For supporting resources, go to Building a Nation > Life in the Colonies > Three Colonial Regions > Explore > New England Colonies: Geography and Trade.

Cause	Effect
Puritans Decided They Could Not Fix the Church of England.	
New England Land Is Rocky and Forested.	
New England Has Many Rivers.	
New England Has Ocean Access and Protected Ports.	

Name _____ Date _____

GRAPHIC ORGANIZER: Problem/Solution Chart

Use this Problem/Solution Chart to analyze the political problems of the New England Colonies and their solutions. List political problems in the left column and their solutions in the right column. For supporting resources, go to Building a Nation > Life in the Colonies > Three Colonial Regions > Explore > New England Colonies: Government and Democracy.

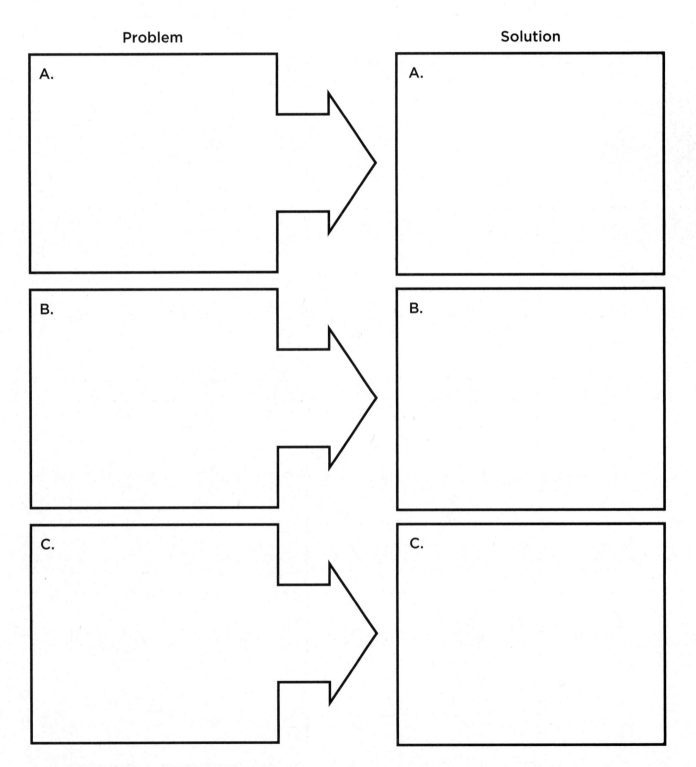

Problem

Solution

A.

A.

B.

B.

C.

C.

Name _____ **Date** _____

GRAPHIC ORGANIZER: GREASES Chart

Use this GREASES Chart to record information about the government, religion, economics, art and architecture, science and technology, environment, and social and cultural values of the Middle Colonies. For supporting resources, go to Building a Nation > Life in the Colonies > Three Colonial Regions > Explore > Middle Colonies: Settlement.

Government	
Religion	
Economic	
Art & Architecture	
Science & Technology	
Environment	
Social & Cultural Values	

Name _____ Date _____

GRAPHIC ORGANIZER: Comparison Chart

Use this Comparison Chart to compare and contrast human and physical characteristics of the five Southern Colonies: Virginia, Maryland, North Carolina, South Carolina, and Georgia. For supporting resources, go to Building a Nation > Life in the Colonies > Three Colonial Regions > Explore > Southern Colonies: Settlement.

Criteria	Virginia	Maryland	North Carolina	South Carolina	Georgia
Type of Colony					
Founder					
Motivation for Settling the Colony					
Geographic Features					
Government					
Economy					

Name _____ **Date** _____

GRAPHIC ORGANIZER: Main Idea Web

Use this Main Idea Web to record information about plantation life. For supporting resources, go to Building a Nation > Life in the Colonies > Three Colonial Regions > Explore > Southern Colonies: Geography and Trade.

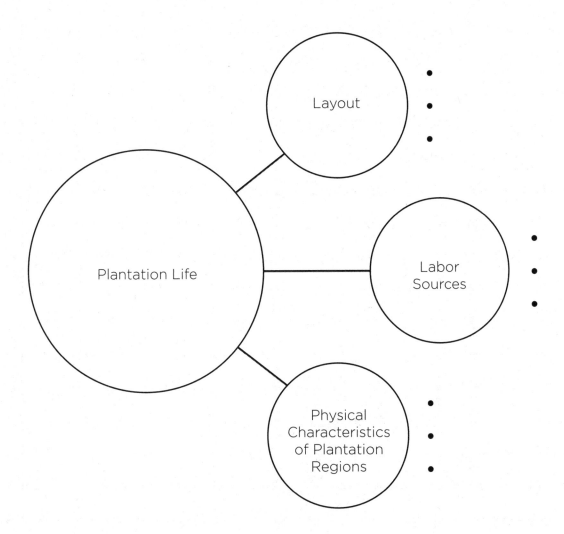

SOCIAL STUDIES TECHBOOK

Name _____ Date _____

GRAPHIC ORGANIZER: Cause/Event/Effect Chart

Use this Cause/Event/Effect Chart to record information about the causes and effects of each event related to Native American and European interactions. For supporting resources, go to Building a Nation > Life in the Colonies > Three Colonial Regions > Explore > Southern Colonies: Native American Interactions.

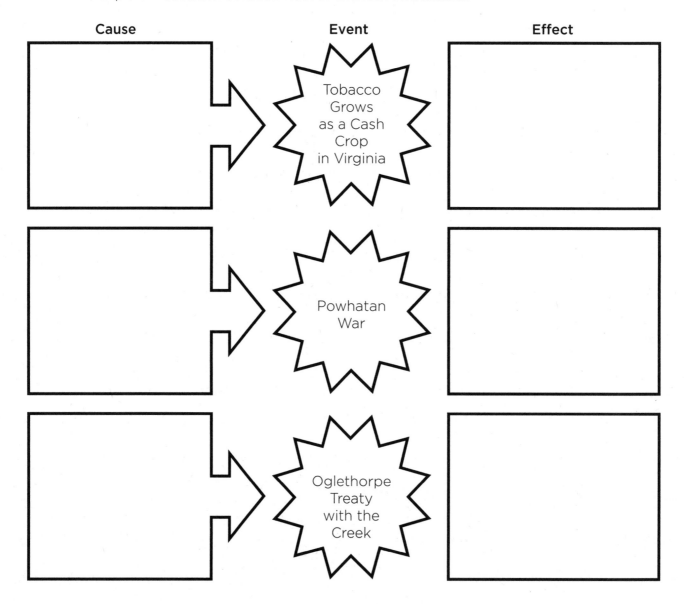

Cause   **Event**   **Effect**

Tobacco Grows as a Cash Crop in Virginia

Powhatan War

Oglethorpe Treaty with the Creek

Name _____   Date _____

EXPLORE: FOCUS QUESTIONS

Using what you learned from the Core Interactive Text, answer each page's focus question:

New England Colonies: Settlement
How were the New England Colonies established?

_____

_____

_____

New England Colonies: Geography and Trade
How did the geography of the New England Colonies affect how people lived?

_____

_____

_____

New England Colonies: Native American Interactions
How did the colonists in the New England Colonies interact with Native Americans?

_____

_____

_____

New England Colonies: Government and Democracy
What democratic practices were formed in colonial New England?

_____

_____

_____

Middle Colonies: Settlement
What were the important politics and religions of the settlers of the Middle Colonies?

_____

_____

Middle Colonies: Geography and Trade
How did the geography of the Middle Colonies affect life in the region?

_____

_____

Name _____ Date _____

EXPLORE: FOCUS QUESTIONS *(continued)*

Middle Colonies: Native American Interactions
How did settlers in the Middle Colonies interact with Native Americans?

_____
_____
_____

Middle Colonies: Government and Democracy
What democratic practices existed in the Middle Colonies?

_____
_____
_____

Southern Colonies: Settlement
How were the Southern Colonies established?

_____
_____
_____

Southern Colonies: Geography and Trade
Why did plantations form in the Southern Colonies?

_____
_____
_____

Southern Colonies: Native American Interactions
How did the Southern Colonists and Native Americans interact with each other?

_____
_____
_____

Southern Colonies: Government and Democracy
How did the Southern Colonies help develop a representative government?

_____
_____
_____

PROJECTS AND ASSESSMENTS

Explain Activities

ACTIVITY TYPE: DIAGRAM

Mapping Colonial America

In this activity, you will create an annotated map of the Thirteen Colonies.

ACTIVITY TYPE: DIAGRAM

The Thirteen Colonies

What is the story behind the establishment of Great Britain's thirteen American colonies? Was each colony founded for similar or different reasons?

ACTIVITY TYPE: GRAPHIC ORGANIZER

Colonial America

In this Comparison Chart, you will compare and contrast human and physical characteristics of the New England Colonies, the Middle Colonies, and the Southern Colonies.

ACTIVITY TYPE: QUICK WRITE

Religious Changes

Imagine you are a Puritan Separatist living in England. Think about all that is happening around you in your country. Why might you consider leaving your homeland to start a new life in America?

ACTIVITY TYPE: SOCIAL STUDIES EXPLANATION

Three Colonial Regions

In this activity, you will use the template to assemble evidence from the sources you have explored. Then, you will write an answer to the Essential Question and defend your answer with supporting evidence.

ACTIVITY TYPE: QUICK WRITE

The Middle Colonies

In this Quick Write, you will write a letter from the perspective of a farmer who has recently moved from New England to the Middle Colonies.

ACTIVITY TYPE: DIAGRAM

The Thirteen Colonies

What is the story behind the establishment of Great Britain's thirteen American colonies? Was each colony founded for similar or different reasons?

PROJECTS AND ASSESSMENTS *(continued)*

Activity Type: Social Studies Explanation

INVESTIGATION TYPE: HISTORICAL PERSPECTIVES

Life in the New England Colonies

Life in colonial New England was challenging. The colonists worked to support themselves while they developed their governments and refined their ideas about their religions. In this activity, you will use the Historical Perspectives interactive tool to explore the perspectives of four individuals who might have lived during this time and faced these challenges.

photo: Library of Congress

INVESTIGATION TYPE: SOURCE ANALYSIS

The Pennsylvania Frame of Government

How did the Pennsylvania Frame of Government shape ideas about democratic government and religious freedom in early America? In this activity, you will answer this question by using evidence from the document to write the script for a discussion or to create a poster about democracy and religious freedom.

photo: Library of Congress

INVESTIGATION TYPE: DATA ANALYSIS

The Three Regions of the Thirteen Colonies

The New England Colonies, the Middle Colonies, and the Southern Colonies were very different. Which colonial region would be the most promising for a new settler? Your mission is to answer this question by determining the differences among the colonial regions after analyzing data about each region's population and economy.

PROJECTS AND ASSESSMENTS *(continued)*

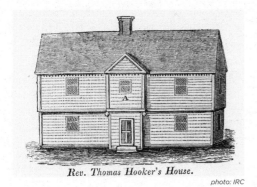

Rev. Thomas Hooker's House.

photo: IRC

ACTIVITY TYPE: SAY WHAT?

Fundamental Orders

In this activity, you will read a portion of the Fundamental Orders and translate it for modern times. Then, you will respond to the analysis questions to decide whether these orders should be used as a model for future governments.

photo: IRC

ACTIVITY TYPE: ROLE PLAY

Life in the Colonies

In this activity, you will take on the role of a New England colonist and conduct an investigation to write a diary entry about your daily life and how contemporary events of the time affect your home.

photo: Library of Congress

ACTIVITY TYPE: DOCUMENT-BASED INVESTIGATION

Plantation Economy in the South

How did the growth of a plantation economy impact society in the Southern Colonies? In this Document-Based Investigation, you will answer this question by analyzing documents and media for information to use in a report to the British King and Parliament or in a letter to the royal governor of another colonial region.

Evaluate Activities

BRIEF-CONSTRUCTED RESPONSE (BCR)

The Middle Colonies

EXTENDED-CONSTRUCTED RESPONSE (ECR)

The Middle Colonies

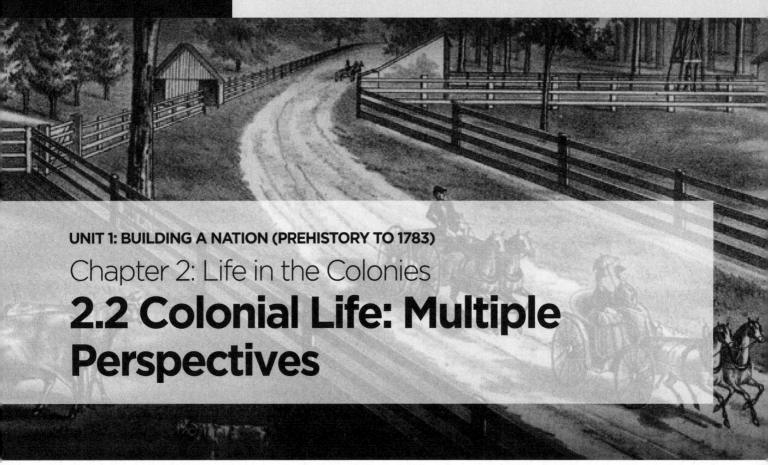

UNIT 1: BUILDING A NATION (PREHISTORY TO 1783)

Chapter 2: Life in the Colonies

2.2 Colonial Life: Multiple Perspectives

LESSON OVERVIEW

Lesson Objectives:

By the end of this lesson, you should be able to:

- Describe and evaluate the quality of life in the colonies from the perspectives of various groups, including city dwellers, farmers, women, children, and different social classes.

Lesson Essential Question:

For various groups, what did it mean to be "American" in 1750?

Key Vocabulary

Benjamin Banneker, Benjamin Franklin, Eliza Lucas Pinckney, encomienda, gentry, George Whitefield, indentured servant, indigo, John Peter Zenger, Pennsylvania, Phillis Wheatley, plantation, Quakers / Religious Society of Friends, slavery, tenant farmer, William Paterson

FLASHCARDS

1 Many "Colonial Americas"

The way people lived in colonial America differed greatly depending on where they lived.

- Though relatively few Americans lived in cities and towns, these were the centers of trade, politics, and industry.
- The pattern of land ownership differed greatly among the colonies.
- Most colonial farms were self-sufficient family farms. Each family member had many responsibilities.
- Larger farms in the North employed tenant farmers. Larger farms in the South were plantations worked by enslaved persons.

Why Does It Matter?

The great majority of colonial Americans lived on farms, but agricultural abundance and trade supported a growing urban culture.

photo: Library of Congress
Faneuil Hall was the location for many public meetings. It is one of many colonial buildings that still stand in Boston.

2 Not a "Classless Society"

The way people lived in colonial America differed greatly depending on gender, age, and degree of personal liberty.

- In most colonies, women had few political or economic rights, but they filled a number of important social and economic roles.
- Childhood and schooling ended early for most Americans, who began working at an early age. Opportunities for education varied according to class and location.
- Although most of the American colonies had more social equality than Europe, there were class divisions.

Why Does It Matter?

The Americans who would come together to create a nation had to overcome strong class divisions and reconcile a great many differences in cultural assumptions.

photo: IRC
The New England Colonies quickly implemented public education; in the Southern Colonies, class differences created discrepancies in schooling and in leisure activities. The lives of enslaved people were nothing like those of plantation owners. In the South, there was virtually no middle class.

Name _____ Date _____

GRAPHIC ORGANIZER: Comparison Chart

Use this Comparison Chart to compare and contrast the various social groups of colonial America. For supporting resources, go to Building a Nation > Colonial America > Colonial Life: Multiple Perspectives > Explore > Urban Islands in a Rural Culture.

Group	Political Rights	Social Standing	Daily Life	Education
Children				
Men				
Women				
Native Americans				
Africans and African Americans				

Name _____ Date _____

GRAPHIC ORGANIZER: Comparison Chart *(continued)*

Group	Political Rights	Social Standing	Daily Life	Education
English				
Gentry				
Middle Class				
Lower Class				
Indentured Servants				
Enslaved People				

Name _____ Date _____

GRAPHIC ORGANIZER: Comparison Chart *(continued)*

Group	Political Rights	Social Standing	Daily Life	Education
Urban Citizens				
Rural Citizens				

Name _____ Date _____

GRAPHIC ORGANIZER: Three-Way Venn Diagram

Use this Venn Diagram to organize facts about colonial farm life in three regions. For supporting resources, go to Building a Nation > Colonial America > Colonial Life: Multiple Perspectives > Explore > Farmsteads and Plantations: New England and the Middle Colonies.

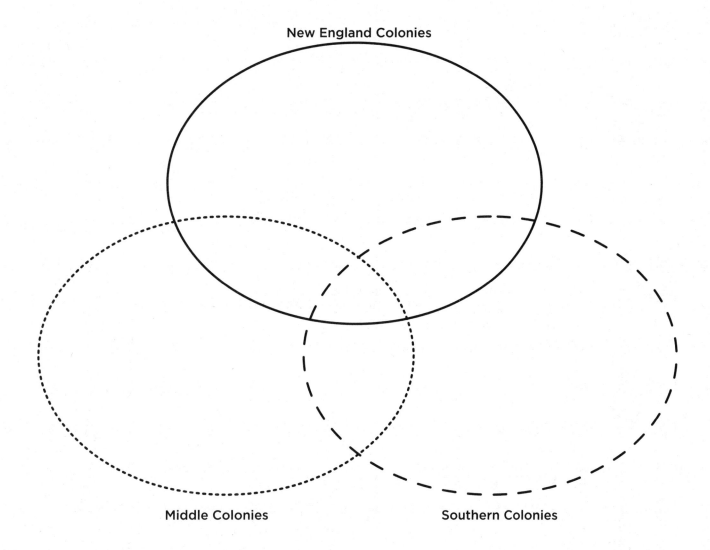

Name _____ Date _____

EXPLORE: FOCUS QUESTIONS

Using what you learned from the Core Interactive Text, answer each page's focus question:

Urban Islands in a Rural Culture

How did the importance of cities shape life there?

_____
_____
_____

Southern Cities

What was life like in Southern cities? How did cities bring different ideas together?

_____
_____
_____

Farmsteads and Plantations: New England and the Middle Colonies

How did daily responsibilities shape family life on colonial farms?

_____
_____
_____

Farmsteads and Plantations: The South and the Backcountry

What was life like on plantations and in the backcountry?

_____
_____
_____

In a Man's World

How did women's roles in the colonies differ from men's?

_____
_____
_____

© Discovery Education | www.DiscoveryEducation.com

Name _____ Date _____

EXPLORE: FOCUS QUESTIONS *(continued)*

Women in Families
What was family life like for women in the colonies?

_____

_____

_____

A Short Childhood
What were work, education, and leisure like for colonial children?

_____

_____

_____

Social Rank
What distinguished colonial social classes?

_____

_____

_____

Consequences of Class Distinctions
What were the differences among colonial social classes?

_____

_____

_____

Slavery and Servitude
What was colonial life like for indentured servants and for enslaved people in the South?

_____

_____

_____

Slavery in the North
What was colonial life like for free and enslaved African Americans in the North?

_____

_____

_____

PROJECTS AND ASSESSMENTS

Explain Activities

ACTIVITY TYPE: DIAGRAM

Colonial Life: Multiple Perspectives

All of Britain's North American colonies in the 1700s had different levels of society, from the wealthy elite to enslaved people. But the occupations of people who belonged to each social class differed from one colonial region to the next. Complete the chart for the following regions: New England, Middle Colonies, and Southern Colonies. Fill in the table by listing the typical occupations of people from each social group for each region. One box has been completed for you.

ACTIVITY TYPE: QUICK WRITE

Effects of European Colonization

Use material in the Core Interactive Text to describe the effects of European colonization on three of the following: Native Americans, democratic government, social classes, religious economies, and religious freedom.

ACTIVITY TYPE: DIAGRAM

European Colonization

Use the Comparison Chart to describe each trend and explain how it contributed to European colonization.

ACTIVITY TYPE: QUICK WRITE

New England Perspectives

In this Quick Write activity, you will take the perspective of a citizen living in the New England colonies.

ACTIVITY TYPE: SOCIAL STUDIES EXPLANATION

Colonial Life: Multiple Perspectives

In this activity, you will use the template to assemble evidence from the sources you have explored. Then, you will write an answer to the Essential Question and defend your answer with supporting evidence.

ACTIVITY TYPE: QUICK WRITE

Women in Colonial Societies

In this activity, use material in the Core Interactive Text, media, and graphic organizers to write a diary entry describing a woman's life in colonial America.

PROJECTS AND ASSESSMENTS *(continued)*

Elaborate Activities

photo: Discovery Education

INVESTIGATION TYPE: HISTORICAL PERSPECTIVES

Colonial Life

Your mission is to get to know four individuals who might have lived in colonial America and then explore the perspectives you think each would have on the issues of the day.

photo: Getty Images

ACTIVITY TYPE: YOU AS ARTIST

Colonial Perspectives

In this activity, you will read and analyze excerpts from two examples of early American verse: a poem by an author from the highest social level of New England and a poem by an enslaved African American female poet in Boston. Then, you will write your own poem.

ACTIVITY TYPE: DOCUMENT-BASED INVESTIGATION

Lives of the Young Virginia Gentry

For young people of the Virginia gentry in the year 1750, what did it mean to be an "American"? How did the meaning differ between boys and girls? In this activity, you will investigate the lives of the Virginia gentry. Then, you will use what you learn to write either a letter from the past or an episode of a reality TV show.

photo: Library of Congress

ACTIVITY TYPE: SAY WHAT?

Shall We Have a Free Press?

In this activity, you will read excerpts from Andrew Hamilton's speech to the jury and "translate" it for modern readers. Then, you will respond to the analysis questions to explain why the Zenger case was historically important.

PROJECTS AND ASSESSMENTS *(continued)*

Evaluate Activities

BRIEF-CONSTRUCTED RESPONSE (BCR)

Colonial Life: Multiple Perspectives

EXTENDED-CONSTRUCTED RESPONSE (ECR)

Colonial Life: Multiple Perspectives

photo: IRC

UNIT 1: BUILDING A NATION (PREHISTORY TO 1783)

Chapter 3: Revolutionary America

3.1 The Colonies Come of Age

LESSON OVERVIEW

Lesson Objectives:

By the end of this lesson, you should be able to:

- Discuss the relationship between the colonial and British governments, including British democratic influences and the degree of colonial autonomy.

- Trace and explain tensions on the frontier between Great Britain, France, American colonists, and Native Americans.

Lesson Essential Question:

In what ways were the American colonies becoming their own nation before 1763? In what ways were they still part of the British Empire?

Key Vocabulary

Albany Plan, Appalachian Mountains, autonomy, Daughters of Liberty, democracy, English Bill of Rights, Enlightenment, French and Indian War, George Washington, House of Burgesses, James Otis, King George III, Magna Carta, Mayflower Compact, mercantilism, monarch, Navigation Acts, nobility, Ohio River Valley, parliament, Plymouth, Pontiac, Pontiac's Rebellion, Proclamation of 1763, propaganda, Quartering Act, representative assembly, representative government, royal governor, self-government, Sons of Liberty, town meeting, William Pitt

FLASHCARDS

1 ▶ **Tradition of Representation and Local Control**

Representative democracy had its roots in the colonies long before the Revolutionary War.

- Colonial governments enjoyed a great deal of autonomy and set up local governments comprised of colonial leaders who made decisions about local matters.
- Southern colonies generally had colonial assemblies, while town meetings were common in northern colonies.
- The British government passed laws for the colonists to follow, but it did not always enforce those laws.
- The ideals of autonomy and self-government in the colonies were expressed by the Magna Carta and the English Bill of Rights.

Why Does It Matter?

The colonists were used to a long tradition of representative government in Britain. They also had grown used to local control over most matters. The desire for self-government would help shape the colonists' reactions when Britain's laws became stricter and the colonists' rights and freedoms were being challenged.

photo: IRC

This image shows the first meeting of the Virginia Assembly, 1619.

2 ▶ **Territorial Troubles**

Clashes between Britain and France in Europe spread to the colonies, impacting the relationship between the colonists, Native Americans, and foreign powers.

- Britain and France fought for control over the Ohio River Valley in what became known as the French and Indian War.
- Native Americans largely supported France in the war, while the colonists supported Britain.
- The conflict united the colonies as they pulled together to aid Britain in the war.
- Britain ultimately won the war and took control of France's territory in the Americas, doubling the size of Britain's American empire.
- The additional territory brought about new problems, such as conflict with Native Americans and increased responsibility for governing.
- Britain issued the Proclamation of 1763, which protected Native American lands and prevented colonists from settling to the west. Colonists were angered by this plan and largely ignored it.

Why Does It Matter?

After the French and Indian War, the relationship between Britain and the colonists began to shift from one of cooperation to conflict.

© 2005 Instructional Resources Corporation

photo: IRC

The British took Quebec on September 13, 1759.

Name _____ Date _____

GRAPHIC ORGANIZER: Democracy

Complete this Vocabulary Chart for the word *democracy*. For supporting resources, go to Building a Nation > Revolutionary America > The Colonies Come of Age > Explore > The Democratic Heritage.

DEFINITION:

Personal (B – 1st):

Techbook Reference (B – 3rd):

EXAMPLES FROM TEXT (drawn or written) (A):

TERM:
democracy

SENTENCES:

Personal (B – 4th):

In Text (A):

RELATED TERMS (A):

WORD PARTS (B – 2nd):

IN COLONIAL AMERICA (Why is this term important to understanding colonial America?) (A – LAST):

Name _____ Date _____

GRAPHIC ORGANIZER: Colonial Government and Politics

Complete this Comparison Chart with information about the various types of governing bodies in colonial America. For supporting resources, go to Building a Nation > Revolutionary America > The Colonies Come of Age > Explore > Local Governments Rule.

Governing Body	What Authority Did This Institution Have in the Colonies?	Describe Limits on This Institution's Power.	In What Ways Was This Institution Democratic?
Parliament			
The King of England			
Royal Governors			
Colonial Assemblies			
Town Hall Meetings			

Name _____ Date _____

GRAPHIC ORGANIZER: Cause/Event/Effect Chart

Use this Cause/Event/Effect Chart to identify the causes and outcomes of four important events that occurred in the colonies leading up to 1763. For supporting resources, go to Building a Nation > Revolutionary America > The Colonies Come of Age > Explore > The Navigation Acts.

Cause	Event	Effect
	Navigation Acts	
	French and Indian War	
	Great Britain's Victory	
	Proclamation of 1763	

Name _____ Date _____

EXPLORE: FOCUS QUESTIONS

Using what you learned from the Core Interactive Text, answer each page's focus question:

The Democratic Heritage

How did democratic traditions emerge in the American colonies?

_____
_____
_____

Local Governments Rule

How were Britain's American colonies governed?

_____
_____
_____

The Navigation Acts

How did Britain hope to profit from its colonies?

_____
_____
_____

A European War on American Soil: 1754–1763

What were the causes of the French and Indian War?

_____
_____
_____

New Troubles on the Horizon: 1763

What events led to Great Britain's victory in the French and Indian War?

_____
_____
_____

Name _____ Date _____

EXPLORE: FOCUS QUESTIONS *(continued)*

More Land, More Problems
Why was Great Britain's victory a mixed blessing?

_____

_____

_____

A King's Proclamation: 1763
How did King George respond to problems on the western frontier?

_____

_____

_____

PROJECTS AND ASSESSMENTS

Explain Activities

ACTIVITY TYPE: QUICK WRITE

Colonial Loyalties

In this Quick Write, you will take a perspective of a resident of the American colonies and describe whether your loyalties lie with the king, the colonists, or neither.

ACTIVITY TYPE: QUICK WRITE

Democratic Champions

For this Quick Write activity, imagine you are a resident of a colonial American city in the 1760s. Then, respond to the following statement: "James Otis is a champion of British democratic traditions."

ACTIVITY TYPE: YOU AS JOURNALIST

Reporting on the Proclamation of 1763

In this activity, you will imagine yourself to be a reporter assigned to write a news story describing how colonists living on the western frontier reacted to the announcement of the Proclamation of 1763. You will explain how this new policy changed the way the colonists viewed the king.

ACTIVITY TYPE: SOCIAL STUDIES EXPLANATION

The Colonies Come of Age

In this activity, you will use the template to assemble evidence from the sources you have explored. Then, you will write an answer to the Essential Questions and defend your answer with supporting evidence.

Elaborate Activities

photo: Discovery Education

INVESTIGATION TYPE: HISTORICAL PERSPECTIVES

The Colonies Move Toward Self-Government

As the colonies became more settled, issues surrounding the relationships between England, the colonies, and Native Americans became more complex. In this activity, you will use the interactive Historical Perspectives tool to analyze some issues faced by people living in the American colonies during the mid-1700s.

PROJECTS AND ASSESSMENTS *(continued)*

photo: IRC

ACTIVITY TYPE: PITCH YOUR IDEA

A Troubled Frontier

It is 1763. The war with France is over—for now. But while the European powers have signed a treaty, colonial life is still in upheaval. In this activity, you will create a slide-show presentation for the king, suggesting new policies for keeping the peace on the western frontier.

photo: Library of Congress

ACTIVITY TYPE: SAY WHAT?

Ackowanothie Speaks

In this speech, Chief Ackowanothie, leader of the Delaware tribe, explains his people's views of the French and Indian War and provides reasons why his tribe aligned with the French during the war. You will translate one excerpt from his speech.

photo: Library of Congress

ACTIVITY TYPE: DOCUMENT-BASED INVESTIGATION

An American National Identity

In this Document-Based Investigation, you will utilize primary documents to investigate the following question: At the conclusion of the French and Indian War, were the 13 American colonies in effect an independent nation with a unique American identity?

Evaluate Activities

BRIEF-CONSTRUCTED RESPONSE (BCR)

The Colonies Come of Age

EXTENDED-CONSTRUCTED RESPONSE (ECR)

The Colonies Come of Age

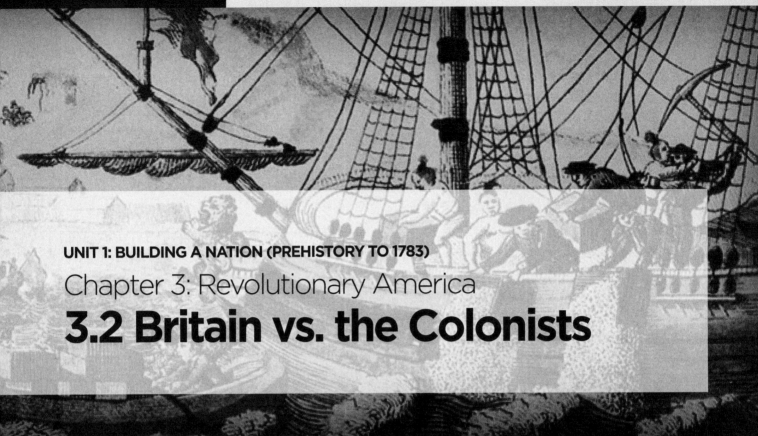

photo: IRC

UNIT 1: BUILDING A NATION (PREHISTORY TO 1783)

Chapter 3: Revolutionary America

3.2 Britain vs. the Colonists

LESSON OVERVIEW

Lesson Objectives:

By the end of this lesson, you should be able to:

- Explain British efforts to tax and increase controls over colonists after the French and Indian War and evaluate American reactions to these policies.

- Trace and explain the significance of events between 1763 and 1775 that led to the outbreak of the Revolutionary War.

Lesson Essential Question:

Why did the colonists risk their lives to fight for independence from Great Britain??

Key Vocabulary

Albany Plan, Battles of Lexington and Concord, Benjamin Franklin, Boston, Boston Massacre, boycott, Charles Thomson, Committees of Correspondence, *Common Sense*, Continental Congress, Continental soldiers, Crispus Attucks, Currency Act, Daughters of Liberty, Declaration and Resolves, Declaration of Rights and Grievances, Declaratory Act, direct tax, First Continental Congress, French and Indian War, Great Britain, import duty, Intolerable Acts, John Hancock, King George III, legislature, mercantilism, Mercy Otis Warren, monarchy, Navigation Acts, "No taxation without representation", Parliament, Paul Revere, Pontiac's Rebellion, Proclamation of 1763, Quartering Act, Redcoats, repeal, representative government, Richard Henry Lee, Samuel Adams, Second Continental Congress, Sons of Liberty, Stamp Act, Sugar Act, taxes, Tea Act, Tea Party, Townshend Acts, Treaty of Paris

FLASHCARDS

1 ▶ The Problem with Taxes

After the French and Indian War, Britain became stricter in the enforcement of laws passed in the colonies

- The French and Indian War left Britain with new territory to protect as well as a lot of debt. Britain turned to the colonies to help pay that debt.
- From 1763 to 1774, Britain passed acts, such as the Sugar Act, the Stamp Act, and the Townshend Acts, that taxed the colonies. It also passed the Proclamation of 1763 to limit colonial settlements on the western frontier.
- The colonists strongly opposed the taxes because they were being taxed without having representation in Parliament. They also wanted to be able to establish settlements as well as purchase and sell western lands.

Why Does It Matter?

The colonists believed that only their elected officials should have the power to pass taxes on them. Because the colonists did not elect representatives to the British Parliament, they did not think they should be subject to British laws. This democratic ideal is a cornerstone of American government today.

photo: IRC

Patrick Henry addresses the Virginia House of Burgesses.

2 ▶ Sparking the Revolutionary Spirit

As Britain continued to pass laws that restricted and taxed the colonists, many colonists sought ways to rebel against British authority.

- Groups such as the Sons of Liberty and the Daughters of Liberty supported boycotts, nonimportation agreements, and other protests in reaction to the laws and taxes.
- The Boston Massacre in 1770 resulted in the deaths of five Americans. The Sons of Liberty publicized the incident to gain support for their cause against the British.
- Leaders in the colonies began to organize and called the First Continental Congress to respond to the Intolerable Acts.
- Britain attempted to seize weapons and arrest colonial leaders on April 18, 1775.
- On April 19, 1775, the British troops and colonial militia met on a field between Lexington and Concord, officially beginning the American Revolution.

Why Does It Matter?

Conflict over taxes increased tensions between Britain and the colonists. Although Britain did repeal or lower some of the taxes, the colonists continued to protest, leading Britain to view the colonists as unreasonable. The colonists in turn viewed Britain's laws as disrespectful and excessive. The tension eventually led to violence and war.

photo: IRC

How did the American Revolution rise out of competition for power and wealth among European nations?

Name _____ Date _____

 GRAPHIC ORGANIZER: Problem/Solution Chart

Use this Problem/Solution Chart to analyze problems faced by the British and by the colonists and the ways in which each group responded to them. Fill out Part 1 with information explaining the challenges the British faced and the actions they took to deal with those challenges after their victory in the French and Indian War. Fill out Part 2 with the reasons colonists were upset about British taxes and governmental controls and the ways that colonists responded to these policies. For supporting resources, go to Building a Nation > Revolutionary America > Britain vs. the Colonists > Explore.

1. The Costs Of Victory: British Policies After the French and Indian War

What PROBLEMS Did Victory in the French and Indian War Bring to the British?	What SOLUTIONS Did the British Devise to Solve These Problems?

2. The American Colonies Respond to British Taxes and Controls

PROBLEMS Why Did American Colonists Object to British Policies?	SOLUTIONS How Did American Colonists Respond to British Policies?

Name _____ Date _____

GRAPHIC ORGANIZER: Road to Revolution

Complete this Road to Revolution Sequencing Chart with information about critical events leading up to the American Revolution. For supporting resources, go to Building a Nation > Revolutionary America > Britain vs. the Colonists > Explore > Tensions Mounting.

Event/Date	Summary	Relevant Symbol

Name _____ **Date** _____

GRAPHIC ORGANIZER: Road to Revolution *(continued)*

Event/Date	Summary	Relevant Symbol

Name _____ Date _____

EXPLORE: FOCUS QUESTIONS

Using what you learned from the Core Interactive Text, answer each page's focus question:

The Cost of Victory
What challenges did victory in the French and Indian War bring for the British?

_____

_____

_____

The British Tighten Control
How did Great Britain tighten control over its North American territory?

_____

_____

_____

No Taxation Without Representation
Why did the colonists oppose the new British policies?

_____

_____

_____

The Colonists Respond
How did colonists respond to the new British policies?

_____

_____

_____

Tensions Mounting
How did tensions continue to rise after the repeal of the Stamp Act?

_____

_____

_____

Name _____ Date _____

EXPLORE: FOCUS QUESTIONS *(continued)*

A "Massacre" in Boston
What was the Boston "Massacre"?

_____
_____
_____
_____

Patriots United
How did the colonies begin to come together?

_____
_____
_____
_____

The Tea Party and Its Aftermath
What happened at the Boston Tea Party? How did the British respond?

_____
_____
_____
_____

From Words to Weapons
What were the final steps leading to war?

_____
_____
_____
_____

The Shot Heard 'Round the World
How did the Revolutionary War begin?

_____
_____
_____

PROJECTS AND ASSESSMENTS

Explain Activities

ACTIVITY TYPE: DIAGRAM

The Road to Revolution

In this activity, you will use a graphic organizer to organize your thoughts about important terms in the concept and use vocabulary words to describe how various events and factors ultimately resulted in the American Revolution.

ACTIVITY TYPE: VISUALIZATION

Britain vs. the Colonists

What were the most important events that led to the outbreak of the Revolutionary War? In this activity, you will select the eight most important events and draw a cartoon, illustration, or symbol to represent each event. Then, you will write an argument to defend your selections.

ACTIVITY TYPE: QUICK WRITE

Britain vs. the Colonists

In this activity, you will imagine yourself to be a reporter assigned to write a news story describing how colonists living on the western frontier reacted to the announcement of the Proclamation of 1763. You will explain how this new policy changed the way the colonists viewed the king.

ACTIVITY TYPE: SOCIAL STUDIES EXPLANATION

Britain vs. the Colonists

In this activity, you will use the template to assemble evidence from the sources you have explored. Then, you will write an answer to the Essential Question and defend your answer with supporting evidence.

Elaborate Activities

photo: Library of Congress

INVESTIGATION TYPE: TIMELINE INQUIRY

Road to Revolution

Why did the relationship between the British government and the American colonies fall apart during the period 1763 to 1775? In this activity, you will use the Interactive Timeline to investigate the tensions that arose between the British government and its American subjects. Then, you may communicate your understanding of the historical events through a comic strip, blog, journal entry, skit, or other presentation.

PROJECTS AND ASSESSMENTS *(continued)*

photo: Library of Congress

ACTIVITY TYPE: YOU AS ARTIST

Britain vs. the Colonists

In this activity, you will analyze a political cartoon created during the time when tensions arose between Britain and the American colonies. Then, you will use the common elements of political cartoons to draw your own cartoon that expresses your opinion, or makes a point, about one or more events presented in the concept Britain vs. the Colonists.

photo: Library of Congress

ACTIVITY TYPE: STUDENT SLEUTH

Paul Revere's Boston Massacre

In this Student Sleuth activity, you will analyze Paul Revere's print of the Boston Massacre, compare his account of the events to the reports of various eyewitnesses, and then write a newspaper article in which you report the facts about the Boston Massacre and point out the accuracies and inaccuracies of events depicted in Revere's engraving.

photo: Library of Congress

ACTIVITY TYPE: DOCUMENT-BASED INVESTIGATION

Reasons to Fight for Independence

Did the colonists risk their lives to fight for independence for economic or political reasons? In this activity, you will review historical documents to prepare an answer to this question. You will deliver your response by writing the opening statement to a public debate or by writing a newspaper article about the issue.

Evaluate Activities

BRIEF-CONSTRUCTED RESPONSE (BCR)

Britain vs. the Colonists

EXTENDED-CONSTRUCTED RESPONSE (ECR)

Britain vs. the Colonists

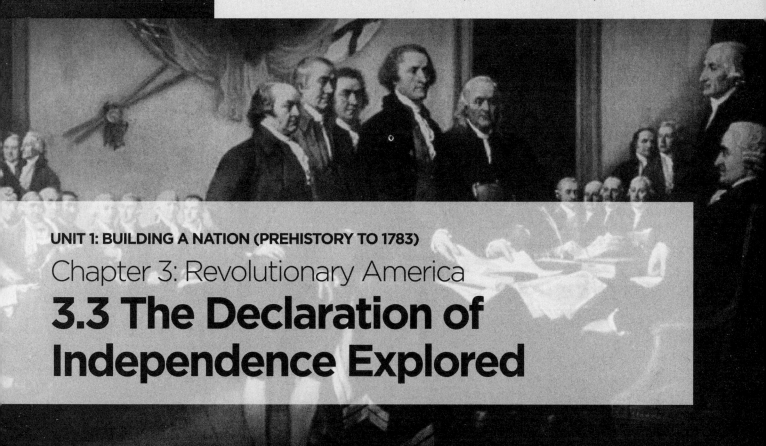

photo: IRC

UNIT 1: BUILDING A NATION (PREHISTORY TO 1783)

Chapter 3: Revolutionary America

3.3 The Declaration of Independence Explored

LESSON OVERVIEW

Lesson Objectives:

By the end of this lesson, you should be able to:

- Trace and summarize key events that resulted in the colonists' decision to declare independence from Great Britain.

- Explain how the Declaration of Independence outlines basic ideas about the purpose and responsibilities of government.

Lesson Essential Question:

How does the Declaration of Independence reflect the colonists' ideas about government?

Key Vocabulary

Abigail Adams, Baron de Montesquieu, Benjamin Franklin, Common Sense, Declaration of Independence, Francis Bacon, George Mason, Indian Removal Act, individualism, John Adams, John Hancock, John Jay, John Locke, John Ross, King George III, natural right, Oklahoma (Indian Territory),Osceola, Patrick Henry, representative, Robert Livingston, Roger Sherman, social contract, Thomas Jefferson, Thomas Paine, Trail of Tears, unalienable right, Voltaire

FLASHCARDS

1 The Road to Independence

After the first blood was drawn at the Battle of Lexington and Concord in 1775, a chain of events led to the decision to declare independence.

- The British Army and colonial militia continued to maneuver for control of Boston, leading to the Battle of Bunker Hill in June 1775.
- Increased British measures to contain the rebellion led to even more abuses and resentment from the colonies.
- The publication of Thomas Paine's Common Sense generated widespread public support for independence.
- The Virginia Resolution called for a united declaration of all 13 colonies by the Continental Congress.

Why Does It Matter?

It took years for the colonists to decide to declare independence. The decision was dangerous, and it quickly expanded the war that had already begun. The Founders' hesitancy to rebel gave them more time to think about how to justify their action, and it helped convince the rest of the world that they were sincere. This helped them win the support of their fellow colonists as well as foreign countries such as France and Holland, which contributed to the colonists' fight for independence.

photo: IRC

Thomas Jefferson and Congress made many adjustments to the original wording of the Declaration of Independence. Why was this document so important?

2 The Role of Government

The Declaration of Independence shows how the Founders understood the American Revolution.

- All "men" are created equal and equally possess the rights of life, liberty, property, and the pursuit of happiness.
- Government is based on a social contract in which the people exchange some of their liberty to enable government to protect their natural rights.
- Government is only legitimate when based on the consent of the governed and when it works to protect citizens' natural, unalienable rights.
- When a government is not legitimate, the people must abolish it and create a new one.
- The British government under King George III repeatedly abused its power, overreached its authority, and ignored the voices and rights of the colonists.
- The British claim to rule America was illegitimate and invalid. Thus, the American colonies declared themselves free and independent.

Why Does It Matter?

The ideas stated in the Declaration of Independence also became the foundation of the entire system of the U.S. government. Even today, these ideas explain many goals of American policy.

photo: IRC

John Hancock was president of the Second Continental Congress from 1775 to 1777 and the first signer of the Declaration of Independence.

FLASHCARDS *(continued)*

3 **The Legacy of the Declaration of Independence**

The Declaration's promise that "all men are created equal" did not necessarily mean that all people in the colonies were treated fairly and equally.

- In 1776, the vast majority of African Americans were enslaved, and they remained so after the Revolutionary War.
- Settlers from the former colonies continued to encroach on Native American lands.
- Women were not considered political equals and had limited rights to vote and to own property.
- The Declaration of Independence was approved unanimously, but the former colonies continued to disagree over the future of the American government.

Why Does It Matter?

The words of the Declaration have continued to inspire civil rights movements in this country and rebellions against oppressive rulers around the world. Disagreements about unity, separateness, and equal rights would lead to an American Civil War and continue to the present.

photo: IRC

Southern rice plantations relied on large numbers of enslaved persons.

Name _____ Date _____

GRAPHIC ORGANIZER: Declaration of Independence

Use this Graphic Organizer to record the main ideas and key phrases from each section of the Declaration of Independence. For supporting resources, go to Building a Nation > Revolutionary America > The Declaration of Independence Explored > Explore > We Hold These Truths.

Part	Main Ideas	Key Phrases
Introduction		
Preamble: Basic Principles		
Grievances: Justification for Independence		
Grievance: Supporting Facts		
Resolution		

Name _____ Date _____

EXPLORE: FOCUS QUESTIONS

Using what you learned from the Core Interactive Text, answer each page's focus question:

Americans Choose Independence

What events led to America's declaring independence from Great Britain?

_____

_____

_____

Old Ideas for a New Nation

How did the writings of John Locke influence ideas expressed in the Declaration of Independence?

_____

_____

_____

We Hold These Truths

What does the Declaration of Independence say?

_____

_____

_____

Congress Makes the Break

How did the Declaration of Independence justify rejecting the British government?

_____

_____

_____

The Legacy of the Declaration of Independence

Why is the Declaration of Independence an important historical document?

_____

_____

_____

PROJECTS AND ASSESSMENTS

Explain Activities

ACTIVITY TYPE: DIAGRAM

Declaration of Independence: Timeline

In this activity, you will create a timeline of at least eight major events described in the Core Interactive Text, the video segments, and information discussed in class that led to the writing and signing of the Declaration of Independence on July 4, 1776. On the reverse side of the paper, you will explain how each event led the United States to break its colonial ties with Great Britain. Then, after reading the Declaration of Independence in the Core Interactive Text, you will choose at least three grievances against King George that are listed in the Declaration and write an explanation of how each grievance relates to a specific event on your timeline.

ACTIVITY TYPE: VISUALIZATION

Visualization: Heroes of Self-Government

In this activity, you will select six figures from colonial history you consider to be heroes of self- government. You will use story frames to illustrate plaques dedicated to each figure you select. Below each plaque, you will explain the role each individual played in the development of self-government in colonial America.

ACTIVITY TYPE: DIAGRAM

Declaration of Independence

How does the Declaration of Independence reveal the Founders' ideas about government? In this activity, you will analyze the Declaration of Independence to identify words and phrases that align to the basic principles of government. You will record your findings in a chart.

ACTIVITY TYPE: SOCIAL STUDIES EXPLANATION

The Declaration of Independence Explored

In this activity, you will use the template to assemble evidence from the sources you have explored. Then, you will write an answer to the Essential Question and defend your answer with supporting evidence.

PROJECTS AND ASSESSMENTS *(continued)*

Elaborate Activities

photo: National Archives

INVESTIGATION TYPE: SOURCE ANALYSIS

Declaration of Independence

What did it mean to the colonists to become an independent nation? In this investigation, you will analyze sections of the Declaration of Independence and explain how they represent the colonists' ideas about the role of government.

photo: IRC

ACTIVITY TYPE: EXPRESS YOUR OPINION

The Declaration of Independence

Imagine that the president has asked you to write your own version of the Declaration of Independence. In this activity, you will choose 10 grievances from those listed in the original Declaration, or you can add other grievances that you identify through historical research. Then, you will rewrite the Declaration of Independence, addressing the grievances that you listed.

ACTIVITY TYPE: CLASSROOM DEBATE

Views on Independence

Should the colonies break ties with Great Britain? In this activity, you will role-play a Patriot, a Loyalist, or an ordinary American citizen to argue your position on this issue. You will gather information for your role from historical documents and then present your opinion in a debate.

PROJECTS AND ASSESSMENTS *(continued)*

photo: IRC

ACTIVITY TYPE: DOCUMENT-BASED INVESTIGATION

Founders United?

How united were the Founders? Did they share common beliefs about representative government? Did they agree that the colonies should break away from Great Britain? In this Document-Based Investigation, you will gather information from historical documents and then present your answers to these questions in a letter or slide show.

Evaluate Activities

BRIEF-CONSTRUCTED RESPONSE (BCR)

The Declaration of Independence Explored

EXTENDED-CONSTRUCTED RESPONSE (ECR)

The Declaration of Independence Explored

Discovery SOCIAL STUDIES
EDUCATION **TECHBOOK**

UNIT 1: BUILDING A NATION (PREHISTORY TO 1783)

Chapter 3: Revolutionary America

3.4 Fighting for Independence

© 2005 Instructional Resources Corporation

photo: IRC

LESSON OVERVIEW

Lesson Objectives:

By the end of this lesson, you should be able to:

- Summarize key battles and events that affected the outcome of the Revolutionary War.
- Describe the accomplishments of key historical figures from the American Revolution.
- Draw conclusions about how the colonists defeated Great Britain in the Revolutionary War.
- Summarize the provisions of the Treaty of Paris and describe its impact on the United States.

Lesson Essential Question:

How did the United States manage to win the Revolutionary War?

Key Vocabulary

American Revolution, Articles of Confederation, Battle of Bunker Hill, Battle of Saratoga, Battle of Trenton, Battle of Yorktown, Battles of Lexington and Concord, Benedict Arnold, Benjamin Franklin, Bernardo de Gálvez, blockade, Bunker Hill, Charles Cornwallis, Charles Thomson, Colonel William Prescott, Concord, Massachusetts, Continental Army, Deborah Sampson, Edmund Randolph, emancipation, Ethan Allen, Francis Marion, Friedrich von Steuben, George Rogers Clark, George Washington, Henry Knox, Hessian mercenaries, Horatio Gates, Hudson River, James Armistead, John Burgoyne, John Paul Jones, Lexington, Massachusetts, Loyalist, Marquis de Lafayette, Mary Ludwig Hays, Mercy Otis Warren, militia, Minutemen, Nathan Hale, Nathanael Greene, Patrick Henry, Patriot, Paul Revere, Peter Salem, Phillis Wheatley, propaganda, Samuel Prescott, Saratoga, Thaddeus Kosciusko, Thomas Gage, treason, treaty, Treaty of Paris, Valley Forge, William Dawes, William Howe, Yorktown

FLASHCARDS

1 Key Events of the American Revolution

The outcome of the American Revolution was a result of American tactics, international assistance, good fortune, and Americans' advantage of fighting in their own communities.

- Americans lost the Battle of Bunker Hill because they ran out of ammunition. But they inflicted heavy casualties using unconventional tactics.
- George Washington's victory at the Battle of Trenton inspired a renewed faith in the rebels' prospects for winning the war.
- General Gates's win for the Americans at the Battle of Saratoga convinced the French to support the colonists' rebellion with arms, troops, and ships.
- After 1778, the British shifted the focus of the war to the South. They captured Charleston, South Carolina, but then made little progress.
- The Battle of Yorktown was the final battle of the war. With the help of the French navy, the Continental Army trapped the British on a small peninsula at Yorktown, Virginia, and bombarded them ceaselessly until General Cornwallis surrendered.
- The Treaty of Paris guaranteed American independence from Britain.

Why Does It Matter?

Victory brought independence and began a new era for Americans.

photo: IRC

George Washington became the United States' first president.

2 Key Figures of the American Revolution

People of all walks of life participated in the American Revolution on one side or the other.

- Many Americans remained loyal to Britain and therefore were called Loyalists.
- Benjamin Franklin worked to persuade France to support the revolution. From 1778 on, France supplied soldiers and ships to the Americans.
- Many women supported the army and militias as nurses, cooks, and seamstresses.
- Civilians collected and passed on crucial information and provided the supplies needed by troops.
- Writers such as Thomas Paine boosted Patriot morale and converted British Loyalists.
- Over 20,000 African American soldiers fought for the British Army. Many were promised emancipation; few received it.
- Roughly 15,000 Native Americans fought on both sides of the war. For most, their main interest was to preserve their homelands.

Why Does It Matter?

Battles were only one aspect of a war that involved the entire society. Civilians, including women, all contributed to the Revolutionary cause. African Americans and Native Americans also contributed.

photo: IRC

How did General Washington create a disciplined army from a group of untrained colonists?

FLASHCARDS *(continued)*

3 ▶ Unlikely Victors

Fighting against powerful, experienced British forces, American colonists used new tactics to gain advantages.

- Instead of fighting in rows on empty fields, Americans relied on unconventional means, such as snipers and ambushes.
- Washington's surprise crossing of the Delaware River the day after Christmas was key to the American victory at Trenton.
- Despite the cold and the lack of adequate food and clothing, Washington's leadership enabled the Continental Army to maintain morale through the winter of 1777–1778 at Valley Forge.
- The military effort benefited from a national information network that relied on civilians.
- Because of distance, the British suffered from poor communications and difficulty in supplying the troops.

Why Does It Matter?

The United States became an inspiration to others who lived under foreign domination. The Patriots' flexibility and determination have remained an inspiring example throughout the country's history.

photo: IRC

The British army surrendered at Yorktown in 1781. This victory ended the American Revolution.

Name _____ Date _____

GRAPHIC ORGANIZER: The Revolutionary War

Use this Sequencing Chart to write down a summary and analysis of important events that happened during the Revolutionary War. For supporting resources, go to Building a Nation > Revolutionary America > Fighting for Independence > Explore.

Event	Date	Summary: Explain Key Issues and Circumstances Surrounding This Event	Analysis: Why Was This Event Important?
Bunker Hill			
Trenton			
Saratoga			
Winter at Valley Forge			

© Discovery Education | www.DiscoveryEducation.com

Name _____ Date _____

GRAPHIC ORGANIZER: The Revolutionary War *(continued)*

Event	Date	Summary: Explain Key Issues and Circumstances Surrounding This Event	Analysis: Why Was This Event Important?
Yorktown			
Treaty of Paris			

Name _____ Date _____

 GRAPHIC ORGANIZER: Minorities in the American Revolutionary War

Complete this Comparison Chart with information about the contributions of various minority groups during the American Revolutionary War. For supporting resources, go to Building a Nation > Revolutionary America > Fighting for Independence > Explore > Civilians Pitch In.

Group	Important Revolutionary War Figures from This Group	Description of This Group's Role(s) in the Revolutionary War
Women		
African Americans		
Native Americans		

© Discovery Education | www.DiscoveryEducation.com

Name _____ Date _____

EXPLORE: FOCUS QUESTIONS

Using what you learned from the Core Interactive Text, answer each page's focus question:

War Begins at Bunker Hill

What was the fighting like at the first major battle of the Revolutionary War?

_____

_____

_____

New Battlefields of America

What tactics did the Americans use to fight the British?

_____

_____

_____

Foreign Influences

How did other countries impact the outcome of the Revolutionary War?

_____

_____

_____

Civilians Pitch In

How did civilian colonists support the Revolution?

_____

_____

_____

Divided Loyalties

What roles did African Americans play in the Revolutionary War?

_____

_____

_____

Name _____ Date _____

EXPLORE: FOCUS QUESTIONS *(continued)*

Native Americans Choose Sides
How did Native Americans participate in the Revolutionary War?

_____
_____
_____

Fruits of Victory
How did the Revolutionary War come to an end?

_____
_____
_____

The Treaty of Paris
What were the provisions of the Treaty of Paris, and what was its impact?

_____
_____
_____

PROJECTS AND ASSESSMENTS

Explain Activities

ACTIVITY TYPE: ADVERTISEMENT

Looking for Support

It is your job to help recruit the people of the colonies to the cause of the Patriots. Select one group of Americans: Loyalists, women, or able-bodied young men. Then, design a poster that would encourage people from the group you have selected to support the Americans' effort against the British.

ACTIVITY TYPE: DIAGRAM

Mapping the American Revolution

Use the map to label places of importance from the American Revolution, including the sites of battles and major events.

ACTIVITY TYPE: VISUALIZATION

War Strategy

In this activity, you will use the boxes to create pages for a pamphlet explaining how the United States managed to win the American Revolutionary War.

ACTIVITY TYPE: YOU AS JOURNALIST

Battlefield Reports

In this You as Journalist activity, you will read sources and view videos about one of the selected battles of the American Revolutionary War. Then, you will create a battlefield news report.

ACTIVITY TYPE: SOCIAL STUDIES EXPLANATION

Fighting for Independence

In this activity, you will use the template to assemble evidence from the sources you have explored. Then, you will write an answer to the Essential Question and defend your answer with supporting evidence.

PROJECTS AND ASSESSMENTS *(continued)*

Elaborate Activities

photo: Library of Congress

INVESTIGATION TYPE: TIMELINE INQUIRY

Fighting for Independence

Investigate the key events and major battles of the American Revolution to understand how and why the Americans won their independence. What gave the United States the edge over Great Britain in the Revolutionary War?

photo: Library of Congress

ACTIVITY TYPE: PITCH YOUR IDEA

Asking for Support

In this activity, you will create an oral presentation to give before the French dignitaries, explaining why their help is needed.

photo: Library of Congress

ACTIVITY TYPE: YOU AS ARTIST

Literary Works and History

In this creative writing exercise, you will analyze Longfellow's take on Paul Revere's Midnight Ride and write a poem about a Revolutionary War figure or battle.

PROJECTS AND ASSESSMENTS *(continued)*

photo: Library of Congress

ACTIVITY TYPE: DOCUMENT-BASED INVESTIGATION

Fighting for Independence

To commemorate Presidents' Day, you have been asked to deliver a lecture to students visiting Mount Vernon, George Washington's home. To prepare for this occasion, write a speech presenting the results of your investigation on the most important factor in the Americans' victory in the Revolutionary War. Also, a popular history magazine has asked you to write an article for an upcoming special issue on the American Revolutionary War. Write a magazine article presenting the results of your investigation on the most important factor in the Americans' victory in the Revolutionary War.

Evaluate Activities

BRIEF-CONSTRUCTED RESPONSE (BCR)

Fighting for Independence

EXTENDED-CONSTRUCTED RESPONSE (ECR)

Fighting for Independence

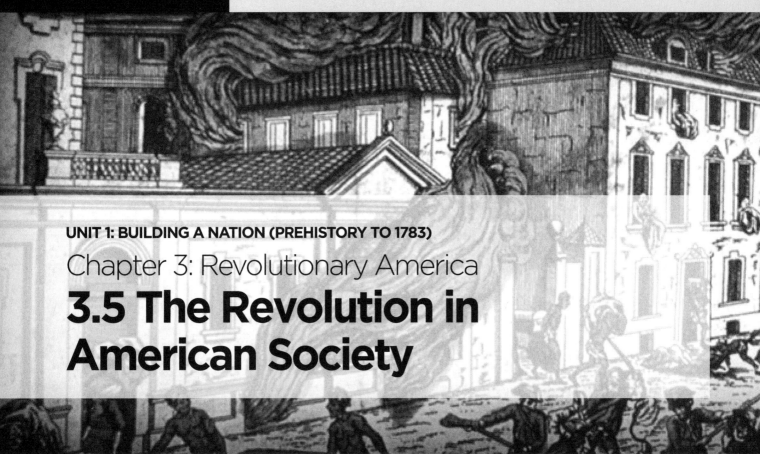

UNIT 1: BUILDING A NATION (PREHISTORY TO 1783)

Chapter 3: Revolutionary America

3.5 The Revolution in American Society

photo: IRC

LESSON OVERVIEW

Lesson Objectives:

By the end of this lesson, you should be able to:

- Describe the roles of various groups of Americans during the Revolutionary War, including women, Native Americans, and African Americans.
- Discuss political, social, and economic outcomes of the Revolutionary War.

Key Vocabulary

Abigail Adams, abolition, American Revolution, Battle of Trenton, Battle of Yorktown, Battles of Lexington and Concord, civil war, democracy, indentured servant, Iroquois League, James Armistead, John Adams, Loyalist, national debt, Patriot, revolution, siege

Lesson Essential Question:

What roles did different groups of Americans play in the Revolutionary War?

FLASHCARDS

1 ▶ Revolutionary Changes

Before the Revolution, the American colonies were a mixture of varied classes of people and groups of nationalities. People from all segments of society contributed to the cause of independence. Not everyone took sides in the war, but everyone experienced the effects.

- **There were shortages of many items because of the lack of imported goods.**
- **There was high unemployment due to the interruption in trade.**
- **Families were displaced because male soldiers were often joined by their wives and children in the forts and encampments.**
- **Enslaved laborers and indentured servants often left to join the battles in the hope of gaining their freedom.**
- **Native Americans fought to defend their lands—in some cases siding with the rebels, in others joining with the British.**

Why Does It Matter?

To fight the war, separate colonies and diverse groups of people stuck together for a common cause. The Patriots' success in the Revolutionary War would serve as an example of how future generations could prosper by working together.

photo: IRC

Women endured hardships during the war and served as supporters and spies.

2 ▶ A New Democracy

At the end of the Revolutionary War, it was time to come together, rebuild, and figure out how to live together without British rule.

- **Americans had fought to oppose taxes. Now the new government would need to find ways to repay its large war debts.**
- **African Americans and women did not yet experience the rights promised by the Declaration of Independence.**
- **Native Americans could no longer rely on any assistance from abroad in stopping or slowing the continued loss of their lands to settlers.**

Why Does It Matter?

After years of struggling for independence, the country faced a new struggle after the Revolution— the struggle for unity. The needs and interests of different groups of Americans needed to be resolved. The post–Revolutionary War answers to conflicts in the 1700s helped make the United States the country it is today.

photo: IRC

After the Revolution, the struggle for unity continued.

Name _____ Date _____

 GRAPHIC ORGANIZER: Comparison Chart

Use this Comparison Chart to compare the Revolutionary War experiences of African Americans, Native Americans, and women. For supporting resources, go to Building a Nation > Revolutionary America > The Revolution in American Society > Explore > African Americans – Patriots and Loyalists.

Group	This Group's Goals/ Reasons for Joining the War Effort	This Group's Contributions to the War Effort/Roles Played During the War	Impact of the War on This Group's Social Status
African Americans			
Native Americans			
Women			

Name _____ Date _____

EXPLORE: FOCUS QUESTIONS

Using what you learned from the Core Interactive Text, answer each page's focus question:

African Americans—Patriots and Loyalists

Did the war change conditions for enslaved African Americans?

_____

_____

_____

Native Americans—Taking Sides

Did the war change conditions for Native Americans?

_____

_____

_____

Female Patriots in the War Effort

How did women participate in the Patriot cause?

_____

_____

_____

The New Nation

What were some political, social, and economic outcomes of the Revolutionary War?

_____

_____

_____

PROJECTS AND ASSESSMENTS

Explain Activities

ACTIVITY TYPE: VISUALIZATION

Looking for Support

In this activity, you will select eight historical figures to be inducted into the "American Revolution Hall of Fame." For each figure selected, you will design an award plaque and write an inscription explaining that person's role in the American Revolution.

ACTIVITY TYPE: DIAGRAM

Revolution and the American Society: Main Idea Web

In this activity, you will use the Main Idea Web below to describe one group's participation in the Revolutionary War. Then, you will work with other students who completed a Main Idea Web for the two other groups to build a more complete understanding of the role of minority groups in the war.

ACTIVITY TYPE: DIAGRAM

Revolution and the American Society: Comparison Chart

In this Comparison Chart, you will compare characteristics of American society, economics, and politics before and after the war.

ACTIVITY TYPE: SOCIAL STUDIES EXPLANATION

Revolution and the American Society

In this activity, you will use the template to assemble evidence from the sources you have explored. Then, you will write an answer to the Essential Question and defend your answer with supporting evidence.

Elaborate Activities

photo: Library of Congress

INVESTIGATION TYPE: DATA ANALYSIS

The Real Impact of the Revolution

Your mission is to analyze data from the era following the American Revolution to find out how much the revolution changed American society.

PROJECTS AND ASSESSMENTS *(continued)*

photo: Library of Congress

ACTIVITY TYPE: PITCH YOUR IDEA

The Revolution and American Society

In this activity, you will act as a Revolutionary War expert who has been asked to advise the historical society. Create a presentation arguing for a permanent exhibit for African Americans, Native Americans, or women and the roles they played in the Revolutionary War.

photo: Corbis

ACTIVITY TYPE: SAY WHAT?

Wheatley to Washington

Phillis Wheatley was the first celebrated African American female poet in the United States. In this poem, written in 1775, Wheatley praises George Washington for his leadership during the Revolutionary War and predicts the future for the American colonies. You will translate one excerpt from her poem.

photo: IRC

ACTIVITY TYPE: DOCUMENT-BASED INVESTIGATION

Impacting the Revolution

In this activity, you will write a title and the introductory text for a museum exhibit that contrasts the roles played by African Americans, Native Americans, and women during the Revolutionary War. The exhibit will focus on the motivations members of these groups had for participating in the war. It will also feature the most important primary source documents from this investigation.

Evaluate Activities

BRIEF-CONSTRUCTED RESPONSE (BCR)

The Revolution in American Society

EXTENDED-CONSTRUCTED RESPONSE (ECR)

The Revolution in American Society

photo: Getty Images

UNIT 2: BECOMING AN INDEPENDENT NATION (1776 TO 1800)

Chapter 4: Establishing a New Government

4.1 The Articles of Confederation

LESSON OVERVIEW

Lesson Objectives:

By the end of this lesson, you should be able to:

- Evaluate the confederate form of government created by the Articles of Confederation.
- Connect key events and trends leading to the Constitutional Convention with weaknesses in the Articles of Confederation.

Lesson Essential Question:

How well did the Articles of Confederation address the needs of the new nation?

Key Vocabulary

alliance, arsenal, Articles of Confederation, Bill of Rights, commerce, confederation, Constitution, Constitutional Convention, currency, Daniel Shays, depression, executive, independence, inflation, John Adams, judicial, Land Ordinance of 1785, legislative, Northwest Ordinance of 1787, Northwest Territory, Richard Henry Lee, Second Continental Congress, Shays's Rebellion, tariff, territory

FLASHCARDS

1 Design Problems of the Articles of Confederation

The government created under the Articles of Confederation was weak and ineffective.

- Congress could raise money only by asking states for it, borrowing it from foreign creditors, or selling western lands.
- Congress had no power to raise an army or govern trade.
- There was no chief executive or judicial branch.
- The two-thirds majority required to pass major laws made it difficult to create needed legislation.
- It was difficult to reach the unanimous agreement required to change the Articles.

Why Does It Matter?

The United States needed a strong central authority to govern its member states and to deal with foreign powers. The lack of a strong central government threatened the survival of the young nation.

photo: Jupiterimages Corporation

Why was it important for America to have an effective form of government?

2 Indicators Here and Elsewhere

The weaknesses of the Articles of Confederation became apparent in the national government's dealings at home and abroad.

- Shays's Rebellion demonstrated the seriousness of many Americans' debt problems.
- Shays's Rebellion shut down courthouses and prevented the operation of the justice system in Massachusetts. It proved that state militias could not guarantee the national defense.
- The government could not force British soldiers to evacuate forts on the western frontier of the United States.
- The government could not enforce its land claims against Spain or secure use of the Mississippi River.

Why Does It Matter?

The inability of the government to settle domestic and foreign problems led to the replacement of the government. The Articles of Confederation would be followed by a framework that gave the central government greater power.

photo: IRC

After realizing that the Articles of Confederation needed to be changed, 12 states sent representatives to the State House of Philadelphia, Pennsylvania. These representatives created a new form of government for the American people.

Name _____ Date _____

GRAPHIC ORGANIZER: Articles of Confederation

Use this Cause/Event/Effect Chart to explain the impacts of different characteristics of government under the Articles of Confederation. For supporting resources, go to Becoming an Independent Nation > Establishing a New Government > The Articles of Confederation > Explore.

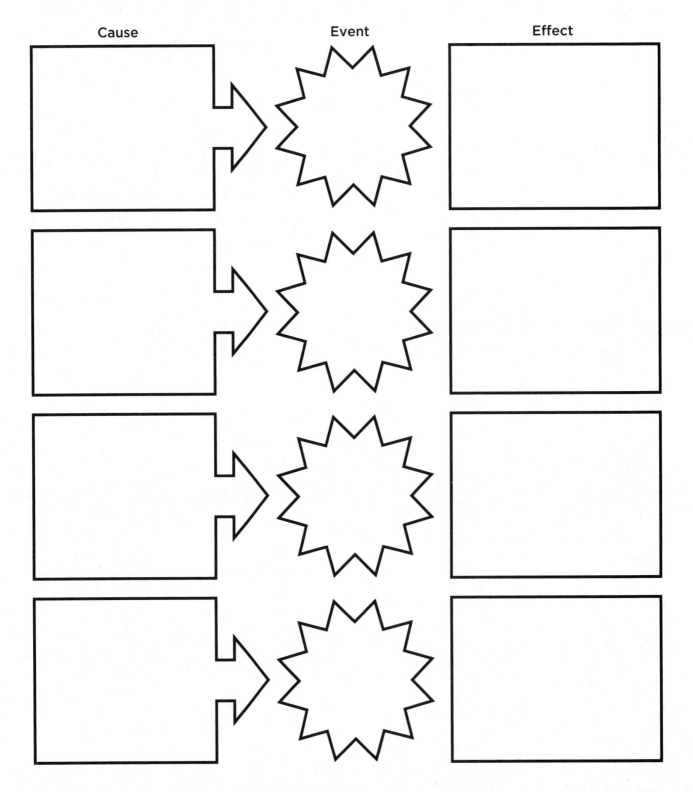

Cause   Event   Effect

Name _____ **Date** _____

GRAPHIC ORGANIZER: Articles of Confederation *(continued)*

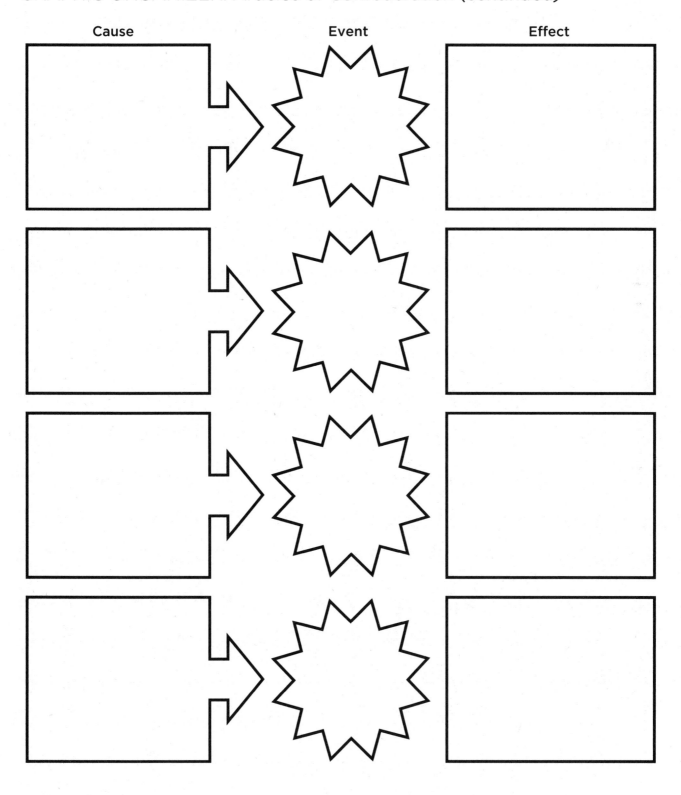

Cause	Event	Effect

Name _____ Date _____

EXPLORE: FOCUS QUESTIONS

Using what you learned from the Core Interactive Text, answer each page's focus question:

Governing a New Nation

How did a new nation begin to govern itself?

_____
_____
_____
_____

Accepting a Central Government

How did the Founders limit the power of the country's first government?

_____
_____
_____
_____

A Blueprint for Expansion

What important laws were made under the Articles of Confederation?

_____
_____
_____
_____

Problems with the Articles of Confederation at Home

What were the major weaknesses of the Articles of Confederation in resolving problems among the states?

_____
_____
_____
_____

Problems Competing with British Commerce

How did the nation's dealings with Great Britain reveal weaknesses in the Articles of Confederation?

_____
_____
_____

Name _____ Date _____

EXPLORE: FOCUS QUESTIONS *(continued)*

Problems with Spanish Land Claims
How did the nation's dealings with Spain reveal weaknesses in the Articles of Confederation?

_____

_____

_____

Rebellion in a New Nation
What did Shays's Rebellion indicate about the United States in the 1780s?

_____

_____

_____

PROJECTS AND ASSESSMENTS

Explain Activities

ACTIVITY TYPE: MAKE A MODEL

America's First Government on Display

In this activity, you will design a museum exhibit about the strengths and weaknesses of the Articles of Confederation and create a sketch of the exhibit.

ACTIVITY TYPE: YOU AS JOURNALIST

In the News: Shays's Rebellion

In this activity, you will take the role of a journalist covering the events of Shays's Rebellion in 1787. In your article, you will describe the events that led to Shays's Rebellion, connecting the rebellion to the effect of a weak federal government under the Articles of Confederation, and state your opinion on steps that could be taken to avoid future rebellions.

ACTIVITY TYPE: SOCIAL STUDIES EXPLANATION

The Articles of Confederation

In this activity, you will use the template to assemble evidence from the sources you have explored. Then, you will write an answer to the Essential Question and defend your answer with supporting evidence.

Elaborate Activities

photo: Discovery Education

INVESTIGATION TYPE: HISTORICAL PERSPECTIVES

The New Nation

In this investigation, you will read the opinions of four individuals who might have lived in the colonies during the 1780s. Then, you will identify how you think each person would respond to three key issues of the day and compare your answers with the historically likely perspectives on each issue.

PROJECTS AND ASSESSMENTS *(continued)*

photo: IRC

ACTIVITY TYPE: SOCRATIC SEMINAR

The Articles of Confederation

How well did the Articles of Confederation address the needs of the new nation? In this activity, you will answer this question in a Socratic Seminar after analyzing excerpts from the Articles of Confederation, discussing the goals of the Articles, and speculating about the effectiveness of the goals for the growth and stability of the new nation.

photo: IRC

ACTIVITY TYPE: ROLE PLAY

The Power of Government

In this activity, you will role-play a member of the Confederation Congress and write a speech to convince opponents of the Northwest Ordinance that the central government must have the power to establish new territories and states.

photo: Library of Congress

ACTIVITY TYPE: DOCUMENT-BASED INVESTIGATION

A More Perfect Union

Should the Articles of Confederation be considered a great American political document? In this activity, you will answer this question by gathering information from historical documents and then either writing a response to a proposal to include the Articles in an online exhibit of great American political documents or creating a paper or digital slide show reporting and defending your answer.

Evaluate Activities

BRIEF-CONSTRUCTED RESPONSE (BCR)

The Articles of Confederation

EXTENDED-CONSTRUCTED RESPONSE (ECR)

The Articles of Confederation

UNIT 2: BECOMING AN INDEPENDENT NATION (1776 TO 1800)

Chapter 4: Establishing a New Government

4.2 Creating a Government

photo: IRC

LESSON OVERVIEW

Lesson Objectives:

By the end of this lesson, you should be able to:

- Identify and analyze key issues addressed by the Framers at the outset of the Constitutional Convention.
- Describe major areas of disagreement among delegates to the Constitutional Convention and explain compromises intended to resolve these issues.

Lesson Essential Question:

How did decisions made at the Constitutional Convention affect the balance of power in the new nation?

Key Vocabulary

amendment, Anti-Federalists, Baron de Montesquieu, Bill of Rights, checks and balances, compromise, Confederacy / Confederate States, constitution, Constitutional Convention, Declaration of Independence, delegate, Edmund Randolph, Enlightenment, enumerated power, executive branch, federal, *Federalist* Papers, Federalists, Framers, George Mason, Great Compromise, habeas corpus, House of Representatives, implied power, interstate commerce, James Madison, judicial branch, Judiciary Act of 1789, legislative branch, levy, New Jersey Plan, nominating conventions, Pierre L'Enfant, pocket veto, precedent, ratification, republic, reserved powers, Roger Sherman, Senate, separation of powers, Three-Fifths Compromise, usurp, veto, Virginia Plan, William Paterson

FLASHCARDS

1 Can We Fix It?

Many delegates who came to the Constitutional Convention believed the Articles of Confederation needed to be reworked to strengthen the government. Others believed a new constitution was needed.

- **The Framers agreed that the national government needed to be strengthened.**
- **To prevent the central government from becoming too powerful, the Framers established a system of separation of powers as well as checks and balances among three branches of government.**
- **The Framers decided to protect states' rights and powers by listing the powers of the national government. Any power not listed was reserved for the states.**

Why Does It Matter?

The Framers wanted to be sure that the new government would not turn into the sort of government they had just fought to escape. Their commitment to the rights of the states and of the people has helped create an enduring democracy.

photo: Jupiterimages Corporation
The State House in Philadelphia, now known as Independence Hall, was the birthplace of the Constitution.

2 Time to Compromise

The delegates of the Constitutional Convention had to come to agreement on many serious issues, and agreement was reached through compromise. Large and small states disagreed about representation. Northern and Southern states disagreed about slavery. People across the nation worried about protecting individual rights and liberties.

- **Disagreements about representation were resolved by the Great Compromise, which created a Congress composed of a Senate, with equal representation for all states, and a House of Representatives, with representation based on population.**
- **Slavery would continue to be legal, but Congress could prohibit importation of enslaved people after 1808.**
- **For both taxation and representation, population counts would include three-fifths of enslaved people.**
- **The rights of the people would be spelled out in a bill of rights, which Congress promised to incorporate as amendments to the Constitution.**

Why Does It Matter?

The work done at the Constitutional Convention is a testament to what a nation can accomplish, even when faced with serious differences. The compromises made at the convention created the U.S. Constitution, which has lasted for more than 200 years.

photo: IRC
George Washington presided over the debates at the Constitutional Convention.

Name _____ Date _____

GRAPHIC ORGANIZER: Problem/Solution Chart

Use this Problem/Solution Chart to record problems that arose during the Constitutional Convention and the solutions the delegates agreed upon. For supporting resources, go to Becoming an Independent Nation > Establishing a New Government > Creating a Government > Explore.

Problem   **Solution**

How will Congress be structured?

Will the slave trade continue?

How will slavery affect representation in the House of Representatives?

How will the power of the national government be limited?

Name _____ Date _____

GRAPHIC ORGANIZER: Comparison Chart

Use this Comparison Chart to compare and contrast the arguments of Federalists and Anti-Federalists. For supporting resources, go to Becoming an Independent Nation > Establishing a New Government > Creating a Government > Explore > The Question Goes to the People.

Criteria	Federalists	Anti-Federalists
Supporters		
Views on the Articles of Confederation		
Views on a Strong National Government		
Arguments For and Against Ratification of the Constitution		

Name _____ Date _____

EXPLORE: FOCUS QUESTIONS

Using what you learned from the Core Interactive Text, answer each page's focus question:

A More Perfect Union?

How did the Philadelphia Convention begin?

_____
_____
_____
_____

Great Compromise

How did a major disagreement lead to one of the key features of the U.S. government?

_____
_____
_____
_____

The Question of Slavery

How did the question of slavery shape the new government?

_____
_____
_____
_____

States' Powers

In what ways does the Constitution limit the powers of the national government?

_____
_____
_____
_____

The Question Goes to the People

How did debate over the Constitution lead to the creation of the Bill of Rights?

_____
_____
_____
_____

Ratification

How was the Constitution finally agreed upon?

_____
_____
_____
_____

PROJECTS AND ASSESSMENTS

Explain Activities

ACTIVITY TYPE: DIAGRAM

Federalists and Anti-Federalists

In this activity, you will analyze arguments advanced by prominent Federalists and
Anti-Federalists during the debate over ratification of the Constitution.

ACTIVITY TYPE: DIAGRAM

Milestones in the Creation of the Constitution

Use this chart to record key dates in the drafting and ratification of the Constitution.

ACTIVITY TYPE: YOU AS JOURNALIST

The Constitutional Convention

In this activity, you will take the role of a delegate at the Constitutional Convention who
is interviewing one of your fellow Framers to clarify his positions on the key issues being
discussed. You will write both your interview questions and your fellow Framer's responses.

ACTIVITY TYPE: DIAGRAM

The Framers of the Constitution: Areas of Disagreement

In this activity, you will use a Comparison Chart to summarize the opposing ideas of
groups at the Constitutional Convention, explain each group's reasoning for its position,
and summarize the compromise that was reached.

ACTIVITY TYPE: SOCIAL STUDIES EXPLANATION

Creating a Government

In this activity, you will use the template to assemble evidence from the sources you
have explored. Then, you will write an answer to the Essential Question and defend your
answer with supporting evidence.

Elaborate Activities

photo: Discovery Education

INVESTIGATION TYPE: HISTORICAL
PERSPECTIVES

The New Nation

In this investigation, you will read the opinions
of four individuals who might have lived in the
colonies during the 1780s. Then, you will identify
how you think each person would respond to
three key issues of the day and compare your
answers with the historically likely perspectives
on each issue.

PROJECTS AND ASSESSMENTS *(continued)*

photo: Library of Congress

ACTIVITY TYPE: EXPRESS YOUR OPINION

Federalists and Anti-Federalists

Do you support the Federalists, who urge ratification of the Constitution, or the Anti-Federalists, who oppose ratification? In this activity, you will write an op-ed article that explains which side you support. You will examine the arguments of Federalists and Anti-Federalists and consider the points raised by both groups when constructing your argument. As an option, you may record your op-ed as a video presentation.

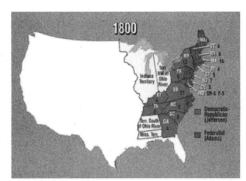

photo: IRC

ACTIVITY TYPE: CURRENT EVENTS CONNECTION

Issues of Power

In this activity, you will create a slide show called "Issues of Power: Then and Now" for a museum exhibit about the U.S. Constitution. Your slide show will show how two issues that were debated in 1787 are still part of the give-and-take of American politics today.

photo: National Archives

ACTIVITY TYPE: DOCUMENT-BASED INVESTIGATION

A Democratic Government?

Did the Framers of the Constitution create a democratic system of government in the United States? In this activity, you will answer this question by writing either a Constitution Day speech or a response to a blog post and supporting your statements with information that you gather from historical documents.

Evaluate Activities

BRIEF-CONSTRUCTED RESPONSE (BCR)

Creating a Government

EXTENDED-CONSTRUCTED RESPONSE (ECR)

Creating a Government

photo: National Archives

UNIT 2: BECOMING AN INDEPENDENT NATION (1776 TO 1800)

Chapter 4: Establishing a New Government
4.3 A More Perfect Union

LESSON OVERVIEW

Lesson Objectives:

By the end of this lesson, you should be able to:

- **Explain the organization of the Constitution and describe its important features.**

- **Explain how the Constitution reflects American democratic principles, including separation of powers, checks and balances, judicial review, individual rights, limited government, and consent of the governed.**

- **Compare the most important features of the government created by the Articles of Confederation with the most important features of the federal form of government created by the Constitution.**

Key Vocabulary

amendment, Articles of Confederation, Baron de Montesquieu, bicameral, Bill of Rights, bond, cabinet, checks and balances, confederation, Congress, Constitution, Elastic Clause, electoral vote, executive branch, federal, impeach, judicial branch, judicial review, legislative branch, limited government, Magna Carta, popular sovereignty, preamble, separation of powers, Supremacy Clause, Supreme Court, treaty, unicameral, veto

Lesson Essential Question:

How does the Constitution reflect major principles of American democracy?

FLASHCARDS

1 ▸ Features of the Constitution

The U.S. Constitution is made up of a Preamble and seven articles that created the structure of our national government.

- **The Preamble is an introduction that lists the purposes of the document.**
- **Articles I, II, and III describe the structure and powers of the three branches of government. They also explain how people become part of each branch.**
- **Articles IV–VII describe other aspects of the government. These include relations among the states, relations between the federal and state governments, and the process of amending the Constitution.**

Why Does It Matter?

The Constitution is one of the shortest national constitutions in the world, but it has lasted the longest and created a form of government that continues to work more than 200 years after its creation.

photo: Jupiterimages Corporation
The U.S. Constitution contains seven articles introduced by a Preamble.

2 ▸ Principles of American Democracy

The Framers of the Constitution crafted a unique form of government to create a balance between the power of the government and the rights of the governed.

- **Consent of the governed: The power of the government comes from the citizens.**
- **Limited government: No one person or group should become too powerful. Separation of powers among three branches, a system of checks and balances, and the federal structure of government are all ways the Constitution limits power.**
- **Individual rights: All people have rights that the government must respect. Individual rights place limits on what powers a government may have.**

Why Does It Matter?

These principles of American democracy still guide U.S. leaders and citizens today.

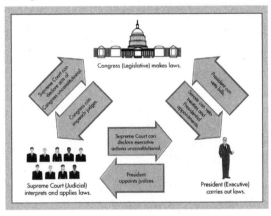

photo: Discovery Education
Important principles of the U.S. government are federalism, separation of powers, checks and balances, and the supremacy of the federal government over the states.

FLASHCARDS *(continued)*

3 **Comparing Forms of Governments**

The government that was created by the Constitution was very different from the previous national government, which had been created by the Articles of Confederation.

- **Federalism:** Under the Articles, the structure of government was a Confederation, which was a loose union of states with little central power. Under the Constitution, the government has a federal structure, which means the national government and the states share power, but the national government is supreme.

- **Complexity:** Under the Articles of Confederation, the government had only one branch, a legislature. The government created by the Constitution has three branches with different powers and responsibilities.

Why Does It Matter?

The government under the Articles of Confederation was not strong enough for the United States to succeed. Under the Constitution, the United States has become a world power that values freedom and individual rights.

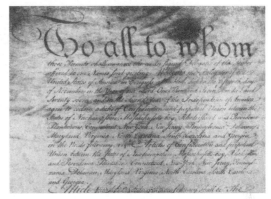

photo: IRC

How did the Constitution address the weaknesses of the Articles of Confederation?

Name _____ Date _____

GRAPHIC ORGANIZER: Categorization Chart

Complete this Categorization Chart with information about the main ideas and significance of each part of the Constitution. For supporting resources, go to Becoming an Independent Nation > Establishing a New Government > A More Perfect Union > Explore.

Section	Main Idea	Significance
1. Preamble		
2. The Parts of the Government (Articles I-III)		
3. How the Government Works (Articles IV-VII)		
4. Amendments		

© Discovery Education | www.DiscoveryEducation.com

Name _____ Date _____

GRAPHIC ORGANIZER: Comparison Chart

Complete this Comparison Chart with information about each branch of the government. For supporting resources, go to Becoming an Independent Nation > Establishing a New Government > A More Perfect Union > Explore > The Legislative Branch (Article I).

Criteria	Legislative Branch	Judicial Branch	Executive Branch
Supporters			
Members			
Structure			
Powers			
Checks			

Name _____ Date _____

 GRAPHIC ORGANIZER: Comparison Chart

Use this Comparison Chart to identify the principles of government found in the new Constitution. For supporting resources, go to Becoming an Independent Nation > Establishing a New Government > A More Perfect Union > Explore > Democratic Principles.

Define the Principle.	Why Is This Principle Important to Maintaining a Democratic System of Government?	How Does the Constitution Support This Principle?
Popular Sovereignty:		
Individual Rights:		
Limited Government:		

Name _____ Date _____

GRAPHIC ORGANIZER: Comparison Chart *(continued)*

Define the Principle.	Why Is This Principle Important to Maintaining a Democratic System of Government?	How Does the Constitution Support This Principle?
Separation of Powers:		
Checks and Balances:		
Federalism:		
Republicanism:		

Name _____ **Date** _____

GRAPHIC ORGANIZER: Comparison Chart

Use this Comparison Chart to compare and contrast information about the Articles of Confederation and the Constitution. For supporting resources, go to Becoming an Independent Nation > Establishing a New Government > A More Perfect Union > Explore > A More Perfect Union?

Criteria	Articles of Confederation	Constitution
Who Held the Power?		
How Was the Government Structured?		
How Was Government Power Limited?		

© Discovery Education | www.DiscoveryEducation.com

Name _____ Date _____

EXPLORE: FOCUS QUESTIONS

Using what you learned from the Core Interactive Text, answer each page's focus question:

Features of the Constitution
How is the Constitution organized?

_____

_____

_____

The Legislative Branch (Article I)
What are the powers of the legislature?

_____

_____

_____

The Legislative Process
What is the basic lawmaking process in the federal government?

_____

_____

_____

Influencing Legislation
How does the Constitution provide opportunities for citizens to participate in the political process?

_____

_____

_____

The Executive Branch (Article II)
What are the powers of the president?

_____

_____

_____

The Judicial Branch (Article III)
What are the powers of the judiciary?

_____

_____

Name _____ Date _____

EXPLORE: FOCUS QUESTIONS *(continued)*

Democratic Principles
What democratic principles are reflected in the Constitution?

_____
_____
_____

How Much Is Too Much?
How does the Constitution limit the powers of the government?

_____
_____
_____

A More Perfect Union?
What is federalism?

_____
_____
_____

Federal Supremacy
How does the Constitution balance power between the federal government and the states?

_____
_____
_____

PROJECTS AND ASSESSMENTS

Explain Activities

ACTIVITY TYPE: VISUALIZATION

Characteristics of Civic Virtue

Use the story frames to illustrate the following characteristics of civic virtue: accepting responsibility for one's behavior, supporting one's family, obeying rules and laws, staying informed, voting, and jury service. Provide an image representing each characteristic of civic virtue and write a caption explaining the importance of each.

ACTIVITY TYPE: DIAGRAM

A More Perfect Union

In this activity, you will restate the Preamble in your own words and then provide examples of how the goals stated in the Preamble are met today.

ACTIVITY TYPE: QUICK WRITE

A More Perfect Union

In this Quick Write activity, you will imagine that you are a member of one branch of the federal government. Explain how your branch of the government limits, and is limited by, the other two branches.

ACTIVITY TYPE: DIAGRAM

Constitutional Principles Scavenger Hunt

In this activity, you will conduct a scavenger hunt to find evidence of democratic principles in the U.S. Constitution.

ACTIVITY TYPE: DIAGRAM

What Does the Constitution Say?

In this activity, you will organize and interpret information from an outline of the U.S. Constitution.

ACTIVITY TYPE: SOCIAL STUDIES EXPLANATION

A More Perfect Union

In this activity, you will use the template to assemble evidence from the sources you have explored. Then, you will write an answer to the Essential Question and defend your answer with supporting evidence.

PROJECTS AND ASSESSMENTS *(continued)*

Elaborate Activities

photo: National Archives

INVESTIGATION TYPE: SOURCE ANALYSIS

Constitution

What are the basic characteristics of the U.S. government as described in the Constitution? In this investigation, you will analyze the main parts of the Constitution and explain the purpose of each.

photo: Library of Congress

ACTIVITY TYPE: PITCH YOUR IDEA

A Constitutional Amendment

In this activity, you will choose one of two constitutional issues and draft a proposal for a constitutional amendment that would resolve the issue.

photo: Getty Images

ACTIVITY TYPE: PITCH YOUR IDEA

Civic Virtue Project

In this activity, you will select one characteristic of civic virtue as a focal point for identifying a problem in your school or local community and evaluate what can be done to help address it through a civic virtue project.

photo: IRC

ACTIVITY TYPE: YOU AS ARTIST

Ratify the Constitution

In this activity, you will create a print advertisement to persuade people that the Constitution will solve the problems created under the Articles of Confederation.

PROJECTS AND ASSESSMENTS *(continued)*

photo: Library of Congress

ACTIVITY TYPE: DOCUMENT-BASED INVESTIGATION

Limited Federal Government

In this activity, you will create a speech that gives historical and modern-day examples of instances in which government action went or tried to go too far or was checked by either the voters or other parts of the government.

Evaluate Activities

BRIEF-CONSTRUCTED RESPONSE (BCR)

A More Perfect Union

EXTENDED-CONSTRUCTED RESPONSE (ECR)

A More Perfect Union

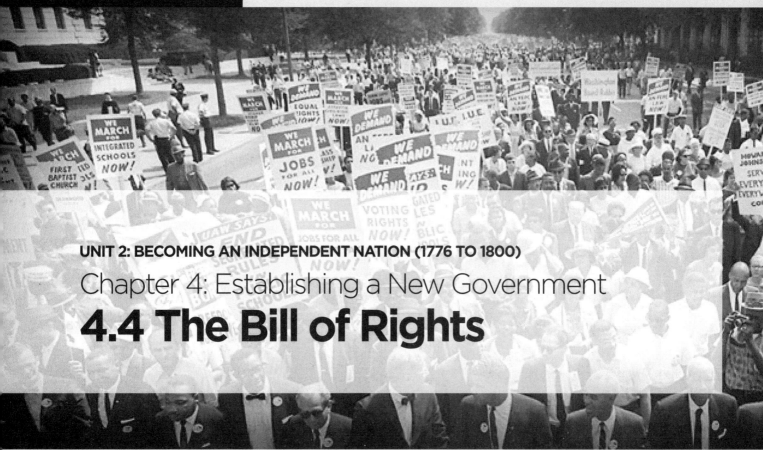

UNIT 2: BECOMING AN INDEPENDENT NATION (1776 TO 1800)

Chapter 4: Establishing a New Government

4.4 The Bill of Rights

photo: Getty Images

LESSON OVERVIEW

Lesson Objectives:

By the end of this lesson, you should be able to:

- Explain the political and historical significance of the Bill of Rights.
- Explain the importance of specific rights and freedoms guaranteed by the Bill of Rights.

Lesson Essential Question:

How does the Bill of Rights help government balance rights and order in the U.S. political system?

Key Vocabulary

amendment, Bill of Rights, civil law, criminal law, defendant, delegated, double jeopardy, due process, Eighth Amendment, eminent domain, English Bill of Rights, exclusionary rule, *Federalist* Papers, Fifth Amendment, First Amendment, Fourth Amendment, George Mason, grand jury, indictment, James Madison, John Hancock, John Peter Zenger, jury, majority rule, Ninth Amendment, Patrick Henry, probable cause, prosecution, protest, Samuel Adams, Second Amendment, seizure, self-incrimination, Seventh Amendment, Sixth Amendment, Tenth Amendment, Third Amendment, tyranny, warrant

FLASHCARDS

1

Keeping Citizens Safe from a Stronger Government

Because the Constitution made the federal government more powerful, the Framers added the Bill of Rights to help protect the rights of citizens and limit the power of government.

- The Constitution proposed in 1787 had seven articles that described the structure and powers of government. These did not explicitly state the rights of the people.
- Anti-Federalists demanded a bill of rights before they would accept the new constitution.
- During the ratification debates, Federalists promised adding a bill of rights as soon as the Constitution was ratified.
- The Bill of Rights, consisting of the first 10 amendments to the Constitution, was adopted by Congress in 1789 and then ratified by the states in 1791.
- The Bill of Rights limited the power of the federal government by explicitly stating rights that the government cannot take away.Why Does It Matter?
- Adding the 10 amendments of the Bill of Rights was crucial for ratification of the Constitution. Debates throughout U.S. history over how to apply and interpret specific rights demonstrate the ongoing importance of the Bill of Rights in limiting government.

Why Does It Matter?

Adding the 10 amendments of the Bill of Rights was crucial for ratification of the Constitution. Debates throughout U.S. history over how to apply and interpret specific rights demonstrate the ongoing importance of the Bill of Rights in limiting government.

photo: Library of Congress
A black-and-white photograph of the Bill of Rights was taken in the 1920s.

2

Safeguarding Specific Rights

The Bill of Rights details personal liberties protected for all citizens.

- The First Amendment guarantees freedom of religion, assembly, speech, and press.
- The Second Amendment guarantees the right of state militia members to bear arms.
- The Third Amendment guarantees that citizens cannot be forced to surrender their homes to soldiers.
- The Fourth through Eighth Amendments prevent abuses by the courts and the police.
- The Ninth Amendment states that citizens have more rights than just those stated in the Constitution.
- The Tenth Amendment reserves all the power not held by the federal government to the people or the states.

Why Does It Matter?

The rights protected by the Bill of Rights help the government balance maintaining order with protecting rights. Debate over the full intent of the amendments has been the subject of thousands of court cases, such as *Tinker v. Des Moines* and *Miranda v. Arizona*, which further clarified the rights of citizens. The continuing debates over these rights prove their enduring importance in the modern United States.

photo: Corbis
The United States fought World War II to preserve our basic freedoms, such as freedom of speech and assembly.

Name _____ Date _____

 GRAPHIC ORGANIZER: Outline

Use this Outline to summarize the rights that each amendment in the Bill of Rights protects and provide an example of that protection. An example has been completed for you. For supporting resources, go to Becoming an Independent Nation > Establishing a New Government > The Bill of Rights > Explore > Protecting the People.

I. Amendment 1	A. Freedom of Speech 1. Journalists can criticize presidents without going to jail.
II. Amendment 2	
III. Amendment 3	
IV. Amendment 4	
V. Amendment 5	

Name _____ Date _____

GRAPHIC ORGANIZER: Outline *(continued)*

VI. Amendment 6	
VII. Amendment 7	
VIII. Amendment 8	
IX. Amendment 9	
X. Amendment 10	

Name _____ Date _____

EXPLORE: FOCUS QUESTIONS

Using what you learned from the Core Interactive Text, answer each page's focus question:

Rights Before the Revolution

Why were Americans fearful of a strong central government?

_____
_____
_____

Protecting the People

How did the Bill of Rights calm peoples' fears about a strong central government?

_____
_____
_____

Personal Liberty

How does the Bill of Rights protect personal freedom?

_____
_____
_____

Rights of the Accused

How does the Bill of Rights protect against abuse of the justice system?

_____
_____
_____

Limited Government

How does the Bill of Rights limit the power of the central government?

_____
_____
_____

PROJECTS AND ASSESSMENTS

Explain Activities

ACTIVITY TYPE: ENCYCLOPEDIA ENTRY

The Bill of Rights

In this activity, you will write an encyclopedia entry describing one of the 10 amendments included in the Bill of Rights.

ACTIVITY TYPE: VISUALIZATION

The First Amendment

In this activity, you will identify key events that led to the addition of the free exercise and establishment clauses of the First Amendment. You will use story frames to trace and illustrate these events and use the captions to explain why these events were important.

ACTIVITY TYPE: QUICK WRITE

The Bill of Rights

In this activity, you will take a position on whether or not the Bill of Rights creates an appropriate balance between governmental power and individual liberty in the United States.

ACTIVITY TYPE: SOCIAL STUDIES EXPLANATION

The Bill of Rights

In this activity, you will use the template to assemble evidence from the sources you have explored. Then, you will write an answer to the Essential Question and defend your answer with supporting evidence.

Elaborate Activities

INVESTIGATION TYPE: ENDURING DEBATE

Liberty vs. Security

Should the government be able to restrict individual rights to preserve order and protect citizens? In this activity, you will analyze two opposing positions. Then, you will join in the debate.

PROJECTS AND ASSESSMENTS *(continued)*

photo: Getty Images

ACTIVITY TYPE: CURRENT EVENTS CONNECTION

Kelo v. City of New London, Connecticut

In this activity, you will write a letter to the Supreme Court justices who decided the case of *Kelo v. City of New London, Connecticut* in 2005.

photo: Getty Images

ACTIVITY TYPE: CLASSROOM DEBATE

The First Amendment and American Democratic Principles

In this activity, you will analyze the amendments in the Bill of Rights and think about their relevance today. You will then participate in a debate on the topic "Resolved: The First Amendment is the most important for preserving American democratic principles."

photo: Library of Congress

ACTIVITY TYPE: DOCUMENT-BASED INVESTIGATION

Was the Bill of Rights Necessary?

In this Document-Based Investigation, you will analyze and synthesize information from primary source documents to develop and defend an argument about whether the Bill of Rights was a necessary addition to the Constitution.

Evaluate Activities

BRIEF-CONSTRUCTED RESPONSE (BCR)

The Bill of Rights

EXTENDED-CONSTRUCTED RESPONSE (ECR)

The Bill of Rights

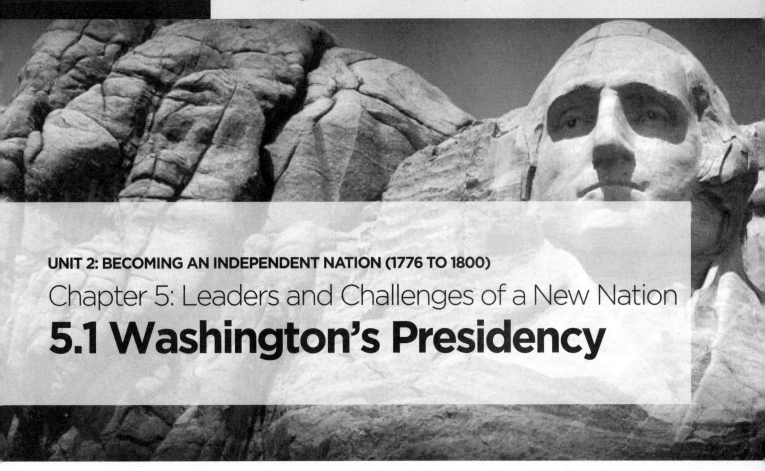

SOCIAL STUDIES TECHBOOK | Discovery EDUCATION

UNIT 2: BECOMING AN INDEPENDENT NATION (1776 TO 1800)

Chapter 5: Leaders and Challenges of a New Nation

5.1 Washington's Presidency

LESSON OVERVIEW

Lesson Objectives:

By the end of this lesson, you should be able to:

- Identify economic and governmental challenges of the new nation and analyze conflicting solutions to these problems proposed by the nation's leaders.

- Describe and explain the significance of precedents established during the presidency of George Washington and evaluate the significance of Washington's Farewell Address.

Lesson Essential Question:

In what ways did George Washington's presidency influence the future of the U.S. political system?

Key Vocabulary

Alexander Hamilton, Benjamin Banneker, cabinet, Democratic-Republican Party, Edmund Randolph, Federalists, French Revolution, George Washington, Henry Knox, Pierre L'Enfant, precedent, Thomas Jefferson, Washington's Farewell Address, Washington, DC

FLASHCARDS

1 ▶ Challenges of the New Nation

The new nation faced problems with its economy and with defining the new government.

- The federal government and the individual states were hampered by huge debts from the American Revolutionary War.
- Alexander Hamilton created a plan for the federal government to assume state debts.
- To pacify the Southern states that had already paid much of their debt, the national capital was relocated to the southern region of the United States.
- The Federalist Party emerged, arguing that the central government should be strong and powerful, while the Democratic-Republican Party called for state and local governments to hold most of the political power.

Why Does It Matter?

tSolving the financial problem strengthened the new U.S. government. Under George Washington's leadership, the United States proved that a government of the people, created by a written constitution, could work.

photo: IRC

The wide streets radiating out from the White House and the U.S. Capitol reflect designer Pierre Charles L'Enfant's vision for the capital city. How is the location and appearance of a nation's capital important?

2 ▶ Showing the Way

As the nation's first chief executive, George Washington set many precedents and gave important advice to the political leaders who followed him.

- Washington created the first panel of presidential advisers, known as the Cabinet.
- Washington decided the president should be called "Mr. President" instead of adopting a royal or monarchical title.
- Washington retired after serving two terms.
- In his Farewell Address, Washington warned Americans about the problems caused by political division.
- He also cautioned Americans about creating "entangling alliances" with other nations.

Why Does It Matter?

Presidents who came after George Washington followed his examples. They used people they trusted for advice to head executive departments, and they stepped down after two terms so that the U.S. government could experience new leadership.

photo: IRC

This painting shows George Washington in 1783.

Name _____ Date _____

EXPLORE: FOCUS QUESTIONS

Using what you learned from the Core Interactive Text, answer each page's focus question:

Washington Sets Some "Firsts"

What examples did George Washington establish that others would follow?

_____

_____

_____

A New Nation, Conceived in Debt

How did the United States deal with its debt problems after the Revolutionary War?

_____

_____

_____

Playing Politics

How did political parties emerge?

_____

_____

_____

Washington Bids Farewell

What advice did George Washington give to the country as he left office?

_____

_____

_____

PROJECTS AND ASSESSMENTS

Explain Activities

ACTIVITY TYPE: MOVIE TRAILER

Washington's Presidency

In this activity, you will use story frames to create a movie trailer for a documentary film, *The First President*.

ACTIVITY TYPE: DIAGRAM

Parties and Issues

In this activity, you will use a Comparison Chart to identify major issues, major political parties, major political parties' views on different issues, and the most important political outcomes for the following time periods.

ACTIVITY TYPE: QUICK WRITE

Washington's Presidency

In this Quick Write activity, you will write from the point of view of an American voter in the election of 1792. Analyze the issues that divide the country, including whether to support France's revolutionary government, whether to support the National Bank, and whether to have a strong federal government controlling the states.

ACTIVITY TYPE: SOCIAL STUDIES EXPLANATION

Washington's Presidency

In this activity, you will use the template to assemble evidence from the sources you have explored. Then, you will write an answer to the Essential Question and defend your answer with supporting evidence.

Elaborate Activities

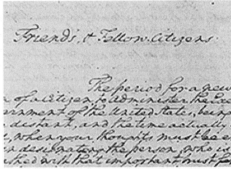

photo: The New York Public Library, Astor, Lenox, and Tilden Foundations

INVESTIGATION TYPE: SOURCE ANALYSIS

Washington's Farewell Address to the Nation

When George Washington completed his last term as president, he published a letter about the issues that concerned him. Why is Washington's Farewell Address still important today? In this investigation, you will use the interactive Source Analysis tool to analyze the address and determine which issues he discussed are still relevant today.

PROJECTS AND ASSESSMENTS *(continued)*

photo: Library of Congress

ACTIVITY TYPE: CLASSROOM DEBATE

A Strong Central Government?

In this activity, you will take a position on the following topic: "Resolved: The Federalist interpretation of the Constitution is the best one for securing freedom and prosperity in our country."

photo: Discovery Education

ACTIVITY TYPE: CURRENT EVENTS CONNECTION

Entangling Alliances

In this activity, you will research how NATO was formed and why it still exists more than 60 years later. You will meet in a panel with other students to discuss the benefits and the costs of the U.S. membership in NATO. You will then write a letter to President Washington explaining why the United States joined NATO and describing aspects of U.S. membership of which he might approve and disapprove.

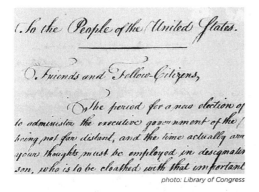

photo: Library of Congress

ACTIVITY TYPE: DOCUMENT-BASED INVESTIGATION

George Washington's Presidency

In this Document-Based Investigation, you will analyze source materials and investigate these questions: How influential was the presidency of George Washington? Based on his presidency alone, did he earn the title of "Father of Our Country"?

Evaluate Activities

BRIEF-CONSTRUCTED RESPONSE (BCR)

Washington's Presidency

EXTENDED-CONSTRUCTED RESPONSE (ECR)

Washington's Presidency

UNIT 2: BECOMING AN INDEPENDENT NATION (1776 TO 1800)

Chapter 5: Leaders and Challenges of a New Nation
5.2 Hamilton vs. Jefferson

photo: Getty Images

LESSON OVERVIEW

Lesson Objectives:

By the end of this lesson, you should be able to:

- Analyze the development of early political parties and ideologies, particularly those supported by Thomas Jefferson and Alexander Hamilton.

- Describe conflicts at home and abroad during the presidencies of George Washington and John Adams.

Lesson Essential Question:

How did the nation's early problems reveal different philosophies about government?

Key Vocabulary

"necessary and proper" clause, Alexander Hamilton, Alien and Sedition Acts, Bank of the United States, cabinet, Democratic-Republican Party, elitist, Federalist Party, implied power, Jay's Treaty, John Adams, Kentucky and Virginia Resolutions, national debt, neutrality, Neutrality Proclamation, political party, speculator, Thomas Jefferson, Whiskey Rebellion, XYZ Affair, *McCulloch v. Maryland*

FLASHCARDS

1 The Development of Political Parties

Disagreements about the powers of the federal government, international relations, and economic policy led to the development of political parties during the administration of George Washington.

- Secretary of the Treasury Alexander Hamilton and Secretary of State Thomas Jefferson both served in President Washington's cabinet.
- Alexander Hamilton and John Adams formed the Federalist Party in 1791.
- In 1792, Thomas Jefferson and James Madison formed what became known as the Democratic-Republican Party.
- Washington tended to agree with Hamilton on matters of policy.
- In the presidential election of 1796, both leading candidates represented political parties.

Why Does It Matter?

Despite George Washington's warnings, political parties became more influential, and national politics became increasingly combative.

photo: Corbis

When Washington first took office, there were no political parties like we know them today. The nation's first political parties, the Federalists and the Democratic-Republicans, soon formed because of political differences. Today, our two main political parties are the Republicans and the Democrats.

2 Challenges Faced by the New United States

Political division made it difficult for the government to deal with challenges in foreign relations and the economy.

- Alexander Hamilton proposed the federal government take action to address economic problems, including paying off Revolutionary War bonds, taking over the states' debts, imposing taxes, and establishing a national bank. All these measures were strongly opposed by Thomas Jefferson.
- War broke out between France and Great Britain in 1793. Federalists supported Britain, while Democratic-Republicans sympathized with France. George Washington issued the Neutrality Proclamation.
- Jay's Treaty with Britain angered the French, who then began to attack American ships.
- Although diplomatic ties with France were damaged by the XYZ Affair, President Adams was still able to negotiate a peace treaty.
- The Federalist majority in Congress enacted the Alien and Sedition Acts, which threatened freedom of the speech and the press.

Why Does It Matter?

The United States' two-party system was not created by the Constitution; it developed out of political conflicts. It has dominated our politics since 1792.

photo: IRC

What were some of the disagreements between the Federalists and the Democratic-Republicans?

Name _____ **Date** _____

GRAPHIC ORGANIZER: Comparison Chart

Use this Comparison Chart to take notes on the differences between the Federalists and the Democratic-Republicans. For supporting resources, go to Becoming an Independent Nation > Leaders and Challenges of a New Nation > Hamilton vs. Jefferson > Explore.

Criteria	Federalist Party	Democratic-Republican Party
Leaders		
Voting		
Economy		
Who Should Make Decisions?		
View on the Power of States		

© Discovery Education | www.DiscoveryEducation.com

Name _____ **Date** _____

GRAPHIC ORGANIZER: Hamilton vs. Jefferson Problem/Solution Chart

Use this Problem/Solution Chart to take notes on the problems faced by the new United States and how Alexander Hamilton proposed to solve them. For supporting resources, go to Becoming an Independent Nation > Leaders and Challenges of a New Nation > Hamilton vs. Jefferson > Explore > Dealing with Debt.

Problem　　　　　　　　　　　　　　　　　**Solution**

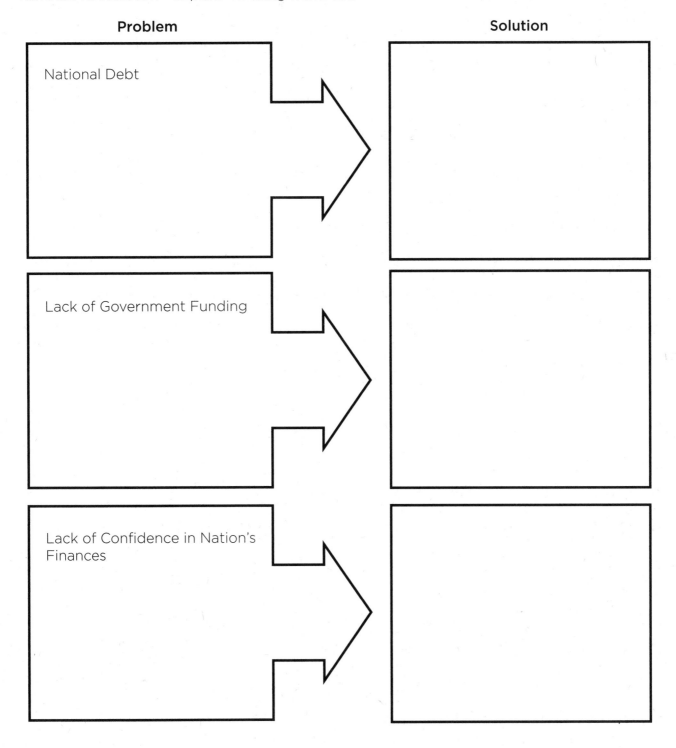

National Debt

Lack of Government Funding

Lack of Confidence in Nation's Finances

Name _____ **Date** _____

GRAPHIC ORGANIZER: Timeline

Use this Timeline to take notes on the major events related to the war between Great Britain and France. For supporting resources, go to Becoming an Independent Nation > Leaders and Challenges of a New Nation > Hamilton vs. Jefferson > Explore.

Date A   Date B

◆──◆

Name _____ Date _____

EXPLORE: FOCUS QUESTIONS

Using what you learned from the Core Interactive Text, answer each page's focus question:

The First U.S. Political Parties
Why did the first U.S. political parties form?

_____

_____

_____

Differing Views About Democracy
How democratic was the new government?

_____

_____

_____

Dealing with Debt
How did Hamilton address the nation's debt problem?

_____

_____

_____

The Business of America
What other economic measures did Hamilton offer?

_____

_____

_____

The National Bank
How did the National Bank become a source of debate?

_____

_____

_____

Name _____ Date _____

EXPLORE: FOCUS QUESTIONS *(continued)*

France vs. Britain
How did political differences affect foreign policy?

_____
_____
_____
_____

U.S. Neutrality Violated
Why did Great Britain and the United States sign Jay's Treaty?

_____
_____
_____

John Adams Takes Office
How did disagreements between the parties continue during John Adams's presidency?

_____
_____
_____

PROJECTS AND ASSESSMENTS

Explain Activities

ACTIVITY TYPE: ADVERTISEMENT

Hamilton vs. Jefferson

In this activity, you will create an advertisement for each political party.

ACTIVITY TYPE: DIAGRAM

Early Years of the Republic

In this activity, you will complete a Cause-Event-Effect diagram to describe causes and effects of key events that took place during the presidencies of George Washington and John Adams.

ACTIVITY TYPE: QUICK WRITE

Hamilton vs. Jefferson

In this activity, you will write a news broadcast covering economic issues facing the United States in the 1780s and early 1790s, Alexander Hamilton's proposed solutions, and various reactions.

ACTIVITY TYPE: SOCIAL STUDIES EXPLANATION

Hamilton vs. Jefferson

In this activity, you will use the template to assemble evidence from the sources you have explored. Then, you will write an answer to the Essential Question and defend your answer with supporting evidence.

Elaborate Activities

INVESTIGATION TYPE: ENDURING DEBATE

Jefferson vs. Hamilton

In this Enduring Debate, you will learn about Thomas Jefferson's and Alexander Hamilton's opposing views on federal power and share your thoughts on the role of national government.

PROJECTS AND ASSESSMENTS *(continued)*

photo: Library of Congress

ACTIVITY TYPE: DOCUMENT-BASED INVESTIGATION

Hamilton vs. Jefferson

In this Document-Based Investigation, you will analyze source materials and investigate this question: During the early national era, what problems did conflicting political philosophies create for the nation's new government?

photo: Library of Congress

ACTIVITY TYPE: SOCRATIC SEMINAR

National Security and Individual Rights

Before participating in the Socratic Seminar, you will read two excerpts—one from the Bill of Rights and one from the Alien and Sedition Acts of 1798. You will first read the text straight through to identify the main points. Keep the following questions in mind as you read: Does a democracy need individual rights protected? Is protecting national security reasonable rationale for the government to set limits on citizens' individual rights?

Evaluate Activities

BRIEF-CONSTRUCTED RESPONSE (BCR)

Hamilton vs. Jefferson

EXTENDED-CONSTRUCTED RESPONSE (ECR)

Hamilton vs. Jefferson

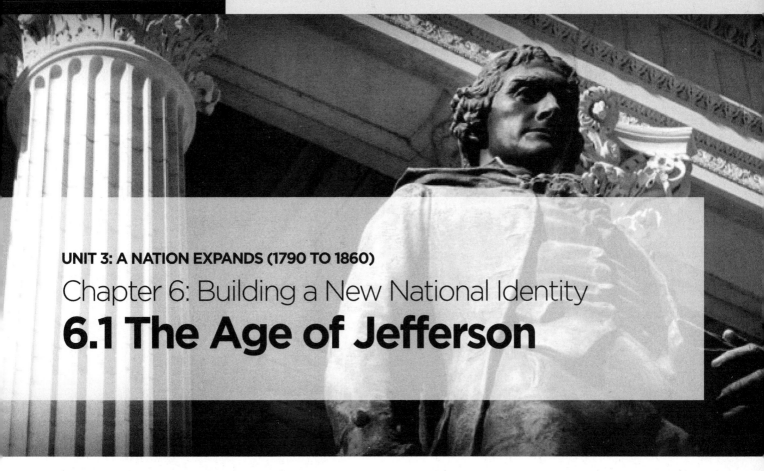

UNIT 3: A NATION EXPANDS (1790 TO 1860)

Chapter 6: Building a New National Identity

6.1 The Age of Jefferson

LESSON OVERVIEW

Lesson Objectives:

By the end of this lesson, you should be able to:

- **Summarize and assess the significance of key events that took place during the presidency of Thomas Jefferson.**

- **Describe provisions of the Louisiana Purchase and analyze its impact on the United States.**

Lesson Essential Question:

To what extent did Jefferson's actions as president reflect his principles?

Key Vocabulary

Aaron Burr, agrarian, Barbary Wars, Charles Maurice de Talleyrand, Chief Black Buffalo, Corps of Discovery, Dolley Madison, James Madison, James Monroe, John Marshall, judicial review, Judiciary Act of 1789, Judiciary Act of 1801, Lewis and Clark expedition, Louisiana Purchase, Louisiana Territory, Meriwether Lewis, national debt, Robert Livingston, Sacagawea, Shoshone, states' rights, states' rights doctrine, Thomas Jefferson, unconstitutional, West Point, William Clark, William Marbury, York

FLASHCARDS

1 Changing Direction of the Country

Thomas Jefferson was elected president in 1800 with Aaron Burr as his vice president.

- Jefferson wanted government to promote agriculture rather than industrialization.
- Jefferson cut funding to the military but preserved the National Bank.
- Anti-Federalism led to the repeal of the Alien and Sedition Acts and attempts to remove the Midnight Judges.
- In Marbury v. Madison, the U.S. Supreme Court, led by Chief Justice John Marshall, firmly established the principle of judicial review.

Why Does It Matter?

Jefferson only changed a portion of John Adams's Federalist actions. By preserving the Bank of the United States and by purchasing the Louisiana Territory, Jefferson seemed to accept some Federalist beliefs.

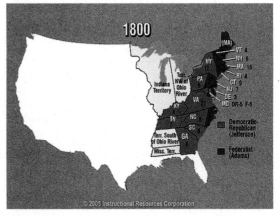

photo: IRC

This map shows the electoral votes by state in the election of 1800.

2 Eyes on the West

The Louisiana Purchase doubled the size of the United States for $15 million.

- In purchasing the Louisiana Territory, President Jefferson used a power that the Constitution did not explicitly delegate to him.
- William Clark and Meriwether Lewis led an expedition to chart the Louisiana Territory.
- The Corps of Discovery documented many previously unknown animals, plants, and Native American groups and reached the Pacific Ocean in 1805.
- The Shoshone woman Sacagawea served as guide to the Corps for a good portion of the expedition.

Why Does It Matter?

The Louisiana Purchase allowed room for westward expansion and also removed the French from North America. Charting Louisiana would benefit the United States, especially if it led to an accessible pathway to the Pacific Ocean. The expedition made peaceful contact with Native Americans in the west, mapped the Louisiana area, and reached the Pacific Ocean.

photo: IRC

The Corps of Discovery reached the Pacific Ocean in November 1805 and built Fort Clatsop to stay in for the winter. They spent that time searching for ship activity on the shores of the Pacific, but there was none.

FLASHCARDS *(continued)*

The World Beyond

Jefferson's Louisiana Purchase resolved problems caused by French and Spanish control of the Mississippi River and the Port of New Orleans.

- **Jefferson refused to make payments to leaders of North African states who demanded ransom and tribute payments for ships seized by the Barbary pirates. The United States sent naval forces to the Barbary Coast to protect American ships. U.S. Marines invaded the coast of present-day Libya in 1805.**

- **U.S. merchant ships faced troubles at sea during Jefferson's administration when another war broke out between Britain and France. This crisis led to the War of 1812.**

Why Does It Matter?

The country's expanded commerce and trade with the outside world had the unintended consequence of creating foreign policy crises in North Africa and Europe. In dealing with these crises, Jefferson was forced to confront his own principles to determine what was best for the future of the country.

photo: IRC

Thomas Jefferson was a designer and founder of the University of Virginia (1819).

Name _____ Date _____

GRAPHIC ORGANIZER: Cause/Event/Effect Chart

Use this Cause/Event/Effect Chart to record information about the causes and effects of major events of Jefferson's presidency. For supporting resources, go to A Nation Expands > Building a New National Identity > The Age of Jefferson > Explore.

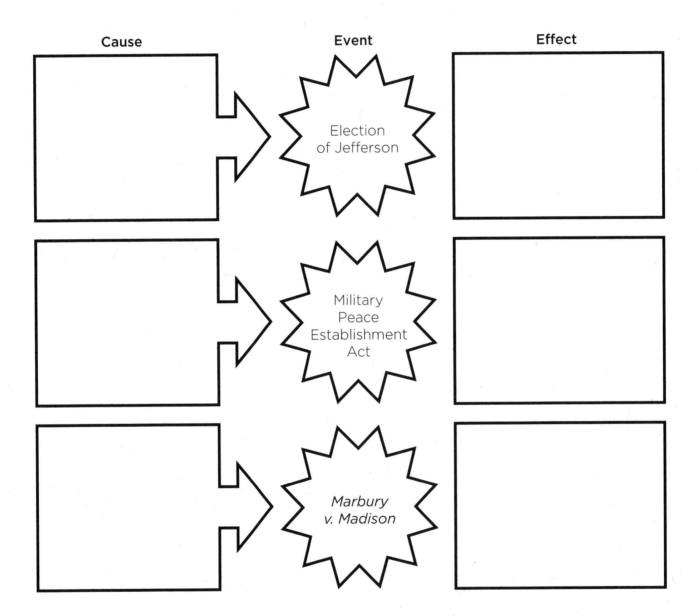

Cause   **Event**   **Effect**

Election of Jefferson

Military Peace Establishment Act

Marbury v. Madison

Name _____ **Date** _____

GRAPHIC ORGANIZER: Cause/Event/Effect Chart *(continued)*

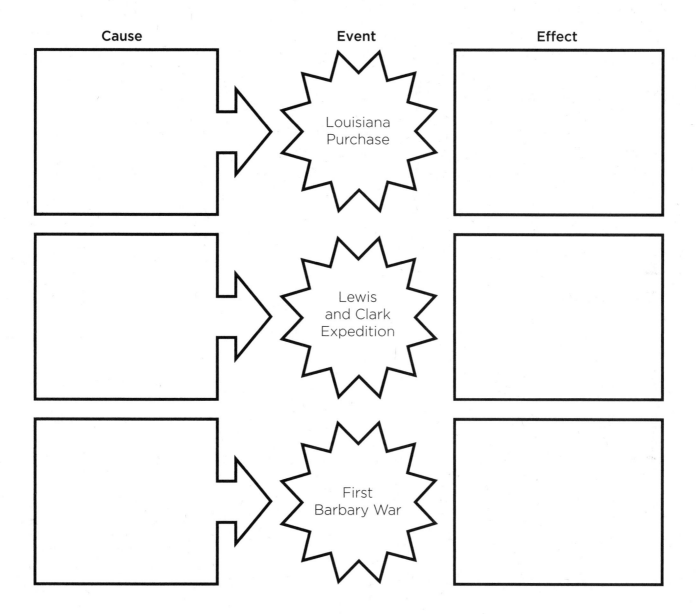

Cause	Event	Effect
	Louisiana Purchase	
	Lewis and Clark Expedition	
	First Barbary War	

Name _____ Date _____

GRAPHIC ORGANIZER: Landmark Case Brief

Use this Graphic Organizer to record important information about the landmark case *Marbury v. Madison*. For supporting resources, go to A Nation Expands > Building a New National Identity > The Age of Jefferson > Explore > *Marbury v. Madison* and Judicial Review.

I. Facts of the Case
Summarize events that took place that led to a dispute between two parties.

II. Question of Law
What questions about the meaning of the Constitution were the justices asked to consider?

Name _____ Date _____

GRAPHIC ORGANIZER: Landmark Case Brief *(continued)*

III. Decision and Outcome

A. How did the justices respond to the questions of law?

B. How did this decision affect the parties in the case?

IV. Reasoning

Why did the justices decide as they did?

V. Significance

In what ways did the impact of the Court's decision extend beyond the parties involved?

Name _____ Date _____

GRAPHIC ORGANIZER: Change Over Time

Use this Change Over Time Chart to record information about the Louisiana Purchase and its impact on the United States. For supporting resources, go to A Nation Expands > Building a New National Identity > The Age of Jefferson > Explore > Eyes on the West.

Before:	After:

Changes:

© Discovery Education | www.DiscoveryEducation.com

Name _____ Date _____

EXPLORE: FOCUS QUESTIONS

Using what you learned from the Core Interactive Text, answer each page's focus question:

Changing Direction of the Country

What ideals did Thomas Jefferson bring to the presidency?

_____

_____

_____

Marbury v. Madison and Judicial Review

What events led to the case of *Marbury v. Madison*, and how was it important?

_____

_____

_____

Eyes on the West

How did trouble with Napoleon lead to a huge land deal?

_____

_____

_____

Closing the Deal

How did the Louisiana Purchase become official?

_____

_____

_____

The Roots of Exploration

How did the famous Lewis and Clark expedition begin?

_____

_____

_____

Name _____ Date _____

EXPLORE: FOCUS QUESTIONS *(continued)*

The Journey West
How did Americans learn about the Louisiana Territory?

_____
_____
_____
_____

Accomplished Explorers
What did the Corps of Discovery accomplish?

_____
_____
_____
_____

Life in the Early Republic
How did American daily life and culture change during the early 1800s?

_____
_____
_____
_____

Foreign Affairs
How did Jefferson deal with foreign affairs?

_____
_____
_____
_____

PROJECTS AND ASSESSMENTS

Explain Activities

ACTIVITY TYPE: DIAGRAM

Judicial Review

Use at least 11 words from the word bank to create a graphic history of judicial review. You may add any other words or symbols, but you must use all of the starred words. Summarize your graphic diagram in a paragraph at the bottom and be prepared to present your thinking.

ACTIVITY TYPE: QUICK WRITE

The Age of Jefferson

In this Quick Write activity, you will write from the perspective of an early 19th-century American in December 1803, just as the Senate is poised to vote on ratification of the Louisiana Purchase treaty.

ACTIVITY TYPE: SOCIAL STUDIES EXPLANATION

The Age of Jefferson

In this activity, you will use the template to assemble evidence from the sources you have explored. Then, you will write an answer to the Essential Question and defend your answer with supporting evidence.

Elaborate Activities

photo: Getty Images

INVESTIGATION TYPE: TIMELINE MAP

Exploring the Louisiana Purchase

How did the Louisiana Purchase change the United States? In this investigation, you will use the Timeline Map interactive tool to trace the journey made by Meriwether Lewis and William Clark and to analyze the information they gained about the new land obtained from the Louisiana Purchase.

ACTIVITY TYPE: ENDURING DEBATE

Jefferson vs. Hamilton

In this Enduring Debate, you will learn about Thomas Jefferson's and Alexander Hamilton's opposing views on federal power and share your thoughts on the role of national government.

PROJECTS AND ASSESSMENTS *(continued)*

photo: Library of Congress

ACTIVITY TYPE: SAY WHAT?

Jefferson's Inaugural Address

In this activity, you will translate Jefferson's first inaugural address for modern times.

photo: Library of Congress

ACTIVITY TYPE: YOU AS ARTIST

The Age of Jefferson

In this activity, you will analyze a political cartoon from the Age of Jefferson. You will use the common elements of political cartoons to draw your own cartoon that will make a point about events during the Age of Jefferson.

photo: Library of Congress

ACTIVITY TYPE: DOCUMENT-BASED INVESTIGATION

The Age of Jefferson

In this Document-Based Investigation, you will analyze source materials and investigate these questions: Why did Thomas Jefferson authorize the Corps of Discovery expedition? Was the expedition motivated by Jefferson's desire for knowledge, his desire for American expansion, or his desire for commerce?

Evaluate Activities

BRIEF-CONSTRUCTED RESPONSE (BCR)

The Age of Jefferson

EXTENDED-CONSTRUCTED RESPONSE (ECR)

The Age of Jefferson

photo: IRC

UNIT 3: A NATION EXPANDS (1790 TO 1860)

Chapter 6: Building a New National Identity
6.2 The War of 1812

LESSON OVERVIEW

Lesson Objectives:

By the end of this lesson, you should be able to:

- Explain underlying issues and trace events that led to the War of 1812.
- Identify and describe key battles and important events from the War of 1812.
- Assess the impact of the War of 1812 on the United States.

Lesson Essential Question:

What was the impact of the War of 1812 on the early history of the United States?

Key Vocabulary

Andrew Jackson, Battle of New Orleans, Battle of Plattsburgh, Battle of Tippecanoe, Battle of York, Confederacy / Confederate States, Dolley Madison, embargo, Embargo Act, Fort McHenry, Francis Scott Key, impressment, James Madison, Non-Intercourse Act, Northwest Ordinance of 1787, Oliver Hazard Perry, Tecumseh, Tenskwatawa, "The Star-Spangled Banner," Treaty of Ghent, War Hawk, War of 1812, William Henry Harrison, Winfield Scott

FLASHCARDS

1 ▶ The United States and Britain Clash

Many factors contributed to the War of 1812, a second armed conflict between the United States and Britain.

- Britain stopped American ships at sea and seized cargo to prevent the French from receiving supplies.
- Britain captured American sailors, whom it accused of deserting, and impressed, or forced, them into service in its navy.
- In the Northwest Territory, the British supplied weapons to Tecumseh's confederacy of Native Americans who attacked settlers.
- The War Hawks successfully roused public sentiment to support the war and, they hoped, to win Canada.

Why Does It Matter?

The British resented the loss of their American colonies and did much to antagonize and bully the United States. Declaring and winning a war against Britain reasserted U.S. independence and increased national pride.

photo: IRC

This imagined scene from the frontier shows a British soldier offering rewards for American scalps.

2 ▶ Land and Sea

The War of 1812 was fought on land and sea in the Northwest, the Mid-Atlantic, and the Southeast.

- At the Battle of York, the Americans captured the capital of Upper Canada and set fire to several public buildings. In this way, the Americans won control of most of the Great Lakes.
- The United States took Lake Champlain in the Battle of Plattsburgh in 1814, securing the northern border of the United States.
- The Americans were unsuccessful in their attempts to invade Canada.
- The British invaded and burned Washington, DC, in 1814.
- U.S. forces repelled the British at Fort McHenry and prevented the capture of Baltimore. Francis Scott Key witnessed the battle and wrote about it in "The Star-Spangled Banner."
- Americans defended a critical port city and Andrew Jackson became a hero at the Battle of New Orleans.

Why Does It Matter?

The War of 1812 was the first contest of the United States against a foreign power since the Revolution. A second U.S. success against the world's mightiest military proved to the rest of the world and to Americans themselves that the United States was to be taken seriously.

photo: IRC

Captain Oliver Hazard Perry managed to defeat the British on Lake Erie, but the U.S. invasion of Canada was an utter failure. Why was it important to control the Great Lakes during the War of 1812?

FLASHCARDS *(continued)*

3 ▶ Results of the War

The War of 1812 did not result in an expansion of the U.S. borders or even a victory over the British. But it had an impact on the United States.

- bullet text Government buildings in Washington, DC, had to be rebuilt.
- The Treaty of Ghent created an armistice, or cease-fire, between the United States and Britain. It did not solve the problems that had caused the war, but it did remove British forces from U.S. territory.
- The relative success of the United States in the War of 1812 led to a surge of national pride.
- The United States gained prestige among other countries for its performance during the war.
- Political bipartisanship eased, and an era of cooperation, known as the Era of Good Feelings, began.

Why Does It Matter?

The War of 1812 was another important step in uniting Americans as a nation. Expelling the British from the Northwest Territory and breaking their alliance with the Native Americans there enabled settlers to continue pushing west.

photo: IRC

Many government buildings, including the U.S. Capitol, pictured here, had to be rebuilt after the British burned them in 1814.

Name _____ **Date** _____

GRAPHIC ORGANIZER: Timeline

Use this Timeline to order important events from 1807 to 1815 regarding the War of 1812. For supporting resources, go to A Nation Expands > Building a New National Identity > The War of 1812 > Explore.

1800   1820

◆━━━◆

Name _____ Date _____

GRAPHIC ORGANIZER: Summary Frames

Use these Summary Frames to summarize important events from 1807 to 1815 regarding the War of 1812. The storyboard should demonstrate the causes, course, and results of the war. For supporting resources, go to A Nation Expands > Building a New National Identity > The War of 1812 > Explore.

Name _____ Date _____

GRAPHIC ORGANIZER: Summary Frames *(continued)*

_____   _____   _____

_____   _____   _____

_____   _____   _____

Name _____ Date _____

EXPLORE: FOCUS QUESTIONS
Using what you learned from the Core Interactive Text, answer each page's focus question:

Great Britain Angers the United States
What caused tensions between the United States and Great Britain?

_____

_____

_____

Tecumseh and His Confederacy
What caused tensions between the U.S. government and Native Americans?

_____

_____

_____

A "Second War for Independence" Begins
What finally started the War of 1812?

_____

_____

_____

War on Land and Sea
What were the major battles of the War of 1812?

_____

_____

_____

An Era of Pride and Good Feelings
What were the results of the War of 1812?

_____

_____

_____

PROJECTS AND ASSESSMENTS

Explain Activities

ACTIVITY TYPE: ENCYCLOPEDIA ENTRY

The War of 1812

In this activity, you will create an encyclopedia entry for the War of 1812.

ACTIVITY TYPE: YOU AS JOURNALIST

The War of 1812

In this activity, you will take on the role of a journalist writing an article on the bicentennial of the War of 1812.

ACTIVITY TYPE: SOCIAL STUDIES EXPLANATION

The War of 1812

In this activity, you will use the template to assemble evidence from the sources you have explored. Then, you will write an answer to the Essential Question and defend your answer with supporting evidence.

Elaborate Activities

photo: Discovery Education

INVESTIGATION TYPE: HISTORICAL PERSPECTIVES

Perspectives on the War of 1812

In this Historical Perspectives investigation, you will hear four different accounts of relations between the United States and Great Britain and analyze the events that led to the War of 1812.

PROJECTS AND ASSESSMENTS *(continued)*

photo: Library of Congress

ACTIVITY TYPE: SAY WHAT?

"The Star-Spangled Banner"

In this activity, you will translate "The Star-Spangled Banner" into modern English.

photo: Library of Congress

ACTIVITY TYPE: CLASSROOM DEBATE

The Hartford Convention

In this activity, you will take a position on the following topic: Resolved: The New England states should secede from the United States of America in 1814 because their interests are not supported by the federal government.

photo: Library of Congress

ACTIVITY TYPE: DOCUMENT-BASED INVESTIGATION

The War of 1812

In this Document-Based Investigation, you will examine sources and investigate this question: Was the War of 1812 America's "Second War for Independence"?

Evaluate Activities

BRIEF-CONSTRUCTED RESPONSE (BCR)

The War of 1812

EXTENDED-CONSTRUCTED RESPONSE (ECR)

The War of 1812

UNIT 3: A NATION EXPANDS (1790 TO 1860)

Chapter 6: Building a New National Identity

6.3 Foreign Affairs

LESSON OVERVIEW

Lesson Objectives:

By the end of this lesson, you should be able to:

- Trace and explain the significance of events after the War of 1812 that led to the announcement of the Monroe Doctrine.
- Explain major provisions of the Monroe Doctrine and assess its immediate and long-term impact on U.S. foreign relations.

Key Vocabulary

Adams-Onís Treaty, Andrew Jackson, Convention of 1818, Democratic-Republican Party, First Seminole War, France, James Monroe, John Jay, John Quincy Adams, Kentucky and Virginia Resolutions, Monroe Doctrine, nationalism, Oregon Country, Rush-Bagot Agreement, Spain, XYZ Affair

Lesson Essential Question:

How did American foreign affairs after the War of 1812 reveal changing attitudes about the United States?

FLASHCARDS

1 ## Creating a Continental Nation

During James Monroe's term in office, the United States signed important treaties with Great Britain and Spain. These treaties established clear boundaries for the United States.

- **Agreements with Great Britain demilitarized the Great Lakes, set the border between Canada and the United States, and established joint ownership of the Oregon Territory.**
- **In the Adams-Onís Treaty, Spain gave up claims to the Oregon Territory and sold Florida to the United States. The treaty established the entire border between the United States and Spanish territory, from the Gulf of Mexico to the Pacific Ocean.**

Why Does It Matter?

The United States gained territory from the Atlantic to the Pacific and asserted power relative to other nations. Resolving international disputes enabled the United States to focus on internal issues such as economic development.

photo: IRC

In 1818 and 1819, the United States signed important treaties that gave the nation new territory and established its boundaries.

2 ## The Monroe Doctrine

As countries in South and Central America gained independence in the early 1800s, John Quincy Adams and James Monroe wanted to be sure European countries would not try to regain control of them.

- **Monroe gave a speech that became known as the Monroe Doctrine.**
- **The doctrine said that European countries should stay out of the affairs of the Western Hemisphere. It also said the United States would stay out of the affairs of Europe.**
- **The statement reflected the nationalism of the United States at the time, although the nation did not have the military power to back it up.**

Why Does It Matter?

The Monroe Doctrine established the principle that the United States would be the dominant power in the Western Hemisphere. Later presidents cited this doctrine to justify their involvement throughout Latin America and the Caribbean.

photo: IRC

The Monroe Doctrine changed the balance of power in the Western Hemisphere.

Name _____ **Date** _____

GRAPHIC ORGANIZER: Sequencing Chart

Use this Sequencing Chart to study how treaties and agreements signed between the United States and other nations benefited the United States. For supporting resources, go to A Nation Expands > Building a New National Identity > Foreign Affairs > Explore.

Agreement	Date	How Did This Agreement Benefit the United States?

Name _____ **Date** _____

GRAPHIC ORGANIZER: Problem/Solution Chart

Use this Problem/Solution Chart to show the problems Adams and Monroe believed would be solved by the Monroe Doctrine. For supporting resources, go to A Nation Expands > Building a New National Identity > Foreign Affairs > Explore > The Monroe Doctrine.

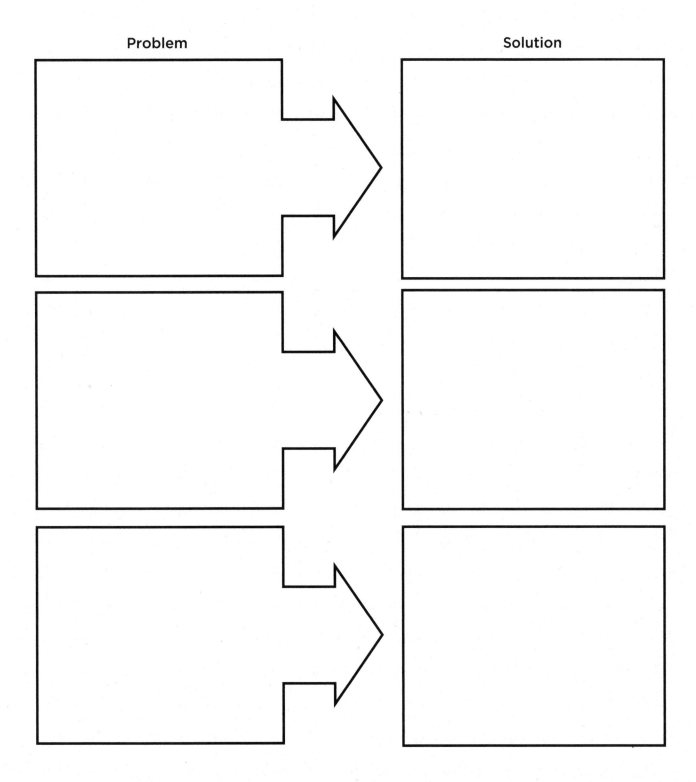

Problem   Solution

Name _____ **Date** _____

GRAPHIC ORGANIZER: Problem/Solution Chart *(continued)*

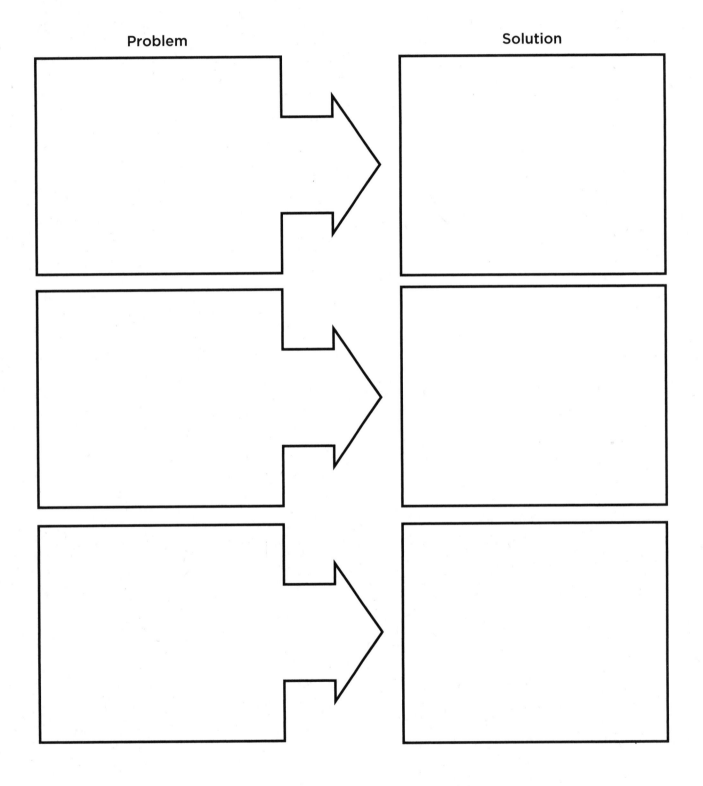

Problem   Solution

Name _____ Date _____

EXPLORE: FOCUS QUESTIONS

Using what you learned from the Core Interactive Text, answer each page's focus question:

Creating a Continental Nation

How did the United States settle its boundary with British Canada?

_____

_____

_____

Agreements with Spain

How did the United States gain territory from Spain?

_____

_____

_____

The Monroe Doctrine

Why did the United States issue the Monroe Doctrine? What was its impact?

_____

_____

_____

PROJECTS AND ASSESSMENTS

Explain Activities

ACTIVITY TYPE: VISUALIZATION

Foreign Affairs

In this activity, you will explore the ways in which the borders of the United States changed from the colonial era to the 1830s.

ACTIVITY TYPE: COMPARISON CHART

Foreign Affairs

Using information from the Core Interactive Text, record the following information: events and other factors leading to, countries involved in, provisions of, and outcomes of the agreements.

ACTIVITY TYPE: SOCIAL STUDIES EXPLANATION

Foreign Affairs

In this activity, you will use the template to assemble evidence from the sources you have explored. Then, you will write an answer to the Essential Question and defend your answer with supporting evidence.

Elaborate Activities

photo: National Archives

INVESTIGATION TYPE: SOURCE ANALYSIS

The Monroe Doctrine

What was the Monroe Doctrine? In this investigation, you will analyze the Monroe Doctrine to understand how it established a U.S. foreign policy.

PROJECTS AND ASSESSMENTS *(continued)*

photo: IRC

ACTIVITY TYPE: PITCH YOUR IDEA

Foreign Affairs

In this activity, you will evaluate the situation that arose in the Americas during the 1820s and decide whether the Monroe Doctrine or another solution of your own creation would be the best way to solve it.

photo: Getty Images

ACTIVITY TYPE: YOU AS ARTIST

Foreign Affairs

In this activity, you will analyze a political cartoon about the Monroe Doctrine to understand its point. Then, you will use the common elements of political cartoons to draw your own cartoon that will make a point about the Monroe Doctrine.

photo: IRC

ACTIVITY TYPE: DOCUMENT-BASED INVESTIGATION

Changing Perceptions

In this Document-Based Investigation, you will analyze source materials and investigate these questions: How did perceptions of the United States change during the tumultuous period between 1800 and 1825? Was the United States viewed on equal footing with foreign powers?

Evaluate Activities

BRIEF-CONSTRUCTED RESPONSE (BCR)

Foreign Affairs

EXTENDED-CONSTRUCTED RESPONSE (ECR)

Foreign Affairs

photo: Getty Images

UNIT 3: A NATION EXPANDS (1790 TO 1860)

Chapter 6: Building a New National Identity

6.4 Challenges of Expansion

LESSON OVERVIEW

Lesson Objectives:

By the end of this lesson, you should be able to:

- Locate and describe the expansion of U.S. territory that followed the War of 1812.
- Analyze consequences of territorial and westward expansion that followed the War of 1812.

Lesson Essential Question:

Did the benefits of American expansion outweigh the costs?

Key Vocabulary

Adams-Onís Treaty, American System, Andrew Jackson, Articles of Confederation, Battle of Horseshoe Bend, Daniel Boone, Erie Canal, *Gibbons v. Ogden*, Henry Clay, James Monroe, John Quincy Adams, Land Ordinance of 1785, Louisiana Purchase, *McCulloch v. Maryland*, meridian, National Road, Northwest Ordinance of 1787, pioneer, Second Bank of the United States, Seminole, Tariff of 1816, Treaty of Ghent

FLASHCARDS

1 ▸ The United States Grows

In the years after the Revolutionary War and the War of 1812, Americans eager for new economic and social opportunity spread to regions south and west of the first 13 states.

- **The Northwest Ordinance provided an orderly system by which territories could become states.**
- **Vermont became a state in 1791.**
- **Kentucky became a state in 1792.**
- **Tennessee became a state in 1796.**
- **Ohio became a state in 1803.**
- **Louisiana became a state in 1812.**
- **Indiana became a state in 1816.**
- **Mississippi became a state in 1817.**
- **Illinois became a state in 1818.**
- **Alabama became a state in 1819.**
- **In 1819, Spain agreed to sell Florida to the United States.**

Why Does It Matter?

The desire to spread across the continent began early in U.S. history. It continued until the United States reached "from sea to shining sea." Today, people come to America from other countries in search of new economic and social opportunities.

photo: IRC

A 20-star American flag like this one flew in 1818.

2 ▸ Costs and Benefits

American expansion came with costs and benefits.

- **As settlers moved west, they clashed with Native Americans.**
- **The American System was created to link the regions of the United States.**
- **Investments led to better roads, canals, and railways.**
- **The Second National Bank helped strengthen and stabilize the economy of the young nation.**
- **Tariffs benefited factory owners in the North but added to the cost of goods for Southerners and Westerners.**

Why Does It Matter?

Westward expansion in the early 1800s continued a bad trend for Native Americans. They would be pushed farther and farther westward onto less desirable land. Once the dominant culture of North America, they would gradually become less populous and powerful. The increasingly different characters of the North, South, and West made it a challenge to view the United States as single, whole nation. By linking the regions through improved transportation, the American System maximized the country's economic resources and helped it feel united.

photo: IRC

Chicago was one of the cities that benefited most from improvements in transportation.

Name _____ Date _____

 GRAPHIC ORGANIZER: Outline Map

Use this Outline Map to label the following items: U.S. territories, new states, and major geographic landmarks. Create a symbol for each geographic landmark that represents its historical importance. In the key on the next page, record each landmark you identify on the map, draw the symbol used to identify the landmark, and briefly describe the landmark's historical importance. Make sure you also label the dates the states were admitted to the Union. For supporting resources, go to A Nation Expands > Building a New National Identity > Challenges of Expansion > Explore.

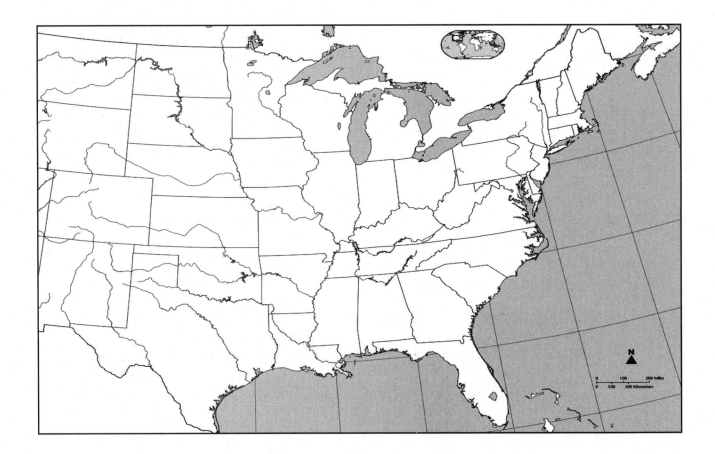

Name _____ **Date** _____

GRAPHIC ORGANIZER: Outline Map *(continued)*

Geographic Feature	Symbol	Description

Name _____ Date _____

GRAPHIC ORGANIZER: Landmark Case Brief

Use this Graphic Organizer to record important information about the landmark cases *McCulloch v. Maryland* (1819) and *Gibbons v. Ogden* (1824). For supporting resources, go to A Nation Expands > Building a New National Identity > Challenges of Expansion > Explore > The American System.

I. Facts of the Case
Summarize events that took place that led to a dispute between two parties.

II. Question of Law
What questions about the meaning of the Constitution were the justices asked to consider?

Name _____ Date _____

GRAPHIC ORGANIZER: Landmark Case Brief *(continued)*

III. Decision and Outcome
A. How did the justices respond to the questions of law?
B. How did this decision affect the parties in the case?

IV. Reasoning
Why did the justices decide as they did?

V. Significance
In what ways did the impact of the Court's decision extend beyond the parties involved?

Name _____ Date _____

EXPLORE: FOCUS QUESTIONS

Using what you learned from the Core Interactive Text, answer each page's focus question:

Settling the Northwest

How did the Northwest Ordinance aid the expansion of the United States?

_____

_____

_____

The Union Grows

Which Northern states were added to the Union at the beginning of the 1800s?

_____

_____

_____

New States in the Southeast

Which Southern states were added to the Union at the beginning of the 1800s?

_____

_____

_____

Native American Resistance

How did Native Americans react to America's early expansion?

_____

_____

_____

A System to Unify America

What was the American System?

_____

_____

_____

Name _____ Date _____

EXPLORE: FOCUS QUESTIONS *(continued)*

A National Transportation System
How does transportation improve?

_____

_____

_____

The American System
What economic measures supported the American System?

_____

_____

_____

PROJECTS AND ASSESSMENTS

Explain Activities

ACTIVITY TYPE: ADVERTISEMENT

The American System

In this activity, you will create an advertisement that either promotes or opposes the American System based on your examination of its costs and benefits.

ACTIVITY TYPE: QUICK WRITE

Westward Expansion

In this activity, you will use a diagram to assess how westward expansion impacted both the Native Americans and the U.S. settlers. You will then write a journal entry from the point of view of either a Native American or a U.S. settler.

ACTIVITY TYPE: SOCIAL STUDIES EXPLANATION

Challenges of Expansion

In this activity, you will use the template to assemble evidence from the sources you have explored. Then, you will write an answer to the Essential Question and defend your answer with supporting evidence.

Elaborate Activities

photo: Corbis

INVESTIGATION TYPE: MAP-GUIDED INQUIRY

Challenges and Opportunities for the Expanding Nation

What challenges and opportunities confronted Americans who settled in new states and territories after 1812? In this investigation, you will use the Map-Guided Inquiry interactive tool to examine whether the benefits of expansion outweighed the difficulties.

PROJECTS AND ASSESSMENTS *(continued)*

photo: Library of Congress

ACTIVITY TYPE: SAY WHAT?

Adams-Onís Treaty

In this activity, you will write a letter to the king of Spain and the president of the United States responding to the terms of the Adams-Onís treaty.

photo: The Macmillan Company

ACTIVITY TYPE: YOU AS ARTIST

The American System

In this activity, you will analyze a political cartoon to understand its point. Then, you will use the common elements of political cartoons to draw your own cartoon that will make a point about the American System.

photo: Library of Congress

ACTIVITY TYPE: DOCUMENT-BASED INVESTIGATION

Challenges of Expansion

In this Document-Based Investigation, you will analyze source materials and investigate this question: How did the treatment of Native Americans by the United States government compare to promises made in the Northwest Ordinance?

Evaluate Activities

BRIEF-CONSTRUCTED RESPONSE (BCR)

Challenges of Expansion

EXTENDED-CONSTRUCTED RESPONSE (ECR)

Challenges of Expansion

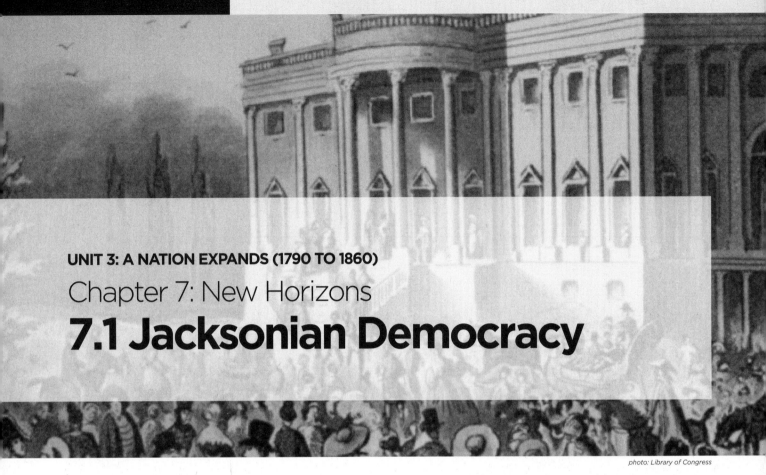

UNIT 3: A NATION EXPANDS (1790 TO 1860)

Chapter 7: New Horizons
7.1 Jacksonian Democracy

photo: Library of Congress

LESSON OVERVIEW

Lesson Objectives:

By the end of this lesson, you should be able to:

- Identify and describe philosophies and policies associated with Jacksonian democracy.

Lesson Essential Question:

Was Andrew Jackson a champion of democracy?

Key Vocabulary

Andrew Jackson, Corrupt Bargain, Democratic Party, Democratic-Republican Party, Henry Clay, Indian Removal Act, John C. Calhoun, John Quincy Adams, Kitchen Cabinet, nullification, Panic of 1837, Second Bank of the United States, spoils system, suffrage, veto, Whig Party

FLASHCARDS

1 The First "People's" President

Jackson won the election by assembling a coalition of voters including common laborers, small farmers, and factory workers. Many of these people had previously been denied the vote because they did not meet a property requirement.

- The Democratic Party based its campaign on recruiting many different groups of voters. They rallied under the accusation of a "corrupt bargain" between wealthy politicians and aristocrats.
- Parties became central to campaigns. No national politician could expect to be elected without the support of a party.
- Suffrage laws had changed to allow more men to vote.
- The 1828 election ushered in the "age of the common man," in which politicians realized they had to appeal to all American voters, rich and poor, to be successful.

Why Does It Matter?

The 1828 election was the most democratic election since the creation of the United States, with white men of all means allowed to vote in most states. The strategies used in the election of 1828 would influence the campaigns of candidates for years to come, including today. The election of 1828 also helped set a precedent for the dominance of the two-party system in U.S. politics.

photo: IRC

Andrew Jackson's Democratic Party changed elections forever in 1828.

FLASHCARDS *(continued)*

2 Jacksonian Policies

Jackson increased the power of the executive branch during his tenure as president. As president, Andrew Jackson:

- challenged South Carolina's attempt at nullification;
- attacked and destroyed the national bank and helped to create a private, more sectional banking system;
- formed the policy of removal of Native Americans to reservations, which was followed for decades to come;
- was the first president to use the spoils system to fill positions in the federal government; and
- used veto powers more than all six of the prior presidents combined.

Why Does It Matter?

Andrew Jackson was the first president of the United States to come from a family without wealth and not have a formal education. He wanted to reform the federal government policies to allow the people to be heard and erase corruption and made several long-lasting policy changes. He was extremely popular with the "common people" of the era, but the way he made the changes led his opponents to label him a king and tyrant.

photo: IRC

"To the Victors Belong the Spoils." Although this cartoon was published by Thomas Nast in 1877 to ridicule the "fraud, bribery, spoils, and plunder" of political corruption of that day, Andrew Jackson was credited with inventing the "spoils" system of giving the victors in an election the rewards of making job appointments. Jackson believed that governmental jobs required no special skills and could be held by any man, regardless of his education. Federal appointments were given without regard to skills or training to men who had helped Jackson win the presidency.

Name _____ **Date** _____

GRAPHIC ORGANIZER: Sequencing Chart

Use this Sequencing Chart by listing events in Andrew Jackson's life in chronological order. For supporting resources, go to A Nation Expands > New Horizons > Jacksonian Democracy > Explore.

Event	Date	Summary	Effect on Jackson's Route to the Presidency

Name _____ Date _____

GRAPHIC ORGANIZER: Sequencing Chart *(continued)*

Event	Date	Summary	Effect on Jackson's Route to the Presidency

Name _____ Date _____

GRAPHIC ORGANIZER: Comparison Chart

Use this Comparison Chart to note important aspects and features of Jackson's Democratic Party and his campaign and compare them to those of Clay and the Republicans. For supporting resources, go to A Nation Expands > New Horizons > Jacksonian Democracy > Explore > A Hotly Contested Election.

Criteria	Democratic Party	National Republican Party
Key Leaders		
Supporters		
Beliefs/Philosophies		

Name _____ Date _____

GRAPHIC ORGANIZER: Cause/Event/Effect Chart

Use this Cause/Event/Effect Chart to identify causes and effects for each event related to Andrew Jackson's presidency. For supporting resources, go to A Nation Expands > New Horizons > Jacksonian Democracy > Explore > "Old Hickory" Becomes "King Andrew."

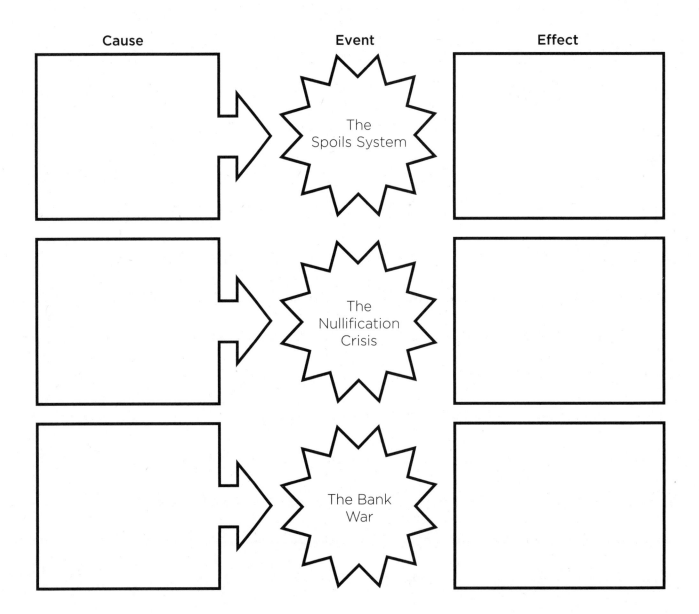

Cause	Event	Effect
	The Spoils System	
	The Nullification Crisis	
	The Bank War	

Name _____   Date _____

EXPLORE: FOCUS QUESTIONS

Using what you learned from the Core Interactive Text, answer each page's focus questions:

A Self-Made Man
Who was Andrew Jackson?

_____

_____

_____

Jackson Enters Politics
What inspired Jackson to enter politics?

_____

_____

_____

A Corrupt Bargain?
How could Andrew Jackson win the popular vote yet lose the election?

_____

_____

_____

A Hotly Contested Election
How did the Democratic Party win the 1828 presidential election?

_____

_____

_____

Jackson's Rivals
Who challenged Jackson in 1828—and why?

_____

_____

_____

Name _____ Date _____

EXPLORE: FOCUS QUESTIONS *(continued)*

"Old Hickory" Becomes "King Andrew"
How did Jackson's policies change American politics and government?

_____
_____
_____
_____

Jackson Resists Nullification
What did the Nullification Crisis show about Andrew Jackson?

_____
_____
_____
_____

Andrew Jackson's Bank War
Why did Americans disagree about the National Bank?

_____
_____
_____
_____

The End of the Bank
What steps did Andrew Jackson take to destroy the bank?

_____
_____
_____
_____

PROJECTS AND ASSESSMENTS

Explain Activities

ACTIVITY TYPE: MOVIE TRAILER

A Historic Veto

In this activity, you will create a movie trailer that will excite viewers and make them want to see this film about a key event in Andrew Jackson's presidency.

ACTIVITY TYPE: YOU AS JOURNALIST

Jacksonian Democracy

In the graphic organizer, identify the three events that you chose. Then, write two or three bullet points for each of the three events, explaining how the events shaped the presidency of Andrew Jackson and how they affected the American people.

ACTIVITY TYPE: DIAGRAM

Parties and Issues

In this activity, you will use a Comparison Chart to identify major issues, major political parties, major political parties' views on different issues, and the most important political outcomes for the following time periods.

ACTIVITY TYPE: SOCIAL STUDIES EXPLANATION

Jacksonian Democracy

In this activity, you will use the template to assemble evidence from the sources you have explored. Then, you will write an answer to the Essential Question and defend your answer with supporting evidence.

Elaborate Activities

photo: Library of Congress

INVESTIGATION TYPE: SOURCE ANALYSIS

King Andrew the First

What was the cartoonist's message in "King Andrew the First"? In this investigation, you will use the Source Analysis tool to identify important details in a famous political cartoon about Andrew Jackson. You will then analyze the cartoon, interpret its meaning, and respond to its message.

PROJECTS AND ASSESSMENTS *(continued)*

photo: IRC

ACTIVITY TYPE: EXPRESS YOUR OPINION

Jackson's Second Term

In this activity, you will create a report card grading Andrew Jackson on his performance in various areas of his presidency.

photo: IRC

ACTIVITY TYPE: PITCH YOUR IDEA

The Spoils System

In this activity, you will evaluate the spoils system and determine whether it was the most effective way of running the federal government.

photo: Library of Congress

ACTIVITY TYPE: DOCUMENT-BASED INVESTIGATION

Jacksonian Democracy

In this Document-Based Investigation, you will analyze source materials and investigate this question: Was Andrew Jackson a champion of democracy?

Evaluate Activities

BRIEF-CONSTRUCTED RESPONSE (BCR)

Jacksonian Democracy

EXTENDED-CONSTRUCTED RESPONSE (ECR)

Jacksonian Democracy

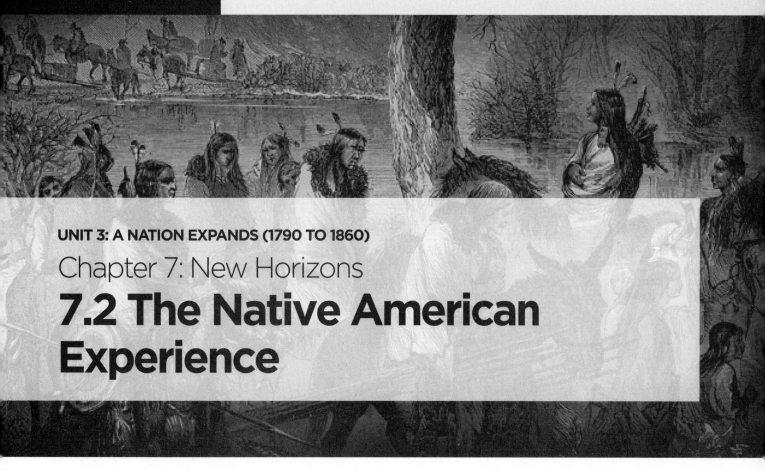

UNIT 3: A NATION EXPANDS (1790 TO 1860)

Chapter 7: New Horizons

7.2 The Native American Experience

LESSON OVERVIEW

Lesson Objectives:

By the end of this lesson, you should be able to:

- Evaluate American Indian relocation policies implemented during the presidency of Andrew Jackson.

Lesson Essential Question:

What were the causes and effects of Indian Removal policies during the 1830s?

Key Vocabulary

Andrew Jackson, Cherokee, *Cherokee Nation v. Georgia*, "Five Civilized Tribes", Indian Removal Act, Indian Territory, John Marshall, John Ross, *Johnson v. M'Intosh*, Oklahoma Territory, Osceola, Trail of Tears, *Worcester v. Georgia*

FLASHCARDS

1 ### The Tragedy of Native American Relocation

The government sought to displace Native Americans east of the Mississippi River so white settlers could take over their land.

- The Indian Removal Act required the federal government to negotiate treaties with Native Americans in the East.
- A series of Supreme Court decisions established the federal government's ownership of Native American lands and determined that Native American tribes were "domestic dependent nations."
- Some Native American groups signed treaties and relocated.
- The federal government fought a war in Florida to expel the Seminole.

Why Does It Matter?

The Native Americans lost their homes and their traditional ways of life. The United States continued to grow.

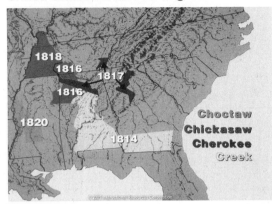

photo: IRC

How did the borders of the United States change under President Andrew Jackson?

2 ### The Trail of Tears

After being displaced from their homes, the Cherokee were forced to trek from Georgia to Oklahoma.

- The Cherokee were rounded up and held by the U.S. Army before being forced on the Trail of Tears.
- From 1838 to 1839, 4,000 Cherokee perished of starvation and disease.

Why Does It Matter?

The Cherokee resisted relocation by creating a constitutional government and battling the state of Georgia in court. Despite their peaceful attempts to appeal removal from their land, the tribe was forced into Indian Territory.

photo: IRC

What impact did settlers have on the Cherokee Nation, and how were the Cherokee removed from their native lands?

Name _____ Date _____

GRAPHIC ORGANIZER: Cause/Event/Effect Chart

Use this Cause/Event/Effect Chart to list the important causes and effects of each event related to the Native American experience during the 1800s. For supporting resources, go to A Nation Expands > New Horizons > The Native American Experience > Explore.

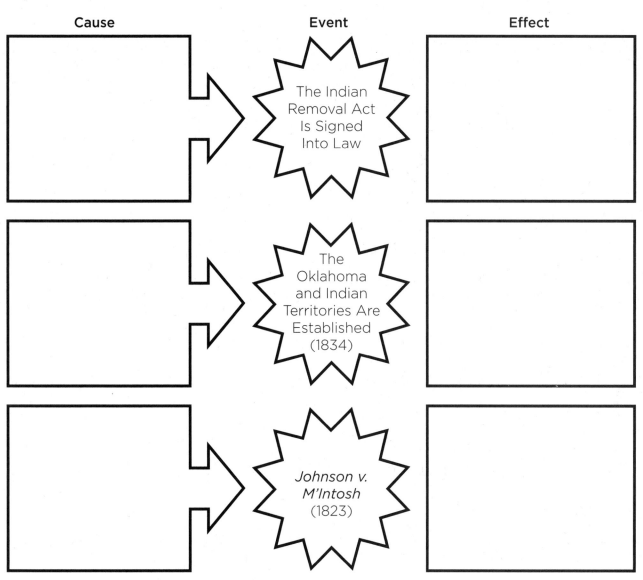

Cause	Event	Effect
	The Indian Removal Act Is Signed Into Law	
	The Oklahoma and Indian Territories Are Established (1834)	
	Johnson v. M'Intosh (1823)	

Name _____ Date _____

GRAPHIC ORGANIZER: Cause/Event/Effect Chart *(continued)*

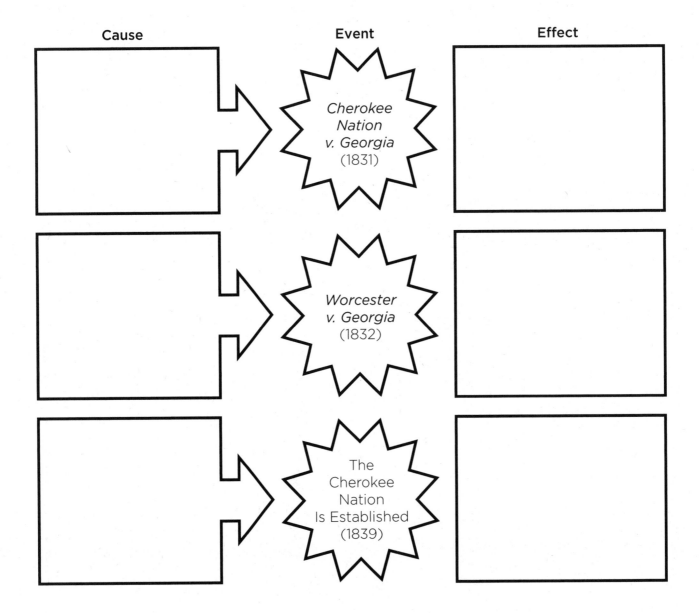

Cause	Event	Effect
	Cherokee Nation v. Georgia (1831)	
	Worcester v. Georgia (1832)	
	The Cherokee Nation Is Established (1839)	

Name _____ **Date** _____

GRAPHIC ORGANIZER: Cause/Event/Effect Chart *(continued)*

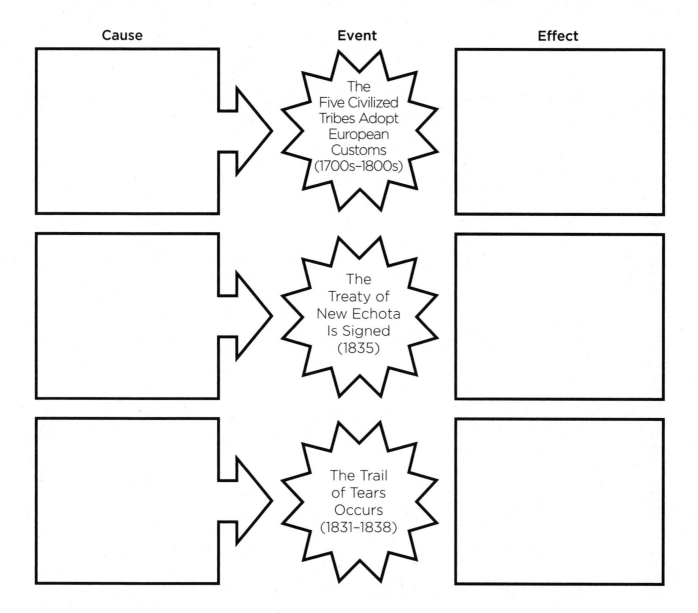

Cause	Event	Effect
	The Five Civilized Tribes Adopt European Customs (1700s–1800s)	
	The Treaty of New Echota Is Signed (1835)	
	The Trail of Tears Occurs (1831–1838)	

Name _____ Date _____

EXPLORE: FOCUS QUESTIONS

Using what you learned from the Core Interactive Text, answer each page's focus question:

Involuntary Exchange of Lands

What was the Indian Removal Act?

_____
_____
_____
_____

Native Americans and the Supreme Court

How did the Supreme Court influence government policies toward Native Americans?

_____
_____
_____
_____

An Attempt at Assimilation

Why did the "Five Civilized Tribes" adopt European customs?

_____
_____
_____
_____

Two Illegal Treaties

How did the attempts to gain Native American land end?

_____
_____
_____
_____

Betrayal and a Forced March

What happened during the Trail of Tears?

_____
_____
_____
_____

PROJECTS AND ASSESSMENTS

Explain Activities

ACTIVITY TYPE: VISUALIZATION

Native Americans

In this Story Frames activity, you will select the key events that you think were most important between 1829 and 1838 that led to the forced relocation of Native Americans. Then, you will represent each event by drawing pictures or finding images that tell the story.

ACTIVITY TYPE: CLASSROOM DEBATE

Indian Removal Act

You will conduct a short, informal debate with a partner on the Indian Removal Act.

ACTIVITY TYPE: SOCIAL STUDIES EXPLANATION

The Native American Experience

In this activity, you will use the template to assemble evidence from the sources you have explored. Then, you will write an answer to the Essential Question and defend your answer with supporting evidence.

Elaborate Activities

photo: Getty Images

INVESTIGATION TYPE: TIMELINE MAP

The Roots of Native American Removal

What problems were created when settlers pushed into Native American lands from eastern states? In this investigation, you will use the Timeline Map interactive tool to analyze the interactions between Native Americans and European settlers in what is now the southeastern United States.

PROJECTS AND ASSESSMENTS *(continued)*

photo: Library of Congress

ACTIVITY TYPE: ROLE PLAY

On the Trail of Tears

In this activity, you will imagine yourself as a news reporter who is witnessing the Cherokee on the Trail of Tears and write at least four diary entries describing the march.

photo: Library of Congress

ACTIVITY TYPE: DOCUMENT-BASED INVESTIGATION

A Cherokee Nation?

In this activity, you will create a museum exhibit that either supports or challenges the idea that the Cherokee Nation was an independent foreign country beginning in 1827. You will also prepare a speech that either supports or challenges this idea.

photo: Library of Congress

ACTIVITY TYPE: DOCUMENT-BASED INVESTIGATION

The Native American Experience

In this Document-Based Investigation, you will analyze source materials and investigate this question: Who was most responsible for the forced relocation of Native Americans from their homelands in the southeastern United States to Oklahoma?

Evaluate Activities

BRIEF-CONSTRUCTED RESPONSE (BCR)

The Native American Experience

EXTENDED-CONSTRUCTED RESPONSE (ECR)

The Native American Experience

photo: Getty Images

UNIT 3: A NATION EXPANDS (1790 TO 1860)

Chapter 7: New Horizons

7.3 Westward Expansion

LESSON OVERVIEW

Lesson Objectives:

By the end of this lesson, you should be able to:

- Explain the concept of Manifest Destiny and describe its effect on the territorial growth of the United States.
- Locate and identify areas acquired by the United States between 1836 and 1853.
- Discuss the causes, key events, and consequences of the Mexican-American War.

Lesson Essential Question:

What impact did Manifest Destiny have on the growth and development of the United States?

Key Vocabulary

49th parallel, abolition, Alamo, American River, California, Antonio López de Santa Anna, Arizona, Brigham Young, California, California Gold Rush, Californios, Donner Party, empresario, Father Miguel Hidalgo y Costilla, forty-niners, Franklin Pierce, Gadsden Purchase, James K. Polk, James Marshall, John Sutter, Juan Seguin, Junipero Serra, Kansas, Levi Strauss, Luzena Stanley Wilson, Manifest Destiny, Marcus Whitman, merchant, Mexican Cession, Mexican War / Mexican–American War, Mexico, Missouri, Mormons, Narcissa Whitman, Nebraska, New Mexico, Oklahoma (Indian Territory), Oregon Country, Oregon Territory, Oregon Trail, prospect, Republic of Texas, Sam Houston, Santa Fe Trail, Stephen Austin, subsistence farming, Texas, Texas Annexation, Texas Revolution, Treaty of Guadalupe Hidalgo, Wilmot Proviso, Zachary Taylor

FLASHCARDS

1 ▶ Manifest Destiny

In the 1840s, many Americans believed in the idea of Manifest Destiny.

- Manifest Destiny was the belief that the United States was destined to stretch all the way across the continent of North America.
- President James Polk was a supporter of Manifest Destiny. Soon after Polk was elected in 1844, he promised to enact policies to gain territory in the West.

Why Does It Matter?

Belief in this ideal led the United States to acquire a great deal of land.

photo: IRC

To Americans in the mid-1800s, Manifest Destiny meant that it was obvious, or manifest, that the fate, or destiny, of the United States was to expand from the Atlantic Ocean to the Pacific Ocean.

2 ▶ New Territories

From 1845 to 1853, the United States gained a large amount of new territory.

- In 1845, the United States annexed the Republic of Texas.
- In 1846, the United States and Great Britain signed a treaty giving the United States full control over the part of the Oregon Country that is south of the 49th parallel.
- As a result of winning the Mexican-American War, the United States gained most of the Southwest.
- In 1853, the United States bought a strip of land in what is now southern Arizona and New Mexico from Mexico.

Why Does It Matter?

In a relatively short period of time, the United States made territorial gains that stretched across the continent and created the continental boundaries that it has today.

photo: IRC

The United States gained more than 1.2 million square miles of land during this time period.

FLASHCARDS *(continued)*

3 ▶ The Mexican-American War

The United States fought a war against Mexico from 1846 to 1848.

- The United States and Mexico disagreed about the location of the Texas border.
- The war began after President James Polk sent U.S. forces into disputed territory and fighting broke out.
- U.S. troops won battles in New Mexico, California, northern Mexico, and southern Mexico.
- The war ended when the two sides signed the Treaty of Guadalupe Hidalgo in 1848, which took away almost half of Mexico's territory.

Why Does It Matter?

The Mexican-American War allowed the United States to gain a huge amount of territory, including states that make up much of the American Southwest and Pacific Coast. The country also gained new citizens who had been citizens of Mexico.

photo: IRC

Fighting and winning the Mexican-American War led to the Treaty of Guadalupe Hidalgo, which added the Southwest to the United States.

Name _____   **Date** _____

GRAPHIC ORGANIZER: Main Idea Web

Complete this Main Idea Web examining the political, social, and economic roots of Manifest Destiny. For supporting resources, go to A Nation Expands > New Horizons > Westward Expansion > Explore.

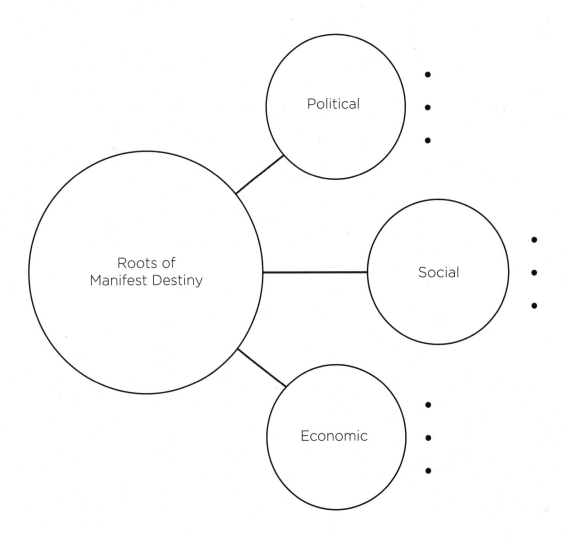

Name _____ Date _____

GRAPHIC ORGANIZER: Sequencing Chart

Use this Sequencing Chart to sequence the events in U.S. westward expansion 1836–1853. For supporting resources, go to A Nation Expands > New Horizons > Westward Expansion > Explore > The Oregon Country.

Event	Date	Summary	Significance

Name _____ Date _____

GRAPHIC ORGANIZER: Sequencing Chart *(continued)*

Event	Date	Summary	Significance

© Discovery Education | www.DiscoveryEducation.com

Name _____ **Date** _____

GRAPHIC ORGANIZER: Cause/Event/Effect Chart

Use this Cause/Event/Effect Chart to summarize the information on the causes, key events, and consequences of the Mexican-American War. For supporting resources, go to A Nation Expands > New Horizons > Westward Expansion > Explore > The Mexican-American War.

Causes	Event	Effects

Mexican-American War

Name _____ Date _____

EXPLORE: FOCUS QUESTIONS

Using what you learned from the Core Interactive Text, answer each page's focus question:

Manifest Destiny

What was Manifest Destiny, and what impact did it have on the United States in the mid-1800s?

_____
_____
_____

The Oregon Country

How did the United States acquire the Oregon Country?

_____
_____
_____

The Republic of Texas

How did the United States acquire Texas?

_____
_____
_____

The Mexican-American War

What were the causes and main events of the Mexican-American War?

_____
_____
_____

The Southwest

How did the United States gain control of the Southwest?

_____
_____
_____

Trailblazers

Who were some of the most famous explorers of the western United States?

_____
_____
_____

PROJECTS AND ASSESSMENTS

Explain Activities

ACTIVITY TYPE: DIAGRAM

Westward Expansion

In this Mind Map activity, use at least eight words from the word bank to make a graphic organizer that illustrates westward expansion in the United States from 1845 to 1848.

ACTIVITY TYPE: VISUALIZATION

Westward Expansion

In this Visualization activity, you will use the lesson content to illustrate the sequence of events that took place during the expansion of U.S. territory in the mid-1800s.

ACTIVITY TYPE: SOCIAL STUDIES EXPLANATION

Westward Expansion

In this activity, you will use the template to assemble evidence from the sources you have explored. Then, you will write an answer to the Essential Question and defend your answer with supporting evidence.

Elaborate Activities

photo: Getty Images

INVESTIGATION TYPE: TIMELINE MAP

Westward Expansion

What were the economic, political, and other motivations that drove the United States to expand to the Pacific coast? Your mission is to examine the changes made to U.S. borders between 1830 and 1853 and explain what motivated these changes.

photo: Corbis

ACTIVITY TYPE: CURRENT EVENTS CONNECTION

Civil Disobedience

In this activity, you will read a quote from *Civil Disobedience* and view video clips on acts of civil disobedience in the 1900s. You will write a moral position paper defending or countering the right of citizens to engage in acts of civil disobedience. You will explain the circumstances under which such actions might be acceptable.

PROJECTS AND ASSESSMENTS *(continued)*

photo: Library of Congress

ACTIVITY TYPE: YOU AS ARTIST

Propaganda Poster

In this activity, you will analyze a piece of propaganda from the Mexican-American War. Then, you will use common elements of propaganda and your understanding of the events leading up the war to make your own propaganda or protest poster about the Mexican-American War.

photo: Library of Congress

ACTIVITY TYPE: DOCUMENT-BASED INVESTIGATION

The Mexican-American War, 1846–1848

In this activity, your task is to draft an opening statement in which you cite the Mexican-American War as an example of either a war of choice or necessity and explain whether subsequent territorial gains for the United States were worth the cost. Alternately, you may decide to write a letter to the editor of a congressperson's hometown newspaper either in support of or in opposition to a statue commemorating the Treaty of Guadalupe Hidalgo.

photo: IRC

ACTIVITY TYPE: DOCUMENT-BASED INVESTIGATION

Westward Expansion

In this Document-Based Investigation, you will analyze source materials and investigate the following questions: How did the American republic respond to the Mexican-American War? What does this response reveal about the country's motivations for war?

Evaluate Activities

BRIEF-CONSTRUCTED RESPONSE (BCR)

Westward Expansion

EXTENDED-CONSTRUCTED RESPONSE (ECR)

Westward Expansion

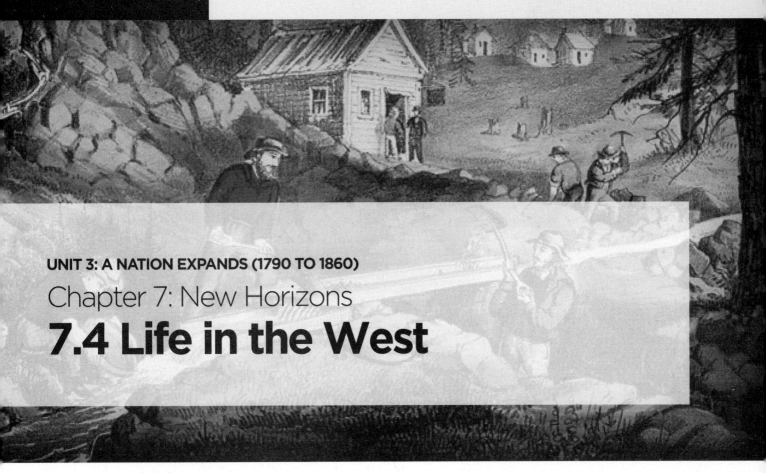

UNIT 3: A NATION EXPANDS (1790 TO 1860)

Chapter 7: New Horizons
7.4 Life in the West

LESSON OVERVIEW

Lesson Objectives:

By the end of this lesson, you should be able to:

- Describe dynamics of daily life in the West from a variety of perspectives.
- Explain political, geographic, economic, and cultural factors that affected the population of the West during the first half of the 1800s.

Key Vocabulary

Andrew Johnson, Brigham Young, California, California Gold Rush, forty-niners, Fugitive Slave Laws, missionary, Mormons, Oregon Trail, reservation, Santa Fe Trail, vaquero

Lesson Essential Question:

For various groups, what was life like in newly settled areas of the West?

FLASHCARDS

1 Western Daily Life

Both settlers and prospectors faced numerous challenges as they migrated west of the Mississippi River. Daily life could be very difficult, and success was not guaranteed, but inexpensive farmland and rich natural resources such as gold could make the journey worthwhile.

- All members of a pioneer family worked hard at daily tasks associated with raising cattle, growing crops, and keeping the farm running smoothly.

- Prospectors dug and panned for gold in their quest to strike it rich, but harsh living conditions and high prices took their toll.

Why Does It Matter?

Ranchers, prospectors, and vaqueros or cowboys became legendary for their bold independence, courage, and hard work.

photo: IRC

In the mid-1800s, following the Treaty of Guadalupe Hidalgo, farmers and immigrants arrived in the West. The arrival of these settlers and their greed for land pushed the Native American tribes onto reservations.

2 A Diverse Population

As the United States expanded its borders westward during the first half of the 1800s, an assortment of settlers arrived, seeking various aspects of the American Dream, including freedom, prosperity, and land. Nonwhites were excluded from many aspects of these opportunities.

- Native American tribes were concentrated on reservations by the U.S. government when white settlers demanded their land.

- Mormons seeking a safe location to practice their religion settled in Utah.

- Asian immigrants arrived from China during the California Gold Rush, seeking wealth by panning for gold and providing services to miners.

- When territories from Mexico were added to the United States, Mexicans became American citizens. Vaqueros taught inexperienced settlers how to herd cattle.

- Both enslaved and free African Americans discovered freedoms and prejudice as they mined for gold alongside other settlers.

Why Does It Matter?

A diverse population of new western settlers was shaped and influenced by an assortment of political, geographical, economic, and cultural factors. These people possessed an independent pioneering spirit that shaped the western frontier and the American Dream.

© 2005 Instructional Resources Corporation

photo: IRC

The United States expanded west into Texas, California, and Utah, attracting new populations.

Name _____ Date _____

GRAPHIC ORGANIZER: Sequencing Chart

Complete this Sequencing Chart to show events that helped expand the United States westward. For supporting resources, go to A Nation Expands > New Horizons > Life in the West > Explore > Traders and Fortune Seekers.

Event/Date	Summary

Name _____ Date _____

GRAPHIC ORGANIZER: Sequencing Chart *(continued)*

Event/Date	Summary

Name _____ Date _____

GRAPHIC ORGANIZER: Sequencing Chart *(continued)*

Answer the following question:

- **Which event had the biggest impact on U.S. expansion? Why?**

Name _____ **Date** _____

GRAPHIC ORGANIZER: Venn Diagram

Complete this 3-Way Venn Diagram to show similarities and differences among Chinese immigrants, Mormon settlers, and Mexican-American vaqueros. For supporting resources, go to A Nation Expands > New Horizons > Life in the West > Explore > A New Wave of Immigrants.

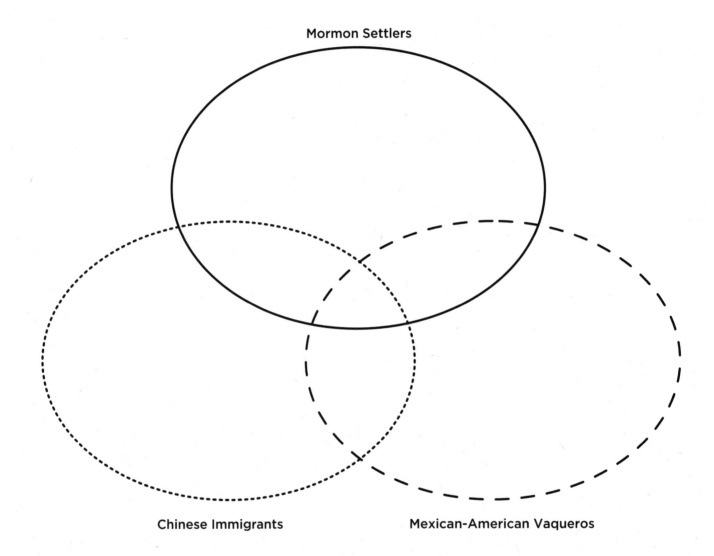

Mormon Settlers

Chinese Immigrants

Mexican-American Vaqueros

Name _____ Date _____

EXPLORE: FOCUS QUESTIONS

Using what you learned from the Core Interactive Text, answer each page's focus question:

Lure of the West
Why did the western frontier beckon to settlers?

_____

_____

_____

Endless Labor on the Farm
What was life like for a farmer in the West?

_____

_____

_____

Traders and Fortune Seekers
What events attracted settlers to New Mexico and California?

_____

_____

_____

Rushing Toward Riches
What was life like for a miner in the West?

_____

_____

_____

Claiming Native Tribal Lands
Why were Native Americans of the West confined to reservations?

_____

_____

_____

Name _____ Date _____

EXPLORE: FOCUS QUESTIONS *(continued)*

A New Wave of Immigrants
Why did Asians immigrate to California?

_____
_____
_____

The Mormon Trail to Salt Lake City
Why did Mormons relocate to Utah?

_____
_____
_____

Expanding into the Southwest
Who were America's first cowboys?

_____
_____
_____

The Struggle for Freedom in the West
Why did African Americans migrate West?

_____
_____
_____

Women in the West
How did life in the West create opportunities for women?

_____
_____
_____

PROJECTS AND ASSESSMENTS

Explain Activities

ACTIVITY TYPE: ADVERTISEMENT

Encouraging People to Come West
In this activity, you will create an advertisement that encourages migration to the gold fields of California.

ACTIVITY TYPE: QUICK WRITE

Daily Life in the West
In this Quick Write activity, you will write a diary entry that describes the daily life of a farmer or miner in the West during the mid-1800s.

ACTIVITY TYPE: SOCIAL STUDIES EXPLANATION

Life in the West
In this activity, you will use the template to assemble evidence from the sources you have explored. Then, you will write an answer to the Essential Question and defend your answer with supporting evidence.

Elaborate Activities

photo: Jupiterimages Corporation

INVESTIGATION TYPE: DATA ANALYSIS

The Making of the West
The western United States changed dramatically during the final part of the 1800s. This leads us to consider what the population of the West was really like during the time period. Your mission is to analyze the growing population of the western United States during the first half of the 1800s, as well as the reasons for this population boom.

PROJECTS AND ASSESSMENTS *(continued)*

photo: Library of Congress

ACTIVITY TYPE: EXPRESS YOUR OPINION

Chinese Immigration to California

In this activity, you will use primary sources to write a letter home from the perspective of a Chinese immigrant to California. In the letter, you will either encourage a relative to come to California or encourage him or her to stay at home rather than emigrating.

photo: IRC

ACTIVITY TYPE: ROLE PLAY

Life for African Americans in the West

In this activity, you will use the primary sources to write a transcript of an interview with a fictional African American resident of the West in the 1840s or 1850s.

photo: Getty Images

ACTIVITY TYPE: DOCUMENT-BASED INVESTIGATION

Life in the West

In this Document-Based Investigation, you will analyze source materials and investigate this question: What role did women play in the westward expansion of the United States in the mid-1800s?

Evaluate Activities

BRIEF-CONSTRUCTED RESPONSE (BCR)

Life in the West

EXTENDED-CONSTRUCTED RESPONSE (ECR)

Life in the West

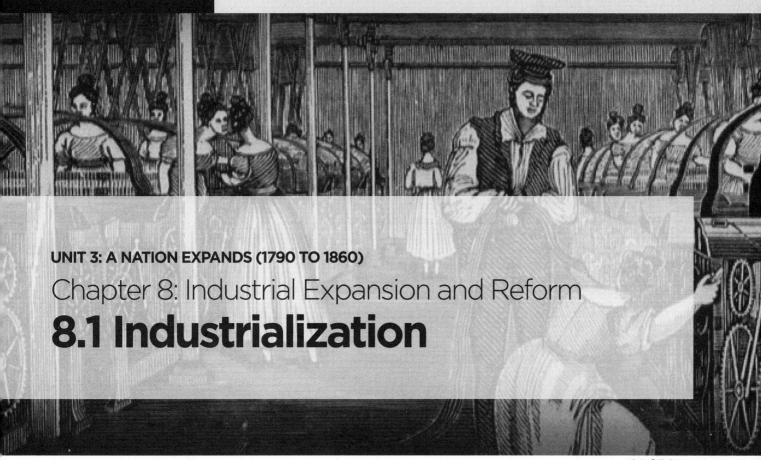

photo: Getty Images

UNIT 3: A NATION EXPANDS (1790 TO 1860)
Chapter 8: Industrial Expansion and Reform
8.1 Industrialization

LESSON OVERVIEW

Lesson Objectives:

By the end of this lesson, you should be able to:

- Explain the Industrial Revolution and discuss its impact on the production of goods and the workplace in the United States.
- Describe key inventions of the Industrial Revolution, such as the cotton gin, reaper, steamboat, and steam locomotive, and analyze their impact on life in the United States.

Lesson Essential Question:

Did the benefits of technological advances made during the Industrial Revolution outweigh the costs?

Key Vocabulary

automate, cotton gin, Cyrus McCormick, economy, Eli Whitney, Elias Howe, Erie Canal, Francis Cabot Lowell, Industrial Revolution, industrialization, interchangeable parts, Isaac M. Singer, John Deere, Lowell System, Lowell, Massachusetts, mass production, mercantilism, Rhode Island System, Richard Arkwright, Robert Fulton, Samuel Morse, Samuel Slater, socialism, steam locomotive, technology, telegraph, textile

FLASHCARDS

1 The Industrial Revolution

Industrialization, which means changing from hand production at home to machine production in factories, led to so many changes in society that the time in which it occurred is called the Industrial Revolution.

- In the United States, the Industrial Revolution began with textile factories in New England, where rivers provided water power to run the machines in the factories.
- Eli Whitney, the inventor of the cotton gin, also developed the idea of interchangeable parts, which allowed many goods to be mass-produced.
- During the 1800s, an increasing number of Americans went to work in factories. Many of the goods that people bought and used were made in these factories.

Why Does It Matter?

The Industrial Revolution began with small changes in manufacturing but ended up affecting many different aspects of people's lives all over the United States.

photo: IRC

During the Industrial Revolution, people used machines to do work that they had previously done by hand.

2 New Inventions

Throughout the 1800s, new inventions changed transportation, communication, farm life, and home life.

- Steamboats, canals, and railroads made transportation faster and easier during the 1800s.
- Samuel Morse's invention of the telegraph allowed people to communicate quickly over long distances.
- New tools such as the mechanical reaper and steel plow improved productivity on farms.
- Sewing machines, iceboxes, and cook stoves changed the way people made clothing and stored and prepared their food, saving them a good deal of time and effort.

Why Does It Matter?

The inventions of the 1800s greatly changed the way people lived and worked. These changes helped the United States become more productive and economically stronger.

photo: IRC

Changes in transportation, such as steamships and railroads, were an important part of the Industrial Revolution.

Name _____ Date _____

GRAPHIC ORGANIZER: Cause/Event/Effect Chart

Use this Cause/Event/Effect Chart to note the main aspects of industrialization and their causes. For supporting resources, go to A Nation Expands > Industrial Expansion and Reform > Industrialization > Explore > The Industrial Revolution Begins.

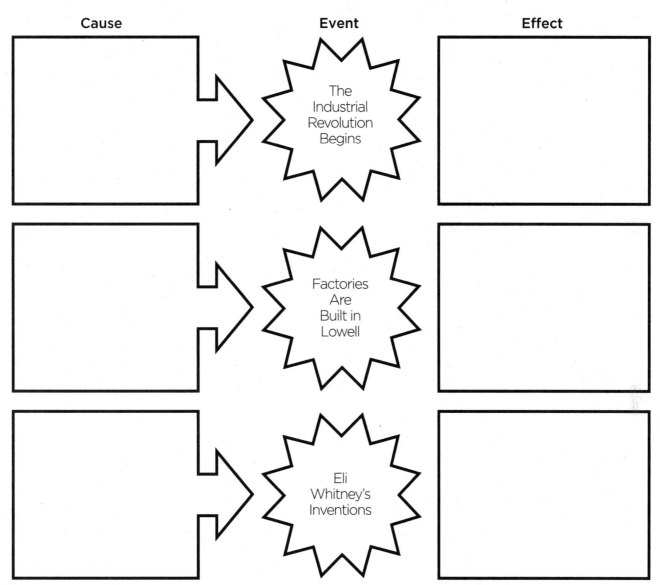

Cause	Event	Effect
	The Industrial Revolution Begins	
	Factories Are Built in Lowell	
	Eli Whitney's Inventions	

Name _____ Date _____

EXPLORE: FOCUS QUESTIONS

Using what you learned from the Core Interactive Text, answer each page's focus question:

The Rise of Free Enterprise in the United States

How did the free enterprise economic system develop in the United States?

_____
_____
_____

The Industrial Revolution Begins

How did the Industrial Revolution begin?

_____
_____
_____

The Industrial Revolution Comes to New England

How were the first factories in the United States built?

_____
_____
_____

Eli Whitney

What role did Eli Whitney play in the Industrial Revolution?

_____
_____
_____

Changes in Transportation

How did transportation change during the Industrial Revolution?

_____
_____
_____

Name _____ Date _____

EXPLORE: FOCUS QUESTIONS *(continued)*

The Telegraph
How did the telegraph change communication in the early 1800s?

_____

_____

_____

Changes in Farming
How did new inventions change life for farmers?

_____

_____

_____

Changes in Daily Life
How did new inventions change the way people lived at home?

_____

_____

_____

PROJECTS AND ASSESSMENTS

Explain Activities

ACTIVITY TYPE: DIAGRAM

Free Enterprise

Use the Cause and Effect Chart to explain how a free enterprise system developed in the United States during the 1700s and 1800s.

ACTIVITY TYPE: ENCYCLOPEDIA ENTRY

Industrialization

In this activity, you will create an encyclopedia entry for a class Inventions Encyclopedia. Write an entry that clearly describes the function of the invention and the ways in which it impacted society.

ACTIVITY TYPE: QUICK WRITE

Industrialization

In this Quick Write activity, you will take the perspective of a factory worker who once made an item by hand. You should address both benefits and challenges of your new life in the age of industrialization.

ACTIVITY TYPE: SOCIAL STUDIES EXPLANATION

Industrialization

In this activity, you will use the template to assemble evidence from the sources you have explored. Then, you will write an answer to the Essential Question and defend your answer with supporting evidence.

Elaborate Activities

photo: Library of Congress

INVESTIGATION TYPE: DATA ANALYSIS

The Impact of the Cotton Gin

How could a simple invention increase the political power of the South within the United States? In this Data Analysis, you will analyze the social and economic impacts of technological advancements in cotton production in the 1800s.

PROJECTS AND ASSESSMENTS *(continued)*

photo: Getty Images

ACTIVITY TYPE: CURRENT EVENTS
CONNECTION

Industrial vs. Digital

In this activity, you will explore recent innovations and their impact on society today and compare them with the impact of the Industrial Revolution on society in the early to mid-1800s.

photo: Getty Images

ACTIVITY TYPE: MAKE A MODEL

Inventions of the 1800s

In this activity, you will create a model to depict an invention from the 1800s.

Panoramic View of the City of Lowell, Massachusetts,

photo: Library of Congres

ACTIVITY TYPE: SAY WHAT?

"The Lowell Offering"

In this activity, you will study an image and read several primary source selections from "The Lowell Offering." You will complete the following tasks: paraphrase each excerpt, analyze each selection by answering a series of questions, and prepare a short statement, as if you are the brother, sister, or friend of one of the mill girls.

photo: IRC

ACTIVITY TYPE: DOCUMENT-BASED
INVESTIGATION

Industrialization

In this Document-Based Investigation, you will analyze source materials and investigate this question: Did the benefits of technological advancements made during the Industrial Revolution (1790–1860) outweigh the costs?

PROJECTS AND ASSESSMENTS *(continued)*

Evaluate Activities

 BRIEF-CONSTRUCTED RESPONSE (BCR)

Industrialization

 EXTENDED-CONSTRUCTED RESPONSE (ECR)

Industrialization

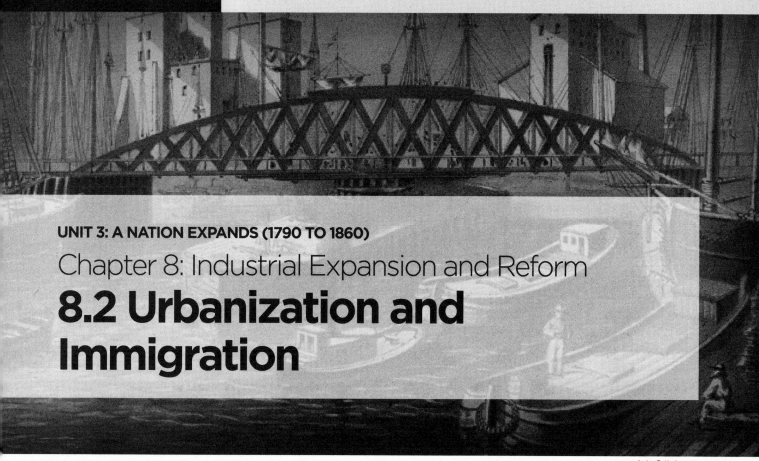

UNIT 3: A NATION EXPANDS (1790 TO 1860)

Chapter 8: Industrial Expansion and Reform

8.2 Urbanization and Immigration

photo: Getty Images

LESSON OVERVIEW

Lesson Objectives:

By the end of this lesson, you should be able to:

- Explain push and pull factors that motivated immigrants to move to the United States in the mid-1800s.
- Discuss key political, cultural, and social dynamics of city life in the mid-1800s.

Key Vocabulary

Erie Canal, ethnic group, factory, immigrant, Industrial Revolution, Irish Potato Famine, Know-Nothing Party, mass production, nativism, nativist, naturalized citizen, peasant, population, race, rural, social class, suburb, tenement, unemployment, urban, urbanization

Lesson Essential Question:

How did urbanization and immigration change the nature of city life in America?

FLASHCARDS

1 Cities and Industry

In the late 1700s, industrialization began to change the ways in which people in Europe and the United States produced goods. The pace and extent of these changes increased dramatically during the 1800s.

- Factories were often built in cities to take advantage of transportation sources, power sources, and a labor force.
- Factories attracted young men and women from the countryside to the cities.
- Factories attracted immigrants who hoped to find work in U.S. cities.

Why Does It Matter?

As cities grew, the complexion of the United States began to change. Industrialized factories brought more economic opportunities for people who had once lived and worked on farms, and immigrants poured into the country in search of jobs and a better life.

photo: IRC

Pittsburgh was ideally located on the shore of the mighty Ohio River with close proximity to the nation's most productive coal mines. By the 1840s, railway transportation had made it possible to use coal as a power source for steel factories in Pittsburgh.

2 Moving to the United States

Political unrest, famine, and poverty were key factors that motivated immigrants to move to the United States in the mid-1800s.

- The Great Irish Famine was the result of the widespread failure of potato crops in Ireland between 1845 and 1852. About 1 million Irish died of starvation and disease during this time, and about 1.5 million Irish immigrants came to the United States in the mid-1800s.
- Nearly 1 million German immigrants came to the United States in the 1850s.
- Most of the Germans left their country because of difficult economic conditions and political unrest.
- Most Irish immigrants were very poor. They often settled in the East Coast cities where they arrived because they did not have the money to go anywhere else.
- The Germans often had more money than the Irish. They were able to move to and settle in the Midwest where there was more land.

Why Does It Matter?

Immigrants from Ireland and Germany came to the United States in search of work and a better life. Because of industrialization, there were plenty of jobs in the cities for them. In the mid-1800s, about 1.5 million Irish and nearly 1 million Germans settled in the United States.

photo: IRC

About 1.5 million Irish immigrants came to the United States in the mid-1800s.

FLASHCARDS *(continued)*

3 ▶ Dynamics of City Life

Urbanization brought political, social, and cultural changes for people living in the cities.

- Once people from a particular immigrant group established a community in a city, others from the same country were attracted to the same area.
- Factory and business owners grew wealthier during the 1800s and began moving into nicer communities separated from factory districts.
- Living quarters for the working class were often crowded, unsanitary, and in need of repair. Landlords subdivided large homes in the inner cities, and the working class moved into apartments there.
- Some free African Americans moved to cities to find work and opportunities. Because they experienced racism and discrimination even in the cities, African Americans created their own neighborhoods, churches, and other establishments.
- As more immigrants came to the United States, anti-immigrant feelings grew among native-born Americans.
- Irish immigrants were discriminated against in part because of their Catholic religious views.
- Immigrants were seen as taking jobs away from unskilled American laborers.
- The Know-Nothing Party was an anti-immigrant political party that fought for native-born rights over immigrant rights.

Why Does It Matter?

Although there were plenty of jobs, industrialization and urbanization created large gaps between the wealthy and the working class, and immigration created tensions between people who were born in the United States and newcomers to the country. People from similar backgrounds and cultures worked together to create their own neighborhoods, churches, and other establishments.

photo: IRC

Working and living conditions were difficult for the poor working class in the 1800s.

Name _____ **Date** _____

GRAPHIC ORGANIZER: Main Idea Web

Fill out this Main Idea Web to explore some reasons people moved to urban areas in the mid-1800s. For supporting resources, go to A Nation Expands > Industrial Expansion and Reform > Urbanization and Immigration > Explore.

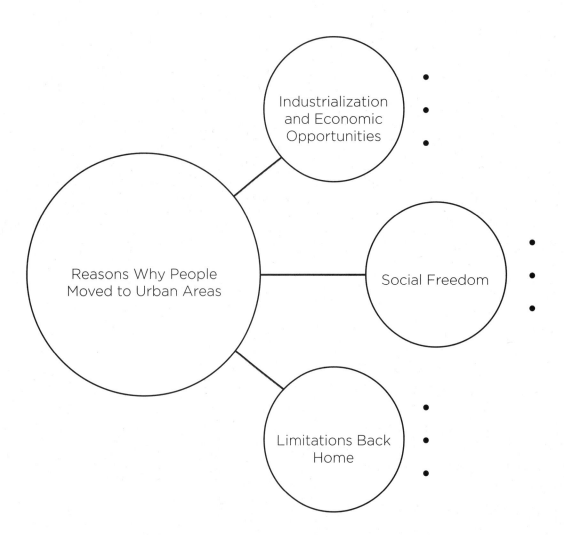

Name _____ Date _____

EXPLORE: FOCUS QUESTIONS

Using what you learned from the Core Interactive Text, answer each page's focus question:

Industrial Rise and Growth of Cities
Why did industrialization cause cities to grow?

_____

_____

_____

Finding a Place to Call Home
Why did Germans migrate to U.S. farms and cities?

_____

_____

_____

Rural Americans
Why did people move from rural areas to the cities?

_____

_____

_____

A Wave of Immigration
Why did Irish people migrate to U.S. cities?

_____

_____

_____

Leaving Home and Family
What was life like for people who moved to the cities?

_____

_____

_____

Name _____ Date _____

EXPLORE: FOCUS QUESTIONS *(continued)*

Gaps Between Rich and Poor

How did urban life differ for the wealthy and the working class?

_____

_____

_____

Anti-Immigrant Sentiments

How did people in the United States react to immigrants?

_____

_____

_____

PROJECTS AND ASSESSMENTS

Explain Activities

ACTIVITY TYPE: DIAGRAM

Urbanization and Immigration

In this activity, you will complete a Comparison Chart focusing on four groups that came to U.S. cities to work in the factories during the first half of the 1800s.

ACTIVITY TYPE: QUICK WRITE

Urbanization and Immigration

In this Quick Write activity, you will take the perspective of a person who has moved to a city to work in the factories that employed growing numbers of immigrants from abroad as well as migrants from rural areas.

ACTIVITY TYPE: SOCIAL STUDIES EXPLANATION

Urbanization and Immigration

In this activity, you will use the template to assemble evidence from the sources you have explored. Then, you will write an answer to the Essential Question and defend your answer with supporting evidence.

Elaborate Activities

photo: Discovery Education

INVESTIGATION TYPE: HISTORICAL PERSPECTIVES

Industry and Immigrants Change American Cities

In this Historical Perspectives investigation, your mission is to analyze three important issues related to urbanization and immigration in the United States from four different perspectives.

photo: Library of Congress

ACTIVITY TYPE: EXPRESS YOUR OPINION

Urbanization and Immigration

In this activity, you will study examples of early American propaganda. Next, you will write a letter of objection to one of the propaganda artists.

PROJECTS AND ASSESSMENTS *(continued)*

photo: Library of Congress

ACTIVITY TYPE: PITCH YOUR IDEA

Life in a Tenement

In this activity, you will analyze the problems associated with the living conditions of the urban poor in the 1800s. Then, you will take the perspective of a citizen in the 1800s and write an open letter to the mayor of New York City pitching a solution to help change these urban living conditions for the better.

photo: Library of Congress

ACTIVITY TYPE: DOCUMENT-BASED INVESTIGATION

Urbanization and Immigration

In this Document-Based Investigation, you will analyze source materials and investigate this question: Did people who moved to U.S. cities in the mid-1800s find what they were looking for?

photo: Library of Congress

ACTIVITY TYPE: DOCUMENT-BASED INVESTIGATION

City Life in the Early to Mid-1800s

In this activity, you will write either a letter or a newspaper article that describes the growth of U.S. cities during the mid-1800s.

Evaluate Activities

BRIEF-CONSTRUCTED RESPONSE (BCR)

Urbanization and Immigration

EXTENDED-CONSTRUCTED RESPONSE (ECR)

Urbanization and Immigration

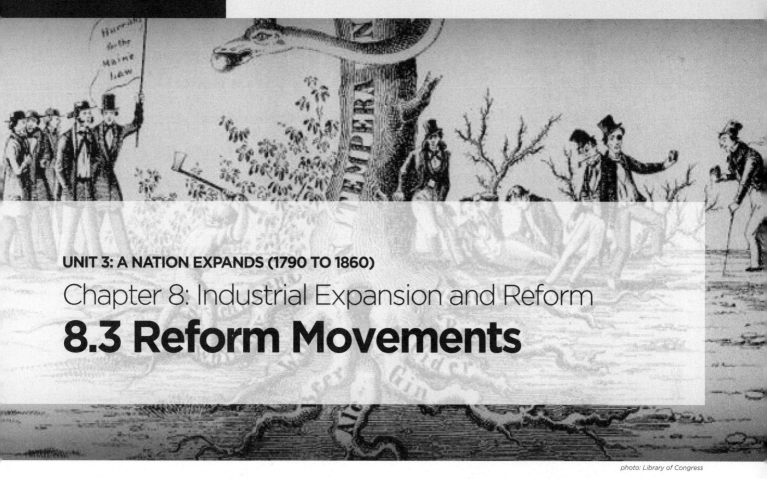

photo: Library of Congress

UNIT 3: A NATION EXPANDS (1790 TO 1860)

Chapter 8: Industrial Expansion and Reform

8.3 Reform Movements

LESSON OVERVIEW

Lesson Objectives:

By the end of this lesson, you should be able to:

- Connect the emergence of mid-1800s reform movements to changes in American life caused by industrialization.
- Trace the rise of the abolitionist and women's suffrage movements.
- Describe key cultural advancements (arts and sciences) and political ideas that emerged before the Civil War.

Lesson Essential Question:

How did the reform movements of the 1840s change American society?

Key Vocabulary

Abigail Adams, abolition, Andrew Jackson, Angelina Grimké, citizen, Elizabeth Cady Stanton, Frederick Douglass, George Whitefield, Harriet Tubman, industrialization, Irish Potato Famine, Know-Nothing Party, Lucretia Mott, mestizo, Olaudah Equiano, Prince Hall, Puritan, reform / social reform, republicanism, Sarah Grimké, Saratoga, Second Great Awakening, Seneca Falls Convention, Seneca Falls, New York, slave codes, Sojourner Truth, suffrage, Susan B. Anthony, temperance, Thomas Jefferson, transcendentalism, Underground Railroad, utopia, William Lloyd Garrison

FLASHCARDS

1 Reforming America

Industrialization created a larger urban population in the United States. The changes that took place economically brought the need for social change as well.

- The temperance movement, a movement to rid American society of alcohol and alcoholism, began in the early 1800s and took on a new life in the 1840s.
- Between 1837 and 1853, every state in the North passed laws establishing public schools.
- Educational reformers worked to increase educational opportunities for women.
- Utopian communities such as Brook Farm sought to create ideal places for people to live.
- The prison reforms during the 1800s created larger prisons in which prisoners were kept in cells and made to engage in physical labor.
- Dorothea Dix helped establish public asylums and mental hospitals and called for the humane treatment of people with mental illnesses.

Why Does It Matter?

The social reforms that were instituted in the 1800s helped shape the societal institutions that we have today.

photo: IRC

In the early 1800s, reformers fought for the creation of institutional facilities to humanely house and school the hearing impaired and care for people with mental illnesses, among other institutional reforms.

2 The Continuing Fight for Rights

Both the abolitionist movement and the women's rights movement were important social reform movements in the mid-1800s.

- Many people supported the abolitionist movement, the movement to end slavery, in the mid-1800s, including William Lloyd Garrison, a newspaper publisher, and Sojourner Truth and Frederick Douglass, two formerly enslaved people who escaped to the North.
- Harriet Tubman led about 300 people to freedom via the Underground Railroad, a secret system of escape routes used to bring enslaved people to freedom in the North and Canada.
- Sisters Sarah and Angelina Grimké were white Southern women who moved to the North to participate in the abolitionist movement. They were also advocates for women's rights.
- Lucretia Mott and Elizabeth Cady Stanton organized the first national women's rights convention in Seneca Falls, New York, in 1848. The convention adopted the "Declaration of Sentiments" that listed grievances of women and their demands for equality.
- Elizabeth Cady Stanton, Lucretia Mott, and Susan B. Anthony were all important women in the fight for women's suffrage, or the right to vote.

Why Does It Matter?

The abolitionists helped bring the issue of slavery to public attention. This was a crucial step in ending slavery in the United States. Women's rights reformers worked for more than 50 years and won women the right to vote.

photo: IRC

After escaping from slavery to the North, Harriet Tubman worked as an abolitionist. She led about 300 enslaved people to freedom via the Underground Railroad.

FLASHCARDS *(continued)*

3 The World of Ideas

After gaining independence from Great Britain, the new United States needed to find its own intellectual and artistic culture.

- Native New Yorker Washington Irving became one of the first internationally recognized American writers.

- American lawyer and scholar Noah Webster wrote the first major dictionary of American English.

- Authors, such as James Fenimore Cooper, wrote stories that created a romantic notion of the people and wilderness in America.

- Artists from the Hudson River School painted landscapes and natural surroundings. They added to the romantic notion of the American wilderness and frontier.

- Transcendentalists and utopianists experimented with living and writing about a "simple life" connected to nature.

- Republicanism was the idea that American citizens needed to be virtuous to maintain the safety and integrity of the country.

Why Does It Matter?

It was during the early 1800s that Americans developed a distinct culture. The writers, artists, and intellectuals that lived in the United States during that time helped create an American culture that is still alive today.

photo: IRC

Washington Irving's tale "The Legend of Sleepy Hollow" was an Americanized version of an old German story.

Name _____ Date _____

GRAPHIC ORGANIZER: Cause/Event/Effect Chart

As you read about the need for social reform, use this Cause/Event/Effect Chart to explain these events and list the causes and effects of each. For supporting resources, go to A Nation Expands > Industrial Expansion and Reform > Reform Movements > Explore.

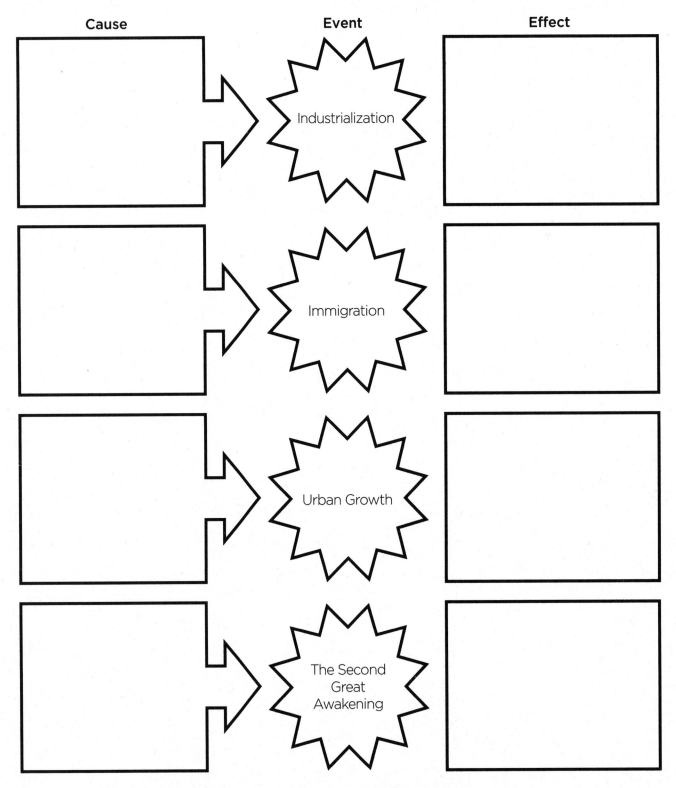

Cause   **Event**   **Effect**

Industrialization

Immigration

Urban Growth

The Second Great Awakening

Name _____ Date _____

GRAPHIC ORGANIZER: Problem/Solution Chart

Use this Problem/Solution Chart to take notes on social problems of the age of urbanization and industrialization and solutions to these problems proposed by social reformers. For supporting resources, go to A Nation Expands > Industrial Expansion and Reform > Reform Movements > Explore > A Movement to End Alcohol Abuse.

Problem   **Solution**

Name _____ Date _____

GRAPHIC ORGANIZER: Problem/Solution Chart *(continued)*

Problem   Solution

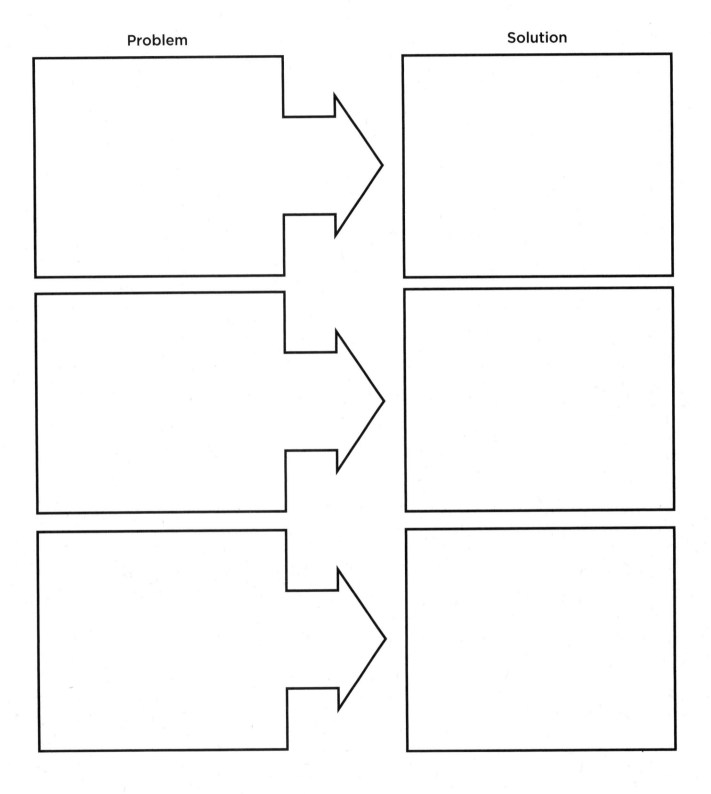

© Discovery Education | www.DiscoveryEducation.com

Name _____ Date _____

GRAPHIC ORGANIZER: Main Idea Web

Complete this Main Idea Web to note important ideas in philosophy, art, and culture. For supporting resources, go to A Nation Expands > Industrial Expansion and Reform > Reform Movements > Explore > A Perfect World.

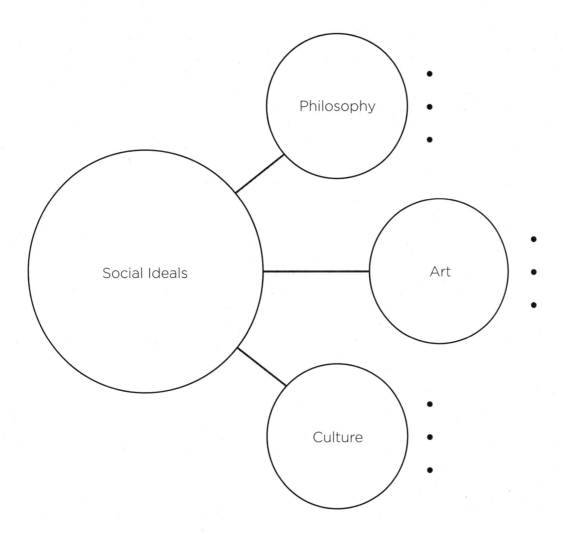

Name _____ Date _____

GRAPHIC ORGANIZER: Sequencing Chart

Use this Sequencing Chart to note important events in the development of women's rights. For supporting resources, go to A Nation Expands > Industrial Expansion and Reform > Reform Movements > Explore > Rights for Women.

Event	Date	Summary	Significance

© Discovery Education | www.DiscoveryEducation.com

Name _____ Date _____

GRAPHIC ORGANIZER: Sequencing Chart *(continued)*

Event	Date	Summary	Significance

Name _____ Date _____

EXPLORE: FOCUS QUESTIONS

Using what you learned from the Core Interactive Text, answer each page's focus question:

The Need for Social Reform

Why did people see a need for social reform in the 1800s?

_____
_____
_____

A Movement to End Alcohol Abuse

What was the temperance movement?

_____
_____
_____

Educating the Public

How did education change during the mid-1800s?

_____
_____
_____

A Perfect World

What social ideals emerged in the mid-1800s?

_____
_____
_____

Crime and Punishment

What did social reformers do for convicts and people with mental illness?

_____
_____
_____

Challenging Slavery

What were the goals of the abolition movement?

_____
_____
_____

Name _____ Date _____

EXPLORE: FOCUS QUESTIONS *(continued)*

A Secret Escape
What was the Underground Railroad? How were free blacks treated in the North?

_____

_____

_____

Rights for Women
What prompted women to begin fighting for their own rights in the mid-1800s?

_____

_____

_____

The First National Convention of Women
Who led the national women's movement? What happened at the Women's Rights Convention in Seneca Falls?

_____

_____

_____

A New Appreciation for America
How did writers and artists cultivate a new American culture in the 1800s?

_____

_____

_____

The Values of the Republic
What was Republicanism?

_____

_____

_____

PROJECTS AND ASSESSMENTS

Explain Activities

ACTIVITY TYPE: ENCYCLOPEDIA ENTRY

Reform Movements

In this activity, you will create an encyclopedia entry (of at least 65 words) describing a social reform movement in the United States.

ACTIVITY TYPE: DIAGRAM

Social Reformers

In this activity, you will use a Comparison Chart to make notes on some important social reformers during the mid-1800s, their backgrounds, the movements they worked for, and how they helped foster change in the United States.

ACTIVITY TYPE: SOCIAL STUDIES EXPLANATION

Reform Movements

In this activity, you will use the template to assemble evidence from the sources you have explored. Then, you will write an answer to the Essential Question and defend your answer with supporting evidence.

Elaborate Activities

photo: Corbis

INVESTIGATION TYPE: MAP-GUIDED INQUIRY

Reform Movements from 1830 to 1860

How did the reform movements of 1830–1860 change American society? In this investigation, you will use the Map-Guided Inquiry interactive tool to explain how the most influential reform movements changed American society.

photo: Getty Images

Continuity and Change in American Fine Arts

In this activity, you will analyze the relationship between fine arts and continuity and change in the American way of life.

© Discovery Education | www.DiscoveryEducation.com

PROJECTS AND ASSESSMENTS (continued)

photo: Corbis

ACTIVITY TYPE: PITCH YOUR IDEA

Presentation to the Council

In this activity, you are a city planner working with your local city council to create a monument or name a public building in honor of one of these social reformers. You will decide which reformer to honor and how you would like to honor him or her. Then, you will present your plan to the city council.

photo: Getty Images

ACTIVITY TYPE: ACT LOCALLY

Promoting Public Health and Safety

According to the U.S. Constitution, one of the federal government's goals is to "promote the general Welfare." Governments at all levels— national, state, and local—develop policies to address public health and safety issues. Some issues, such as contagious diseases and smoking, are more obvious than others, such as chronic diseases or bullying

photo: Library of Congress

ACTIVITY TYPE: YOU AS ARTIST

Reform Cartoon

In this activity, you will analyze a political cartoon from the temperance movement of the 1840s to learn more about common techniques used to make a point. You will then use what you have learned to design your own political cartoon around another social reform movement from the time period.

photo: Getty Images

ACTIVITY TYPE: DOCUMENT-BASED INVESTIGATION

Reform Movements

In this Document-Based Investigation, you will answer the following question: Were the arguments of the women's movement revolutionary or consistent with existing American ideals?

PROJECTS AND ASSESSMENTS *(continued)*

Evaluate Activities

BRIEF-CONSTRUCTED RESPONSE (BCR)

Reform Movements

EXTENDED-CONSTRUCTED RESPONSE (ECR)

Reform Movements

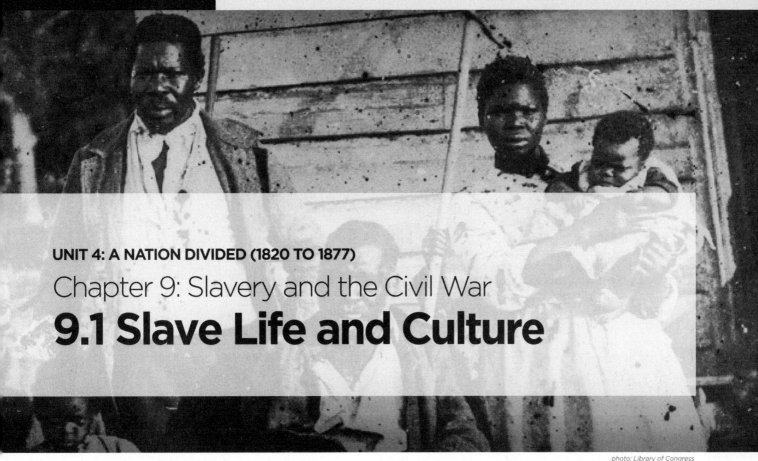

UNIT 4: A NATION DIVIDED (1820 TO 1877)

Chapter 9: Slavery and the Civil War

9.1 Slave Life and Culture

photo: Library of Congress

LESSON OVERVIEW

Lesson Objectives:

By the end of this lesson, you should be able to:

- Analyze the experiences of enslaved and free African Americans in antebellum America.

Lesson Essential Question:

In antebellum America, what did it mean to be an enslaved African American? A free African American?

Key Vocabulary

abolition, Denmark Vesey, discrimination, Frederick Douglass, fugitive, Nat Turner, oral tradition, overseer, plantation, segregation, slave codes

FLASHCARDS

1 ▶ Life in Slavery

African Americans endured a harsh life under slavery.

- **Southern plantations depended on slave labor. Enslaved people worked on farms and plantations from dawn to dusk, often under the watchful eye of an overseer. Slave codes permitted slave owners to punish disobedient enslaved people severely.**
- **Enslaved people usually lived in separate quarters, often just simple cabins with dirt floors. They often had inadequate nutrition.**
- **Slave owners could sell enslaved people, often separating mothers from children or husbands from wives.**
- **Enslaved African Americans developed a rich culture combining African traditions with American culture adapted to the circumstances of an enslaved people.**

Why Does It Matter?

Many people, especially in the North, were beginning to see the institution of slavery as both inhumane and immoral. Conflict over slavery increased tensions between North and South and helped lead to the American Civil War. The institution of slavery sowed the seeds of discrimination and injustice that affect the nation to this day.

photo: IRC

Most enslaved people in the South worked as field hands.

2 ▶ Free African Americans

Free African Americans lived and worked in both the North and the South in a variety of jobs.

- **Free African Americans were among the leaders of the abolition movement.**
- **With few exceptions, free African Americans in both North and South faced segregation and discrimination and were denied civil rights.**

Why Does It Matter?

Free African Americans faced constant danger of being captured and sold as slaves. They supported the Underground Railroad and were vocal and prominent in the abolition movement. Many also pursued careers, raised families, and lived successful lives despite the injustices they faced.

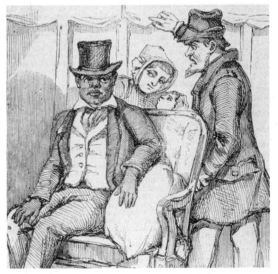

photo: IRC

Even in the North, African Americans faced discrimination and prejudice.

Name _____ Date _____

EXPLORE: FOCUS QUESTIONS

Using what you learned from the Core Interactive Text, answer each page's focus question:

Life in Slavery
What was everyday life like for enslaved African Americans in the South?

_____

_____

_____

Family Life
What was family life like for enslaved people?

_____

_____

_____

African American Culture
What kind of culture did enslaved African Americans develop?

_____

_____

_____

Resistance
How did enslaved African Americans react to slavery?

_____

_____

_____

Free African Americans
What was life like for free African Americans?

_____

_____

_____

PROJECTS AND ASSESSMENTS

Explain Activities

ACTIVITY TYPE: DIAGRAM

Slave Life and Culture

In this activity, you will use a graphic organizer to describe the power and status relationships among enslaved and free people on and around a Southern plantation.

ACTIVITY TYPE: YOU AS JOURNALIST

Slave Uprising

In this activity, imagine you are a reporter covering the story of a slave uprising in a Southern community.

ACTIVITY TYPE: SOCIAL STUDIES EXPLANATION

Slave Life and Culture

In this activity, you will use the template to assemble evidence from the sources you have explored. Then, you will write an answer to the Essential Questions and defend your answer with supporting evidence.

Elaborate Activities

photo: Library of Congress

INVESTIGATION TYPE: SOURCE ANALYSIS

Life in Slavery

What was life like for enslaved people in the South? How did abolitionists make Americans aware of enslaved people's living conditions? In this investigation, you will examine an abolitionist print from 1830 to explain how it demonstrates the realities of slave life and verifies the testimonies of former enslaved people.

photo: IRC

ACTIVITY TYPE: ROLE PLAY

Betsey Merrick Runs Away

In this activity, you will write a conversation between Betsey Merrick and another person about her plans to run away and the possible consequences of her actions.

PROJECTS AND ASSESSMENTS *(continued)*

photo: Babel

ACTIVITY TYPE: YOU AS ARTIST

Songs of Enslavement

In this activity, you will analyze several slave songs and hymns, called spirituals, to understand the emotions behind the music.

photo: Library of Congress

ACTIVITY TYPE: DOCUMENT-BASED INVESTIGATION

Families in Slavery

In this investigation, you will research the impact of slavery on African American families.

photo: Library of Congress

ACTIVITY TYPE: DOCUMENT-BASED INVESTIGATION

Slave Life and Culture

In this Document-Based Investigation, you will analyze source materials and investigate this question: How did enslaved African Americans respond to bondage, and what repercussions did they face? When considering this question, keep in mind that the risks and rewards involved in resistance to slavery may have varied dramatically from one strategy to another.

Evaluate Activities

BRIEF-CONSTRUCTED RESPONSE (BCR)

Slave Life and Culture

EXTENDED-CONSTRUCTED RESPONSE (ECR)

Slave Life and Culture

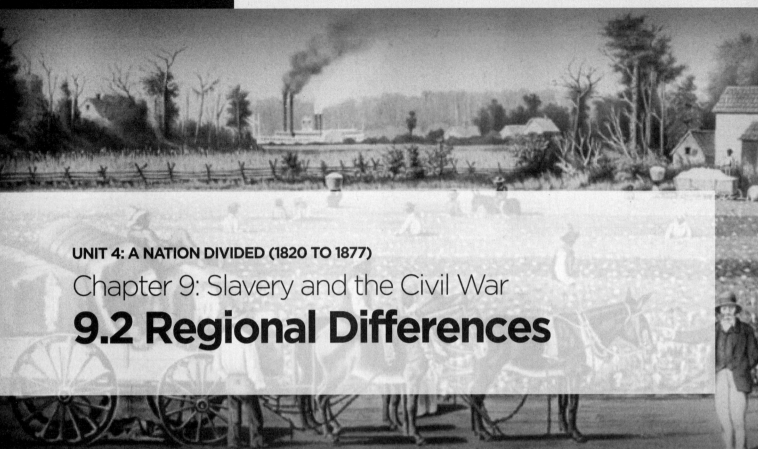

photo: IRC

UNIT 4: A NATION DIVIDED (1820 TO 1877)

Chapter 9: Slavery and the Civil War

9.2 Regional Differences

LESSON OVERVIEW

Lesson Objectives:

By the end of this lesson, you should be able to:

- **Explain economic, social, and cultural differences between the North and the South.**

- **Explain how economic, social, and cultural differences between the North and the South resulted in disagreements over public policy..**

Key Vocabulary

abolition, agriculture, Angelina Grimké, cotton gin, Eli Whitney, export, Frederick Douglass, Industrial Revolution, plantation, Sarah Grimké, sectionalism, tariff, William Lloyd Garrison

Lesson Essential Question:

How did geographical differences between the North and the South lead to conflict?

FLASHCARDS

1 ▸ Different Regions, Different Economies

The North and the South developed very different economies and ways of life during the first half of the 1800s.

- The North became a center of industry and manufacturing, while the South remained dependent on agriculture, especially cotton.
- The North had more cities and railroads, and the South remained rural with fewer railroads.
- Northern states gradually abolished slavery and became dependent on wage labor, while Southerners relied on enslaved African Americans to work on plantations.

Why Does It Matter?

The difference in the economic activities of the two regions grew increasingly significant, and over time, people felt they had little in common with residents of the other region.

photo: IRC

The North and the South had many significant differences in the early 1800s.

2 ▸ Sectionalism Causes Disagreements

The differences between the regions led to sectionalism, which meant that the people of each region had different priorities and wanted different public policies that would benefit their own region.

- Northerners wanted the government to pay for internal improvements such as roads and other forms of transportation, while Southerners did not need these improvements.
- Northerners supported high tariffs that would help manufacturers, and Southerners wanted low tariffs to keep the price of imports down and avoid any retaliatory tariffs on their exported cotton.
- As the abolition movement grew in the North, Southerners became outraged that outsiders would try to tell them how to live and take away their livelihoods.

Why Does It Matter?

The disagreements caused by sectionalism became stronger as the century progressed and would eventually become so strong that they led to the Civil War.

photo: IRC

The differences between the North and the South led to strong disagreements about national policies.

Name _____ **Date** _____

GRAPHIC ORGANIZER: Cause/Event/Effect Chart

Complete this Cause/Event/Effect Chart to show how the geography of the North led to industrialization, which led to urbanization and railroads and the gradual abolition of slavery there. For supporting resources, go to A Nation Divided > Slavery and the Civil War > Regional Differences > Explore > The Northern Economy.

Northern Economy

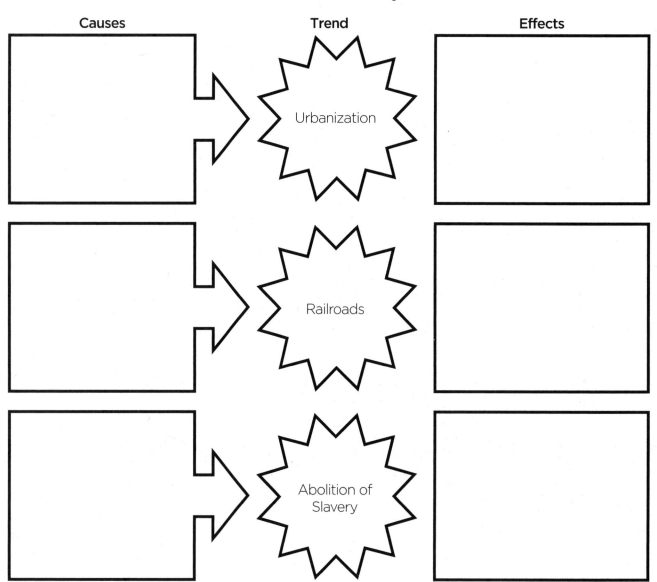

Causes	Trend	Effects
	Urbanization	
	Railroads	
	Abolition of Slavery	

SOCIAL STUDIES TECHBOOK

Name _____ **Date** _____

GRAPHIC ORGANIZER: Cause/Event/Effect Chart

Complete this Cause/Event/Effect Chart to show how the geography of the South led to reliance on agriculture instead of industry, which led to few cities and railroads and the growth of slavery. For supporting resources, go to A Nation Divided > Slavery and the Civil War > Regional Differences > Explore > The Southern Economy.

Southern Economy

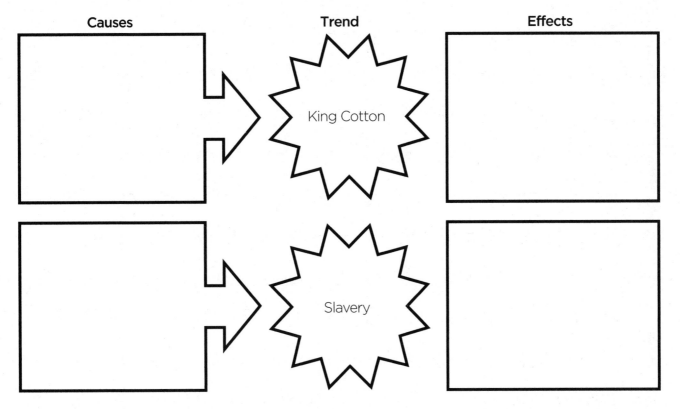

Causes | Trend | Effects

King Cotton

Slavery

Name _____ Date _____

EXPLORE: FOCUS QUESTIONS

Using what you learned from the Core Interactive Text, answer each page's focus question:

The Northern Economy

What was the economy of the North like in the first half of the 1800s?

_____
_____
_____

The Southern Economy

What was the economy of the South like in the first half of the 1800s?

_____
_____
_____

Sectionalism

How did the differences between the North and the South lead to disagreements?

_____
_____
_____

The Abolition Movement Grows

How did the abolition movement affect relations between the North and the South?

_____
_____
_____

PROJECTS AND ASSESSMENTS

Explain Activities

ACTIVITY TYPE: VISUALIZATION

Regional Differences

In this Visualization activity, you will illustrate the effects that import tariffs had on Northern manufacturers, Southern cotton growers, and American consumers in the 1800s.

ACTIVITY TYPE: DIAGRAM

Regional Differences

In this activity, you will use a Comparison Chart to record notes on the geographic characteristics, main economic activities, workforce characteristics, and role of the cities in the Northern and Southern United States during the early 1800s.

ACTIVITY TYPE: SOCIAL STUDIES EXPLANATION

Regional Differences

In this activity, you will use the template to assemble evidence from the sources you have explored. Then, you will write an answer to the Essential Question and defend your answer with supporting evidence.

Elaborate Activities

photo: Library of Congress

INVESTIGATION TYPE: DATA ANALYSIS

Same Nation, Different Worlds

The first half of the 1800s was characterized by increasing conflict between the Northern and Southern regions of the United States. What made these regions so different from each other? Your mission is to investigate and analyze the economic differences between the North and South before the Civil War.

ACTIVITY TYPE: CLASSROOM SPEECH

Regional Differences

In this activity, you will write an abolitionist speech explaining why slavery should be abolished.

A FAMILY QUARREL.

photo: Library of Congress

PROJECTS AND ASSESSMENTS *(continued)*

photo: Getty Images

ACTIVITY TYPE: ROLE PLAY

Regional Differences

In this activity, you will assume the perspective of a Southerner traveling through the North or a Northerner traveling through the South. Write a detailed travel diary about your journey.

NEW METHOD OF ASSORTING THE MAIL, AS PRACTISED BY SOUTHERN SLAVE-HOLDERS, OR

ATTACK ON THE POST OFFICE, CHARLESTON, S.C.

photo: Getty Images

ACTIVITY TYPE: DOCUMENT-BASED INVESTIGATION

Regional Differences

In this Document-Based Investigation, you will analyze source materials and investigate this question: Given regional differences between the North and the South, could the breakup of the Union have been avoided?

photo: Getty Images

ACTIVITY TYPE: VISUALIZATION

Top Five List: Regional Differences

In this Visualization activity, you will illustrate the top five reasons for regional differences between the North and South in the early 1800s.

Evaluate Activities

BRIEF-CONSTRUCTED RESPONSE (BCR)

Regional Differences

EXTENDED-CONSTRUCTED RESPONSE (ECR)

Regional Differences

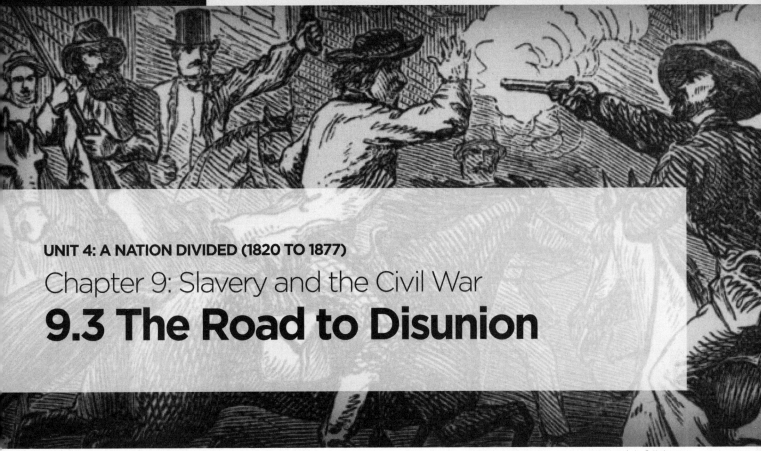

UNIT 4: A NATION DIVIDED (1820 TO 1877)

Chapter 9: Slavery and the Civil War

9.3 The Road to Disunion

photo: Getty Images

LESSON OVERVIEW

Lesson Objectives:

By the end of this lesson, you should be able to:

- **Connect divergent positions on slavery and states' rights with failed attempts at congressional compromise.**

- **Trace and explain the significance of key events between 1850 and 1860 that deepened the crisis between the North and the South.**

Lesson Essential Question:

By 1860, why were the nation's leaders unable to keep the Union together?

Key Vocabulary

Abraham Lincoln, Battle of Harpers Ferry, Bleeding Kansas, Compromise of 1850, Daniel Webster, Dred Scott, fire-eaters, free soiler, free state, Fugitive Slave Laws, gag rule, Harpers Ferry, Virginia, Harriet Beecher Stowe, Henry Clay, John Brown, John Brown's raid, John C. Calhoun, John Quincy Adams, Kansas, Kansas-Nebraska Act, Lincoln-Douglas debates, mandate, Missouri, Missouri Compromise, Nebraska, nullification, popular sovereignty, Pottawatomie massacre, Republican Party, Roger Taney, sectionalism, slave state, Stephen Douglas, Tariff of Abominations, *Uncle Tom's Cabin*, Union

FLASHCARDS

1 Disagreements Divide the Nation

In the early to mid-1800s, the North and South grew apart as the regions disagreed over several issues.

- Southerners argued for states' rights and nullification, the idea that a state could nullify a federal law it thought was unconstitutional. However, Southerners supported strong national policies that restricted states' rights as long as they protected slavery. The Fugitive Slave Act, which outlawed personal liberty laws enacted by some Northern states, is an example of this.
- Some Northerners pressed for the immediate abolition of slavery, while others opposed its spread into new territories.
- Southerners who saw slavery as essential to their way of life and economic well-being feared that the federal government would outlaw slavery in the United States.
- As new territories asked to enter the Union, Congress tried to rein in tensions by using compromises to maintain a balance between free states and slave states.

Why Does It Matter?

Despite Congress's attempts at compromise over slavery, the struggle split the nation when Southern states seceded from the Union.

photo: IRC

The slavery issue threatened to tear the nation apart.

2 A Series of Crises

A series of events between 1850 and 1860 deepened the divide between the North and the South.

- When California sought to enter the Union as a free state, the balance of free states and slave states was threatened.
- The Fugitive Slave Act, which was part of the Compromise of 1850, further angered Northerners.
- Harriet Beecher Stowe's *Uncle Tom's Cabin* turned many more Northerners against slavery.
- The Kansas-Nebraska Act angered Northerners who resented the repeal of the Missouri Compromise and led to violence in Kansas between proslavery and antislavery activists.
- The Democratic Party split in two, and a new party, the Republican Party, was formed in 1854.
- The Lincoln-Douglas debates made Lincoln's name known across the nation and clarified the Democratic and Republican positions on the slavery issue.
- The *Dred Scott* case declared enslaved people to be property and said Congress could not stop the spread of slavery into any territory. Many Northerners vowed to ignore the Supreme Court's ruling, and this increased paranoia about the slave power conspiracy.
- John Brown's unsuccessful raid on Harpers Ferry infuriated and alarmed Southerners.
- Republican Party candidate Abraham Lincoln, a free soiler, was elected president in 1860. In response, Southern states seceded.

Why Does It Matter?

Conflict over slavery increased tensions between the North and the South. Although Congress tried various compromises, events continued to escalate tensions and led to secession. While Southern states thought they had the right to leave the Union, Lincoln refused to recognize the legitimacy of secession and fought to maintain control over federal property in the South.

UNION AND LIBERTY!   AND   UNION AND SLAVERY!

photo: Discovery Education

Slavery divided the nation and brought about civil war in the United States.

Name _____ Date _____

GRAPHIC ORGANIZER: K-W-L Chart

Complete this K-W-L Chart. First, think about why the nation divided; write your ideas in the first column of the chart. In the second column, write things you would like to find out about the causes of disunion or questions that you would like answers to. As you read, fill in the last column with things you learn about the causes of disunion. For supporting resources, go to A Nation Divided > Slavery and the Civil War > The Road to Disunion > Engage.

What I Know	What I Want to Know	What I Learned

Name _____ Date _____

GRAPHIC ORGANIZER: Problem/Solution Chart

Use this Problem/Solution Chart to take notes to identify congressional compromises and the disagreements and problems they were intended to address. For supporting resources, go to A Nation Divided > Slavery and the Civil War > The Road to Disunion > Disagreements Divide.

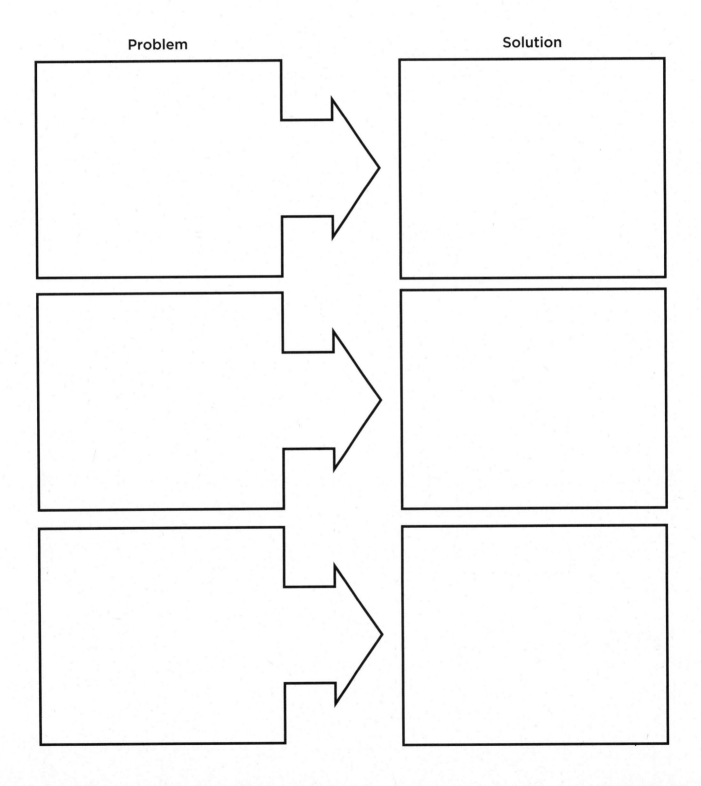

Problem

Solution

© Discovery Education | www.DiscoveryEducation.com

Name_____ Date _____

GRAPHIC ORGANIZER: Problem/Solution Chart *(continued)*

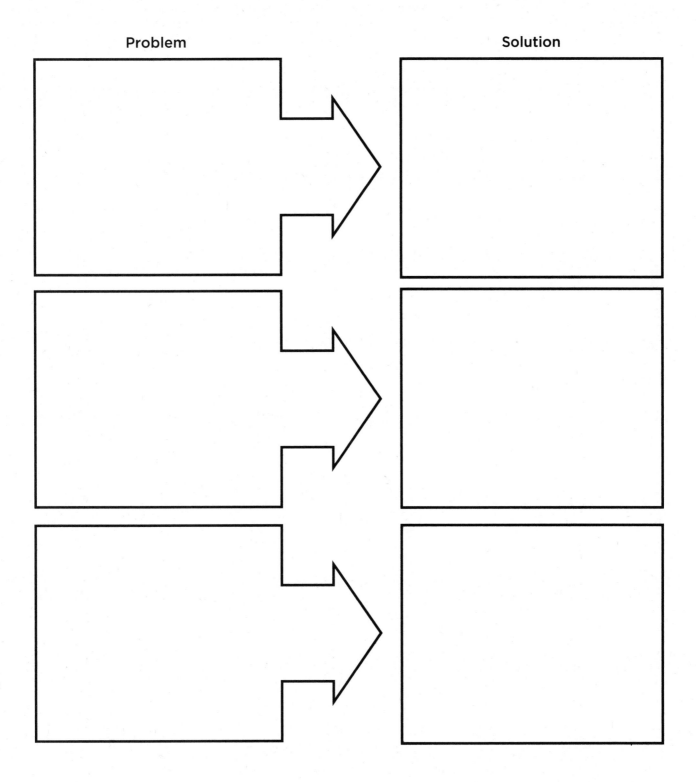

Problem

Solution

Name _____ **Date** _____

GRAPHIC ORGANIZER: Timeline

Make a timeline of important events from 1850 through 1860 that contributed to secession. For supporting resources, go to A Nation Divided > Slavery and the Civil War > The Road to Disunion > Explore > Keeping the Balance.

1820   1860

◆━━◆

© Discovery Education | www.DiscoveryEducation.com

Name _____ Date _____

GRAPHIC ORGANIZER: Timeline *(continued)*

Summarize the Event	How Did This Event Lead to Sectional Tensions Between the North and South?

Name _____ Date _____

GRAPHIC ORGANIZER: Landmark Case Brief

Use this Graphic Organizer to record important information about the landmark case *Dred Scott v. Sandford* (1857). For supporting resources, go to A Nation Divided > Slavery and the Civil War > The Road to Disunion > Explore > A Lawsuit and a Decision.

I. Facts of the Case
Summarize events that took place that led to a dispute between two parties.

II. Question of Law
What questions about the meaning of the Constitution were the justices asked to consider?

Name _____ Date _____

GRAPHIC ORGANIZER: Landmark Case Brief *(continued)*

III. Decision and Outcome

A. How did the justices respond to the questions of law?

B. How did this decision affect the parties in the case?

IV. Reasoning

Why did the justices decide as they did?

V. Significance

In what ways did the impact of the Court's decision extend beyond the parties involved?

Name _____ Date _____

EXPLORE: FOCUS QUESTIONS

Using what you learned from the Core Interactive Text, answer each page's focus question:

Disagreements Divide

How did economics divide the nation?

_____
_____
_____
_____

The Nullification Crisis

How did the country almost go to war in 1833?

_____
_____
_____

Division over Slavery

How were arguments over slavery dividing the nation?

_____
_____
_____
_____

Keeping the Balance

How did settling the western territories cause further tension?

_____
_____
_____

Bleeding Kansas

What were the effects of the Kansas-Nebraska Act?

_____
_____
_____

Name _____ Date _____

EXPLORE: FOCUS QUESTIONS *(continued)*

Divisive Politics
How did the nation's political parties reorganize in the 1850s?

_____

_____

_____

A Lawsuit and a Decision
How did a Supreme Court decision inflame passions?

_____

_____

_____

The Lincoln-Douglas Debates
Why was a senatorial election significant?

_____

_____

_____

John Brown Leads an Uprising
What happened at Harpers Ferry, Virginia?

_____

_____

_____

The Last Straw
What were the outcome and impact of the election of 1860?

_____

_____

_____

PROJECTS AND ASSESSMENTS

Explain Activities

ACTIVITY TYPE: VISUALIZATION

Parties and Issues

In this activity, you will use a Comparison Chart to identify major issues, major political parties, major political parties' views on different issues, and the most important political outcomes for the following time periods.

ACTIVITY TYPE: DIAGRAM

The Road to Disunion

Think about how the terms given in this activity are important to understanding the congressional conflicts and compromises that led to the secession of Southern states after Abraham Lincoln's election in 1860. Next, consider how these terms might be categorized or connected with one another. Then, using all of the words in the word bank, design your own diagram or graphic illustration of events in Congress that led to secession and the Civil War.

ACTIVITY TYPE: VISUALIZATION

The Road to Disunion

In this activity, you will select, illustrate, and summarize the main events from the early and mid-1800s that led to Southern states seceding from the Union.

ACTIVITY TYPE: COMPARISON CHART

Regional Differences

In this activity, you will use a Comparison Chart to record notes on the geographic characteristics, main economic activities, workforce characteristics, and role of the cities in the Northern and Southern United States during the early 1800s.

ACTIVITY TYPE: QUICK WRITE

The Road to Disunion

In this Quick Write activity, you will write a brief essay explaining which of the events listed best demonstrates why the Union was unable to stay together.

ACTIVITY TYPE: SOCIAL STUDIES EXPLANATION

The Road to Disunion

In this activity, you will use the template to assemble evidence from the sources you have explored. Then, you will write an answer to the Essential Question and defend your answer with supporting evidence.

PROJECTS AND ASSESSMENTS *(continued)*

Elaborate Activities

photo: Discovery Education

INVESTIGATION TYPE: HISTORICAL PERSPECTIVES

A Nation Divided

Your mission is to analyze three important issues impacting the United States in 1860 from four different perspectives.

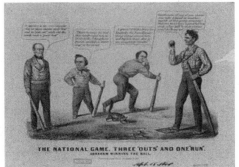

photo: Library of Congress

ACTIVITY TYPE: CLASSROOM DEBATE

Election of 1860

In this activity, you will write a stump speech in support of a Republican, Northern Democratic, Southern Democratic, or Constitutional Union Party candidate. You will then participate in a debate with classmates representing the other parties.

photo: Harpweek

ACTIVITY TYPE: EXPRESS YOUR OPINION

Walking a Tightrope

In this activity, you will perform an in-depth analysis of a political cartoon from the pre–Civil War era.

photo: Library of Congress

ACTIVITY TYPE: DOCUMENT-BASED INVESTIGATION

Road to Disunion

In this Document-Based Investigation, you will analyze source materials and investigate this question: Was the expansion of slavery into new western territories the primary cause of secession and the Civil War?

PROJECTS AND ASSESSMENTS *(continued)*

Evaluate Activities

BRIEF-CONSTRUCTED RESPONSE (BCR)

The Road to Disunion

EXTENDED-CONSTRUCTED RESPONSE (ECR)

The Road to Disunion

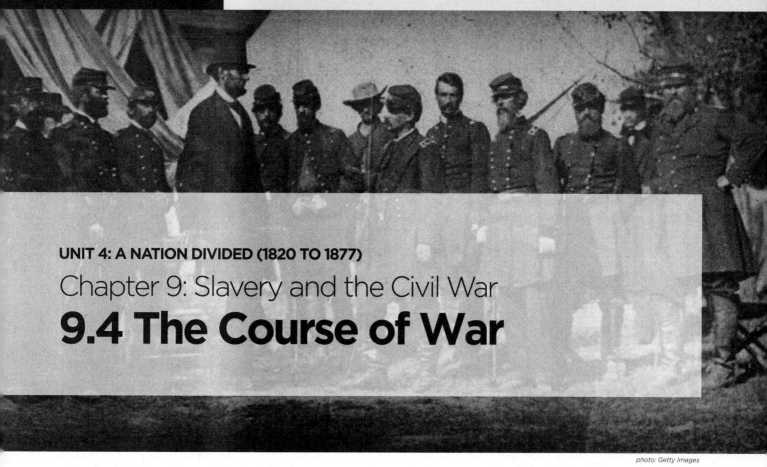

UNIT 4: A NATION DIVIDED (1820 TO 1877)

Chapter 9: Slavery and the Civil War

9.4 The Course of War

photo: Getty Images

LESSON OVERVIEW

Lesson Objectives:

By the end of this lesson, you should be able to:

- Compare and contrast the characteristics of the Union and Confederate armies (size, access to resources).
- Describe the outbreak, major battles, turning points (Emancipation Proclamation/Gettysburg Address), and conclusion of the Civil War.

Lesson Essential Question:

How did the Union win the Civil War?

Key Vocabulary

90-day men, Abraham Lincoln, Anaconda Plan, Antietam, Appomattox Court House, Battle of Antietam, Battle of Fort Sumter, Battle of Gettysburg, Battle of Shiloh, Belle Boyd, blockade, border state, Bull Run, Civil War, Confederacy / Confederate States, Confederate States of America, conscription, cotton diplomacy, emancipation, Emancipation Proclamation, First Battle of Bull Run, Fort Sumter, George McClellan, Gettysburg Address, greenback, habeas corpus, Harpers Ferry, Virginia, Jefferson Davis, Juneteenth, martial law, Mathew Brady, Robert E. Lee, secession, Second Battle of Bull Run, Seven Days' Battle, Siege of Vicksburg, Thomas Jonathan "Stonewall" Jackson, total war, Ulysses S. Grant, Vicksburg, Mississippi, William Tecumseh Sherman, Winfield Scott

FLASHCARDS

1 Choosing Sides

In 1861, 11 states seceded from the United States (the Union) and established their own country, which they called the Confederate States of America (the Confederacy).

- **The Confederate states were Georgia, South Carolina, Virginia, North Carolina, Tennessee, Louisiana, Mississippi, Alabama, Arkansas, Florida, and Texas.**
- **The border states remained in the Union and allowed slavery.**
- **Union advantages included a larger population, stronger economy, more effective transportation system, and more natural resources.**
- **Confederate advantages included stronger motivation and military leadership.**

Why Does It Matter?

Slavery was one of the primary sources of conflict between the Union and the Confederacy, but it wasn't the only factor when states chose sides. The comparative advantages of each side explain why the Civil War lasted so long.

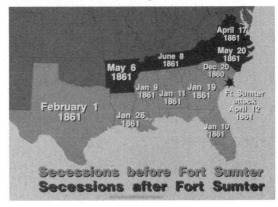

photo: IRC

Four states seceded after the attack on Fort Sumter.

2 Key Events and Mounting Casualties

The first shot of the Civil War was fired at Fort Sumter near Charleston, South Carolina.

- **The first major battle of the Civil War occurred on July 21, 1861, near Manassas, Virginia, and a creek named Bull Run.**
- **Confederates attacked a Union camp at Shiloh. Two days of fighting caused more than 23,000 casualties.**
- **On September 16, 1862, Union Major General George McClellan attacked Confederate General Robert E. Lee at Sharpsburg, Maryland. Fought on Union territory, the Battle of Antietam included the bloodiest day in America's history.**
- **The Emancipation Proclamation in 1863 granted freedom to enslaved people in the Confederate states and enabled African Americans to serve in the Union military.**
- **The Confederate army was seriously weakened at Gettysburg in Confederate General Lee's second attempt to invade the North.**
- **President Lincoln's Gettysburg Address reinforced the purpose of the Civil War as a war for freedom and equality.**
- **After several weeks under siege, Vicksburg surrendered to the Union on July 4, 1863. The Union gained control of the Mississippi River and split the Confederacy.**
- **Union General Sherman captured Atlanta and Savannah on his March to the Sea and subjected Georgia to total war.**
- **Confederate General Robert E. Lee surrendered at the town of Appomattox Court House on April 9, 1865.**

Why Does It Matter?

Four states seceded after the attack on Fort Sumter. The Emancipation Proclamation changed the focus of the Civil War from holding the Union together to abolishing slavery. The policy of total war was new to American warfare; it terrified and demoralized the Confederate army as well as the civilian population of the South.

photo: Paul Fuqua

The First Battle of Manassas or Bull Run showed that the Civil War would not be brief.

Name _____ Date _____

GRAPHIC ORGANIZER: Sequence Chart

Complete this Sequence Chart to identify major events of the Civil War. Be sure to briefly describe and explain the significance of each event. For supporting resources, go to A Nation Divided > Slavery and the Civil War > The Course of War > Explore.

Event/Date	Summary of Event	Significance of Event
Fort Sumter		
First Battle of Bull Run		
Battle of Shiloh		
Battle of Antietam		

Name _____ **Date** _____

GRAPHIC ORGANIZER: Sequence Chart *(continued)*

Event/Date	Summary of Event	Significance of Event
Emancipation Proclamation		
Battle of Gettysburg		
Siege of Vicksburg		
Gettysburg Address		

Name _____ Date _____

GRAPHIC ORGANIZER: Sequence Chart *(continued)*

Event/Date	Summary of Event	Significance of Event
Sherman's March to the Sea		
Siege of Petersburg		
Surrender at Appomattox		
Lincoln's Assassination		

Discovery SOCIAL STUDIES
EDUCATION **TECHBOOK**

Name _____ Date _____

EXPLORE: FOCUS QUESTIONS

Using what you learned from the Core Interactive Text, answer each page's focus question:

Secession Leads to War
How did the Civil War begin?

_____
_____
_____
_____

President Lincoln Responds
What continued efforts did President Lincoln make to preserve the Union?

_____
_____
_____
_____

Economic Strength
How did the Union's and the Confederacy's economies compare?

_____
_____
_____
_____

Soldiers and Weapons
Who fought in the Civil War? What weapons were used?

_____
_____
_____
_____

War Strategies and Results
How did the Union win the Civil War?

_____
_____
_____

The Real Fighting Begins
What happened in the first major Civil War battles?

_____
_____
_____
_____

Name _____ Date _____

EXPLORE: FOCUS QUESTIONS *(continued)*

Turning Point
How did Antietam and the Emancipation Proclamation change the war?

_____
_____
_____

Gettysburg
What happened at Gettysburg?

_____
_____
_____

Turning Point: Siege of Vicksburg
How was the Siege of Vicksburg important?

_____
_____
_____

Sherman's March to the Sea
What events convinced many Confederates that the time to surrender had come?

_____
_____
_____

Surrender
How did the Civil War end?

_____
_____
_____

Assassination
How was Abraham Lincoln assassinated?

_____
_____
_____

PROJECTS AND ASSESSMENTS

Explain Activities

ACTIVITY TYPE: DIAGRAM

Mapping the Civil War

In this activity, you will create an annotated map of the Civil War, including the sites of battles and major events, and then describe the important events that occurred at each place on the map.

ACTIVITY TYPE: ADVERTISEMENT

Recruitment and the Emancipation Proclamation

In this activity, you will study a Union recruitment poster issued in 1861. Next, you will create a similar poster for an 1863 campaign.

ACTIVITY TYPE: VISUALIZATION

The Civil War

In this activity, you will use illustrations and captions to tell the story of an important event from the Civil War.

ACTIVITY TYPE: VISUALIZATION

Top Five List: Why Did the Union Win?

In this Visualization activity, you will identify what you think are the top five reasons for the Union's victory in the Civil War. Then, you will create a slide show of graphs and charts illustrating each of your reasons.

ACTIVITY TYPE: DIAGRAM

Significant Figures of the Civil War

In this activity, you will complete a Comparison Chart to describe and compare the contributions of significant figures from the Civil War.

ACTIVITY TYPE: SOCIAL STUDIES EXPLANATION

The Course of War

In this activity, you will use the template to assemble evidence from the sources you have explored. Then, you will write an answer to the Essential Question and defend your answer with supporting evidence.

PROJECTS AND ASSESSMENTS *(continued)*

Elaborate Activities

photo: Library of Congress

INVESTIGATION TYPE: TIMELINE MAP

The Course of the Civil War

What tactics did the Northern generals and Abraham Lincoln use to win the Civil War in spite of many lost battles? In this investigation, you will use the Timeline Map interactive tool to examine the major movements of the Union and the Confederate armies from 1861 to 1865 and trace the advantages and disadvantages each side had as the war proceeded.

photo: IRC

ACTIVITY TYPE: SOCRATIC SEMINAR

Validating War

In this Socratic Seminar, you will read the Gettysburg Address and complete a discussion that leads to a response to the question: To what extent were the ideas Abraham Lincoln presented in the Gettysburg Address consistent with his initial reasons for fighting the Civil War?

photo: Library of Congress

ACTIVITY TYPE: YOU AS ARTIST

Illustrating Viewpoints

In this activity, you will analyze a political cartoon to understand its message. Then, you will use the common elements of political cartoons to draw your own cartoon that will make a point about one of the controversies of the Civil War.

photo: Library of Congress

ACTIVITY TYPE: SOCRATIC SEMINAR

Lincoln vs. Davis

In this activity, you will analyze excerpts from addresses given by President Lincoln and Jefferson Davis to compare their ideas on government, equality, and liberty.

PROJECTS AND ASSESSMENTS *(continued)*

photo: Library of Congress

ACTIVITY TYPE: SOCRATIC SEMINAR

Lincoln's Gettysburg Address

In this Socratic Seminar, you will read the Gettysburg Address and complete a discussion that leads to a response to the question: What can we learn from the Gettysburg Address about the Union's purpose for fighting the Civil War?

photo: Library of Congress

ACTIVITY TYPE: DOCUMENT-BASED INVESTIGATION

A Turning Point?

In this activity, you will either write a newspaper article commemorating the 150th anniversary of the Civil War or create a slide show on the turning point in the Civil War.

photo: Library of Congress

ACTIVITY TYPE: DOCUMENT-BASED INVESTIGATION

The Course of War

In this Document-Based Investigation, you will analyze source materials and investigate this question: Why did the Civil War last longer than many expected?

Evaluate Activities

BRIEF-CONSTRUCTED RESPONSE (BCR)

The Course of War

EXTENDED-CONSTRUCTED RESPONSE (ECR)

The Course of War

© Discovery Education | www.DiscoveryEducation.com

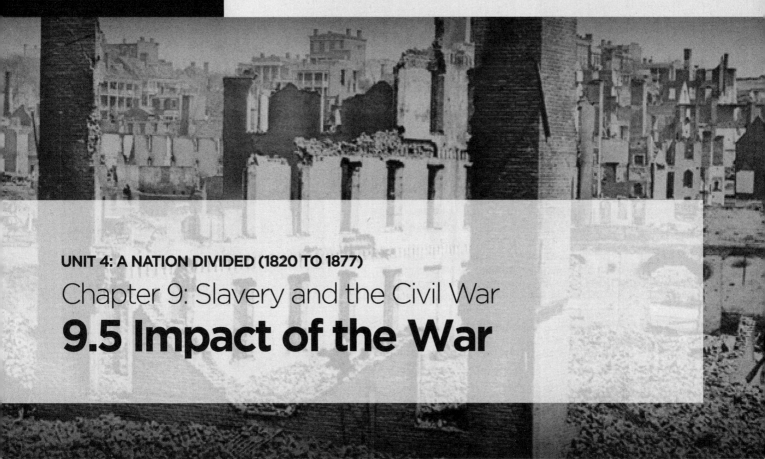

UNIT 4: A NATION DIVIDED (1820 TO 1877)

Chapter 9: Slavery and the Civil War

9.5 Impact of the War

LESSON OVERVIEW

Lesson Objectives:

By the end of this lesson, you should be able to:

- Analyze key immediate outcomes of the Civil War on various groups and regions in the United States.
- Analyze the political, economic, and social effects of the Civil War.

Key Vocabulary

Abraham Lincoln, Appomattox Court House, Civil War, Clara Barton, Compromise of 1877, emancipation, Emancipation Proclamation, greenback, inflation, infrastructure, nationalism, Robert E. Lee, Thirteenth Amendment, Ulysses S. Grant

Lesson Essential Question:

To what extent was the Civil War America's second revolution?

FLASHCARDS

1 Immediate Outcomes of the Civil War

When the Civil War ended in April 1865, it was time to pick up the pieces and rebuild the country. Enslaved persons, women, and the South in general had experienced a great deal of change because of the war.

- All enslaved persons were freed by the passage of the Thirteenth Amendment in 1865.
- African Americans were unsure of what their new rights and freedoms meant. They were mostly uneducated and were very poor.
- Much of the South lay in ruins after the war. Major cities like Charleston and Atlanta had been burned nearly to the ground. The Union army had destroyed railroads, barns, farm equipment, and other infrastructure across the Confederacy.
- About three million people fought in the Civil War. Roughly 600,000 of them died. The Union and the Confederacy both suffered from this great loss of life.
- During the war, women worked as nurses and had to take care of their homes, farms, and families. They raised money for the war effort and volunteered making socks, canning food, and doing whatever was needed.
- After the war, women returned to the home. They had no more rights than before and were expected to go back to "business as usual."

Why Does It Matter?

The Civil War created change for the United States as a whole, and its aftermath affected different groups and regions differently. Enslaved people were now free, women were confined to the home once more, and the South needed to be rebuilt.

photo: IRC

Southerner Belle Boyd used her feminine charm to get Union military men to spill their army secrets to her. Although imprisoned on more than one occasion, Belle Boyd continued to attempt to help the South until she fled capture and married a former Union soldier in England.

2 The Spoils of War

The Civil War solidified the economic power of the North and expanded the powers of the federal government.

- More than 600,000 Americans were killed during the Civil War. This is the largest loss of American life of any war in history.
- During the Civil War, people in the North began viewing themselves as "Americans" rather than as belonging to a particular state.
- The federal government expanded its powers during the Civil War to raise taxes and create currency to pay for war.
- After the war, the government's expanded powers remained, and it took on new responsibilities to make sure the Thirteenth Amendment was followed. For the first time, the federal government was charged with guarding the rights and freedoms of the people of the United States.
- Much of the South was burned and destroyed during the Civil War. After the war, the region was devastated economically. It had no factories, had little infrastructure, and had lost its slave labor. The industrialized North emerged as the dominant economic power in the nation.
- About one-fourth of all Southern men were killed in the war. About one in every sixteen white men from the North lost their lives as well. The tremendous loss of life left a small labor pool and touched almost every family.

Why Does It Matter?

The Civil War had wide-reaching effects on the economy, politics, and society of the United States. Government changes, the enormous loss of life, and the devastation of the South created a new nation that was much different than the prewar United States had been.

photo: IRC

Richmond, the capital of Virginia and of the Confederacy, was destroyed during the war.

Name _____ **Date** _____

GRAPHIC ORGANIZER: GREASES Chart

Use this GREASES Chart to track important effects of the Civil War. For supporting resources, go to A Nation Divided > Slavery and the Civil War > Impact of the War > Explore.

Government	
Religion	
Economic	
Art & Architecture	
Science & Technology	
Environment	
Social & Cultural Values	

Name _____ **Date** _____

GRAPHIC ORGANIZER: Main Idea Web

Complete this Main Idea Web. For supporting resources, go to A Nation Divided > Slavery and the Civil War > Impact of the War > Explore > Devastation in the South.

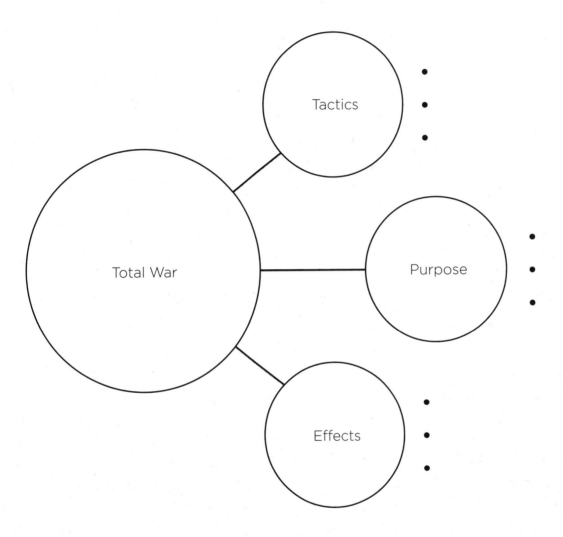

© Discovery Education | www.DiscoveryEducation.com

Name _____ Date _____

EXPLORE: FOCUS QUESTIONS

Using what you learned from the Core Interactive Text, answer each page's focus question:

Free at Last
What happened to the institution of slavery during the Civil War?

_____

_____

_____

Devastation in the South
What did the South look like at the end of the Civil War?

_____

_____

_____

Women and the Civil War
How did the role of women change during and after the Civil War?

_____

_____

_____

"This Mighty Scourge of War"
What were the human costs of the Civil War?

_____

_____

_____

Identifying as an "American"
How did the role of the federal government change during and after the war?

_____

_____

_____

Name _____ Date _____

EXPLORE: FOCUS QUESTIONS *(continued)*

Postwar Economies
What were the economic effects of the Civil War?

_____
_____
_____

A Social Shift
How was society in the North and South changed by the war?

_____
_____
_____

© Discovery Education | www.DiscoveryEducation.com

PROJECTS AND ASSESSMENTS

Explain Activities

ACTIVITY TYPE: VISUALIZATION

Impact of War

In this Visualization activity, you will explore how the South was changed by the Civil War.

ACTIVITY TYPE: DIAGRAM

Impact on Americans

In this activity, you will use a Comparison Chart to make notes on how the immediate aftermath of the Civil War made an impact on African Americans and people from the North and South.

ACTIVITY TYPE: SOCIAL STUDIES EXPLANATION

Impact of the War

In this activity, you will use the template to assemble evidence from the sources you have explored. Then, you will write an answer to the Essential Question and defend your answer with supporting evidence.

Elaborate Activities

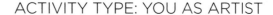

photo: Library of Congress

INVESTIGATION TYPE: SOURCE ANALYSIS

The Civil Rights Amendments

How did the Civil War and the passage of the Thirteenth, Fourteenth, and Fifteenth Amendments change the legal status of African Americans? Analyze the Thirteenth, Fourteenth, and Fifteenth Amendments to the U.S. Constitution to determine how they changed the civil and political roles of African Americans.

ACTIVITY TYPE: YOU AS ARTIST

Rebuilding the Nation

In this activity, you will analyze a political cartoon published in 1865 to learn more about common techniques used to make a point in political cartoons.

photo: Library of Congress

PROJECTS AND ASSESSMENTS *(continued)*

photo: Jupiterimages Corporations

ACTIVITY TYPE: SAY WHAT?

In Lincoln's Footsteps

In this activity, you and your classmates will work together to translate the first section of Abraham Lincoln's second inaugural address.

photo: Library of Congress

ACTIVITY TYPE: DOCUMENT-BASED INVESTIGATION

Lincoln and Emancipation

In this activity, you will write a newspaper article commemorating the 150th anniversary of emancipation. In your article, explain your perspective on the investigation question using evidence and examples from the primary sources. You may also write a letter responding to the artist of a lithograph celebrating Lincoln.

photo: Getty Images

ACTIVITY TYPE: DOCUMENT-BASED INVESTIGATION

Impact of the War

In this Document-Based Investigation you will be looking at post–Civil War perceptions: In what ways did the Civil War change the way Americans perceived themselves?

Evaluate Activities

BRIEF-CONSTRUCTED RESPONSE (BCR)

Impact of the War

EXTENDED-CONSTRUCTED RESPONSE (ECR)

Impact of the War

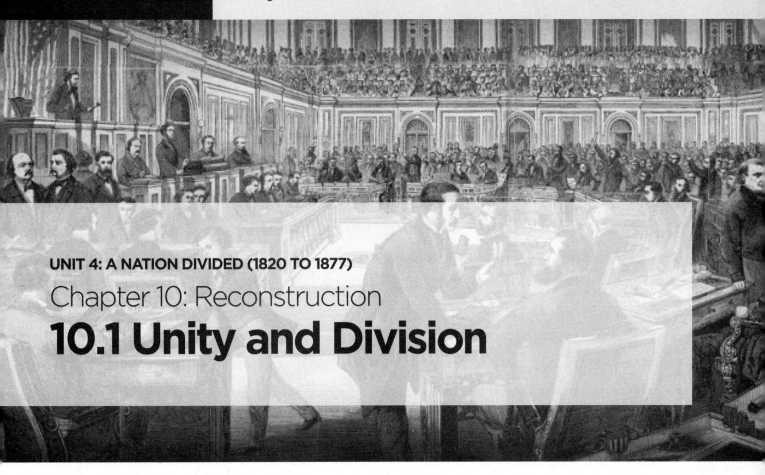

UNIT 4: A NATION DIVIDED (1820 TO 1877)

Chapter 10: Reconstruction

10.1 Unity and Division

LESSON OVERVIEW

Lesson Objectives:

By the end of this lesson, you should be able to:

- Explain social and economic problems faced by the nation following the Civil War.

- Analyze and compare Reconstruction plans proposed by Abraham Lincoln and moderate Republicans, the Radical Republicans, and Andrew Johnson.

- Evaluate the effectiveness of key components of Congressional Reconstruction, including the Freedmen's Bureau and the establishment of military control of the South.

- Describe and evaluate the impact of the Fourteenth and Fifteenth Amendments to the Constitution.

Key Vocabulary

Abraham Lincoln, Andrew Johnson, Black Codes, Civil Rights Act of 1866, Fifteenth Amendment, Fourteenth Amendment, Frederick Douglass, Freedmen's Bureau, Hiram Revels, impeach, infrastructure, Ku Klux Klan, Military Reconstruction Act, Reconstruction, Ten Percent Plan, Thirteenth Amendment, Ulysses S. Grant, Wade-Davis Bill

Lesson Essential Questions:

What problems did Reconstruction resolve?
What problems did it fail to resolve?

FLASHCARDS

1 ## Aftermath of War

The Union faced a number of economic, social, and political problems following the end of the Civil War.

- The South had lost most of its resources in the war, and its land had been looted and burned. The Southern economy had collapsed.
- To pay for the war, Confederate states and the Union had taken on debts that now needed to be repaid.
- African Americans had been freed, but most of them had no money, nowhere to live, and no education.
- Southerners resented the North and were skeptical of Northern intentions.

Why Does It Matter?

The North had to decide on the best way to rebuild and bring the South back into the Union. Problems that were not resolved during Reconstruction troubled the United States into the 21st century.

photo: Discovery Education
A memorial to Confederate soldiers stands in a Kentucky cemetery.

2 ## Plans for Reconstruction

Abraham Lincoln, the Radical Republicans in Congress, and Andrew Johnson all had different ideas about how to reconstruct the South.

- Lincoln and the moderate Republicans wanted to make it easier for the South to reenter the Union and introduce reform for the freed enslaved people gradually.
- Radical Republicans wanted to punish the South and use federal authority to grant rights to the freed enslaved people quickly.
- Johnson's policies allowed the South to rebuild its society with the same social distinctions as before the war.
- Congress and Johnson disagreed on the best plan for Reconstruction. Eventually, Johnson was impeached for attempting to prevent Congress's laws from being enforced.

Why Does It Matter?

The partial solutions adopted during Reconstruction have left a legacy of racial inequality and race-based violence.

photo: IRC
This cartoon represents the collision of two different visions for Reconstruction. Notice how neither figure is willing to move.

FLASHCARDS *(continued)*

3 Congressional Action

Congressional Reconstruction included military control of the South, establishment and continuation of the Freedman's Bureau, and the passing of the Fourteenth and Fifteenth Amendments.

- The Freedman's Bureau was a welfare agency offering services to help formerly enslaved persons transition to their new lives.
- The Freedman's Bureau was originally only intended to be in place for one year, but it lasted until 1872.
- Union troops occupied the South, dividing it into five military districts.
- Southern states could reenter the Union if they wrote new constitutions, swore to be loyal to the Union, and accepted the prohibition of slavery.

Why Does It Matter?

Despite Congress's actions, African Americans faced major problems due to white violence and discrimination. These would last not only through Reconstruction but also through the middle of the next century.

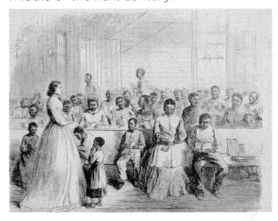

photo: IRC

The Freedmen's Bureau bill called for assistance for former enslaved persons, such as this Mississippi school.

4 Constitutional Amendments

Together with the Thirteenth Amendment, the Fourteenth and Fifteenth Amendments radically reshaped the rights granted to people within the United States.

- The Reconstruction Amendments (Thirteenth, Fourteenth, and Fifteenth) made up the biggest change to the U.S. Constitution since the Bill of Rights.
- The Fourteenth Amendment granted citizenship to formerly enslaved people.
- The Fourteenth Amendment extended federal power to prevent states from passing laws that could strip formerly enslaved people of their rights.
- The Fifteenth Amendment granted African American men suffrage, or the right to vote.

Why Does It Matter?

These amendments meant that rights and reforms were now the letter of U.S. law. They also marked an increase in federal power over that of the states. This would solve some of the problems of Reconstruction (guaranteeing rights for African Americans) but not others (Southern resentment of the Union).

photo: IRC

African Americans registered to vote in federal elections in 1868.

Name _____ Date _____

 GRAPHIC ORGANIZER: Venn Diagram

Use this Venn Diagram to compare and contrast the post–Civil War situations of Southern whites and newly freed African Americans. Be sure to include economic, political, and social factors in your response. For supporting resources, go to A Nation Divided > Reconstruction > Unity and Division > Explore.

Southern Whites   Newly Freed African Americans

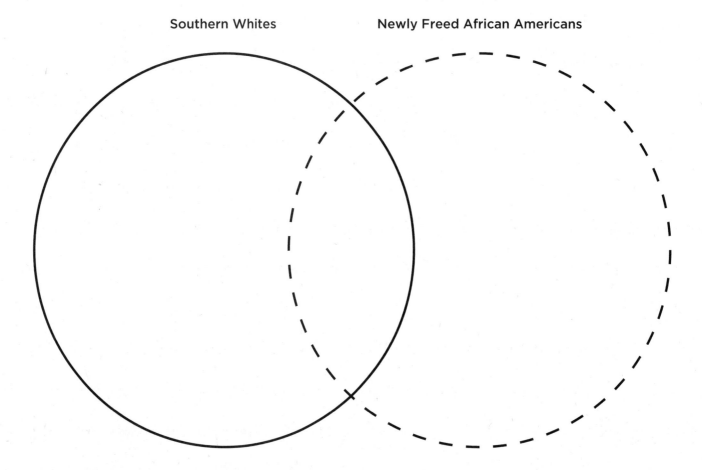

Name _____ **Date** _____

GRAPHIC ORGANIZER: Comparison Chart

Use this Comparison Chart to compare the Reconstruction plans of Lincoln, Johnson, and Congress. For supporting resources, go to A Nation Divided > Reconstruction > Unity and Division > Explore > Lincoln's Plan.

Criteria	Lincoln	Johnson	Congress
Readmission			
Freedmen's Bureau			
Civil Rights			
Citizenship			
Military Rule			
Voting Rights			

Name _____ Date _____

GRAPHIC ORGANIZER: Change Over Time

Complete this Change Over Time Chart by noting the changes to the rights granted to African Americans. For supporting resources, go to A Nation Divided > Reconstruction > Unity and Division > Explore.

Rights Before the Civil War:	Rights Gained During Reconstruction:

Changes:

© Discovery Education | www.DiscoveryEducation.com

Name _____ Date _____

EXPLORE: FOCUS QUESTIONS

Using what you learned from the Core Interactive Text, answer each page's focus question:

Radical Changes

What was life like for Southerners after the war?

_____

_____

_____

Lincoln's Plan

What was Lincoln's plan for Reconstruction?

_____

_____

_____

The Radical Republican Plan

How was the Radical Republican plan different from Lincoln's plan?

_____

_____

_____

The End of Presidential Reconstruction

How did Lincoln's assassination change the course of Reconstruction?

_____

_____

_____

The Civil Rights Act and the Fourteenth Amendment

How did Congress respond to the Black Codes?

_____

_____

_____

Name _____ Date _____

EXPLORE: FOCUS QUESTIONS *(continued)*

Congressional Reconstruction
How did Congress restore unity?

_____
_____
_____
_____

The Impeachment of President Johnson
How did Congress try to defeat Andrew Johnson?

_____
_____
_____
_____

Granting Freedmen the Right to Vote
How did the Fifteenth Amendment affect Reconstruction?

_____
_____
_____
_____

PROJECTS AND ASSESSMENTS

Explain Activities

ACTIVITY TYPE: ADVERTISEMENT

Becoming a Citizen

Imagine that you work for the Citizenship and Immigration Services division of the U.S. Department of Homeland Security. In this activity, you will create an advertisement designed to target foreign-born persons who wish to become citizens of the United States.

ACTIVITY TYPE: MOVIE TRAILER

Lincoln's Presidency

The Great Emancipator will soon be in theaters nationwide! You must develop a movie trailer that will make people want to see this documentary film.

ACTIVITY TYPE: ADVERTISEMENT

Unity and Division

In this activity, you will create an advertisement designed to persuade African Americans to register to vote and participate in an upcoming election.

ACTIVITY TYPE: YOU AS JOURNALIST

Unity and Division

In this activity, you will write an article that briefly describes Lincoln's assassination.

ACTIVITY TYPE: DIAGRAM

Parties and Issues: Diagram

In this activity, you will use a Comparison Chart to identify major issues, major political parties, major political parties' views on different issues, and the most important political outcomes for the following time periods.

ACTIVITY TYPE: SOCIAL STUDIES EXPLANATION

Unity and Division

In this activity, you will use the template to assemble evidence from the sources you have explored. Then, you will write an answer to the Essential Questions and defend your answer with supporting evidence.

PROJECTS AND ASSESSMENTS *(continued)*

Elaborate Activities

photo: Library of Congress

INVESTIGATION TYPE: TIMELINE INQUIRY

Unity and Division

Find out how two presidents, Congress, and the people of the North and South tried to steer the process of reuniting the nation after the Civil War. Was Reconstruction mostly a success or mostly a failure?

photo: Harpweek

ACTIVITY TYPE: YOU AS ARTIST

Reconstruction-Era Literature

In this creative writing exercise, you will read selections from popular Reconstruction-era literature. Then, you will create your own work to add to the canon.

photo: Library of Congress

ACTIVITY TYPE: PITCH YOUR IDEA

The Best Plan to Reunite?

In this activity, you will evaluate the Reconstruction plans of the Radical Republicans, moderate Republicans, and Democrats and select the one you think would be most effective in rebuilding the nation.

photo: Harpweek

ACTIVITY TYPE: DOCUMENT-BASED INVESTIGATION

The Radical Republicans

In this Document-Based Investigation, you will analyze source materials and investigate this question: To what extent did emancipation bring true freedom to African Americans in the South?

PROJECTS AND ASSESSMENTS *(continued)*

photo: IRC

ACTIVITY TYPE: DOCUMENT-BASED INVESTIGATION

Unity and Division

In this Document-Based Investigation, you will analyze source materials and investigate this question: Did Congressional Reconstruction promote or undermine American democratic principles?

Evaluate Activities

BRIEF-CONSTRUCTED RESPONSE (BCR)

Unity and Division

EXTENDED-CONSTRUCTED RESPONSE (ECR)

Unity and Division

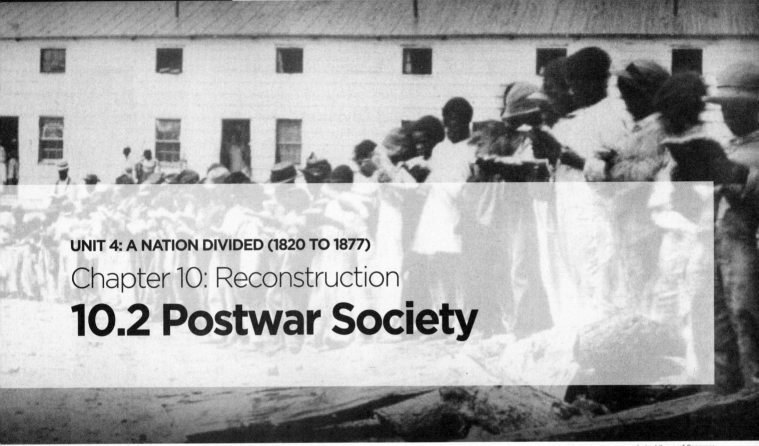

UNIT 4: A NATION DIVIDED (1820 TO 1877)

Chapter 10: Reconstruction

10.2 Postwar Society

photo: Library of Congress

LESSON OVERVIEW

Lesson Objectives:

By the end of this lesson, you should be able to:

- **Assess the long-term social and cultural impacts of Reconstruction on various groups.**
- **Account for Southern distrust of the federal government and Northern interests.**

Lesson Essential Question:

In what ways did Reconstruction change Southern society?

Key Vocabulary

amendment, Black Codes, Blanche K. Bruce, carpetbaggers, Civil Rights Act of 1866, Compromise of 1877, disenfranchise, Fifteenth Amendment, Fourteenth Amendment, Ku Klux Klan, *Plessy v. Ferguson*, Reconstruction Acts, Robert E. Lee, scalawags, sharecropping, tenant farmer, William Tecumseh Sherman

FLASHCARDS

1 **Reconstruction Affects Both African Americans and White Southerners for Decades**

Congressional Reconstruction had harsh consequences for the former leaders of the South and attempted to provide justice for African Americans.

- The Reconstruction Acts required readmitted states to ratify the Fourteenth Amendment and to give African American men the right to vote. By September 1867, more African Americans than white Americans were registered to vote in several Southern states.
- The Freedmen's Bureau built and operated hospitals and distributed clothing.
- The Freedmen's Bureau built and ran schools and teacher training institutions. Many teachers came from the North or were members of abolitionist societies.
- In 1870, the Fifteenth Amendment to the U.S. Constitution guaranteed all African American men the right to vote.

Why Does It Matter?

The end of Reconstruction brought an end to strict federal protection of African Americans and a renewal of discriminatory laws and policies. This development lasted well into the 1960s, when African Americans and others led the fight for the protection of rights for all during the civil rights movement.

photo: Discovery Education

Immediately after Reconstruction ended, Southern states passed discriminatory laws to prevent African Americans from voting and exercising their civil rights. These laws lasted well into the 1960s.

2 **Federal Policies During Reconstruction Led to Long-Term Southern Hostilities**

Through the period of Radical Reconstruction, white Southerners continued their attempts to restore what had been lost of the life they had known. However, they saw their political power reduced and African Americans' political power increased. Over time, they felt increasingly hostile toward not only Northern Republicans and African Americans but also the federal government.

- Many Southerners resented freed African Americans, Congress, the Freedmen's Bureau, carpetbaggers, and scalawags—people who did not want to protect white American privilege.
- Southern legislatures passed Black Codes that limited the rights of African Americans.
- Some Southerners joined hate groups, such as the Ku Klux Klan, that used violence and terror to prevent African Americans from exercising their rights.
- A national financial panic in 1873 led Americans across the country to turn away from Reconstruction.
- As soon as Republicans lost power, Southern legislatures reinstated discriminatory legislation and put an end to Republican reforms and programs.

Why Does It Matter?

The partial solutions adopted during Reconstruction have left a legacy of racial inequality and race-based violence.

photo: IRC

This cartoon focuses on the election of Rutherford B. Hayes as president in 1877. Hayes's policy toward the South was known as the "Let 'em alone policy" and brought an end to Reconstruction. In the cartoon, Hayes is plowing up the "carpetbag and bayonet rule" of the South.

Name _____ **Date** _____

GRAPHIC ORGANIZER: Comparison Chart

Use this Comparison Chart to compare the lives and problems of different groups of people before and after the Civil War. For supporting resources, go to A Nation Divided > Reconstruction > Postwar Society > Explore.

Group:	Life Before the Civil War	Life After the Civil War
White Small Farmers		
Enslaved People / Newly Freed African Americans		
Plantation Owners		
Carpetbaggers		

Discovery SOCIAL STUDIES
EDUCATION **TECHBOOK**

Name _____ Date _____

GRAPHIC ORGANIZER: Problem/Solution Chart

Use this Problem/Solution Chart to identify social and political problems following the Civil War and the solutions adopted by different groups. For supporting resources, go to A Nation Divided > Reconstruction > Postwar Society > Explore.

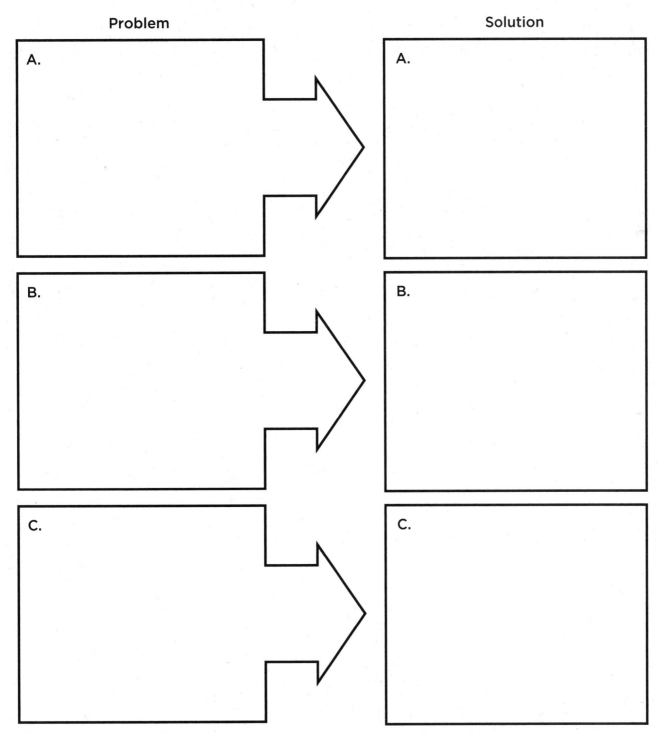

Problem   **Solution**

A.

B.

C.

A.

B.

C.

Name _____ Date _____

EXPLORE: FOCUS QUESTIONS

Using what you learned from the Core Interactive Text, answer each page's focus question:

Congressional Reconstruction Brings Violent Reactions

How did Southerners react to Congressional Reconstruction?

_____

_____

_____

Radical Reconstruction Brings Change

How did Reconstruction affect African American voting rights?

_____

_____

_____

African Americans Want Land for Farming

How did sharecropping affect freed African Americans?

_____

_____

_____

Reconstruction Governments Enact Change

How did Reconstruction aim to improve African Americans' lives?

_____

_____

_____

Carpetbaggers Head South

How did Southern politics reflect social divisions?

_____

_____

_____

PROJECTS AND ASSESSMENTS

Explain Activities

ACTIVITY TYPE: ADVERTISEMENT

Postwar Society

In this activity, you will create a broadside to advertise a meeting to discuss the problem of carpetbaggers in the South.

ACTIVITY TYPE: QUICK WRITE

Postwar Society

In this Quick Write exercise, you will write a diary entry describing the daily life of a person living in the South during Radical Reconstruction.

ACTIVITY TYPE: SOCIAL STUDIES EXPLANATION

Postwar Society

In this activity, you will use the template to assemble evidence from the sources you have explored. Then, you will write an answer to the Essential Question and defend your answer with supporting evidence.

Elaborate Activities

photo: Library of Congress

INVESTIGATION TYPE: DATA ANALYSIS

African Americans in Congress

African Americans held only 2 percent of the congressional offices in 1875. How long would it take for that number to reach 3 percent? Your mission is to investigate how the participation of African Americans in Congress changed following the Civil War.

photo: Library of Congress

ACTIVITY TYPE: PITCH YOUR IDEA

A Proposal for Reconstruction

In this activity, you develop a written proposal for Reconstruction to be presented to a congressional committee.

Postwar Society

PROJECTS AND ASSESSMENTS *(continued)*

photo: Getty Images

ACTIVITY TYPE: DOCUMENT-BASED INVESTIGATION

Postwar Society

In this Document-Based Investigation, you will analyze source materials and investigate this question: To what extent did emancipation bring true freedom to African Americans in the South?

photo: Library of Congress

ACTIVITY TYPE: EXPRESS YOUR OPINION

Results of Radical Republican Actions

In this activity, you will write an essay describing Radical Republican actions and decide whether these actions were necessary to bring about a new and unified nation or if they continued the divisions between North and South and increased Southern hostility and resentment.

photo: Library of Congress

ACTIVITY TYPE: DOCUMENT-BASED INVESTIGATION

The Freedmen's Bureau

In this activity, you will write a newspaper article or the opening argument for a public seminar that discusses whether the Freedmen's Bureau was successful in achieving its purpose.

Evaluate Activities

BRIEF-CONSTRUCTED RESPONSE (BCR)

Postwar Society

EXTENDED-CONSTRUCTED RESPONSE (ECR)

Postwar Society

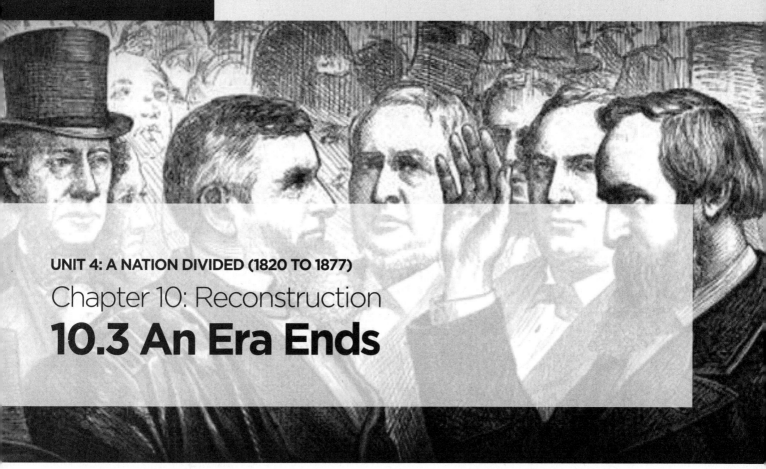

Discovery SOCIAL STUDIES
EDUCATION **TECHBOOK**

UNIT 4: A NATION DIVIDED (1820 TO 1877)

Chapter 10: Reconstruction

10.3 An Era Ends

LESSON OVERVIEW

Lesson Objectives:

By the end of this lesson, you should be able to:

- Summarize events leading to the conclusion of military Reconstruction.
- Evaluate the short- and long-term effects of Reconstruction on various groups.

Lesson Essential Question:

How did the Civil War and Reconstruction affect life for future generations of Americans?

Key Vocabulary

amnesty, Compromise of 1877, electoral college, Fifteenth Amendment, Fourteenth Amendment, Jim Crow laws, Ku Klux Klan, literacy test, *Plessy v. Ferguson*, poll tax, Radical Republicans, Reconstruction, Redeemers, Rutherford B. Hayes, "separate but equal," Thirteenth Amendment

FLASHCARDS

1 ### The Compromise of 1877

In 1877, military Reconstruction ended and federal troops left the South.

- By the 1870s, many people in both the North and the South were weary of Reconstruction.
- The results of the presidential election of 1876 were unclear, so a congressional commission had to settle the conflict.
- Through the Compromise of 1877, Democrats agreed to declare Republican Rutherford B. Hayes president in exchange for the withdrawal of federal troops from the South.

Why Does It Matter?

When the federal troops left the South, African Americans no longer had military protection and lost most of their political rights.

photo: IRC

A congressional Electoral Commission agreed to allow Hayes to become president in exchange for the removal of federal troops from the South.

2 ### The Impact of Reconstruction

Reconstruction had some enduring accomplishments, but its laws and policies were not enough to protect African Americans' rights.

- Reconstruction did bring the North and the South back together and established federal authority over the states.
- The Thirteenth Amendment successfully ended slavery.
- The Fourteenth and Fifteenth Amendments gave African Americans equal treatment and voting rights; however, Jim Crow laws enforced segregation throughout the South.
- For much of the 1900s, Southerners voted Democratic and distrusted the federal government.

Why Does It Matter?

Reconstruction did not achieve all that its leaders had hoped it would, and African Americans continued to face injustice for nearly another century. The Civil War amendments, however, formed the basis for the civil rights movement of the 1950s and 1960s.

photo: Discovery Education

The Thirteenth, Fourteenth, and Fifteenth Amendments were among the most important effects of Reconstruction. However, the Fourteenth and Fifteenth Amendments were not effectively enforced until the civil rights movement of the mid-1900s.

Name _____   **Date** _____

GRAPHIC ORGANIZER: Main Idea Web

Complete this Main Idea Web to show positive, long-lasting achievements of Reconstruction. For supporting resources, go to A Nation Divided > Reconstruction > An Era Ends > Explore > Achievements of Reconstruction.

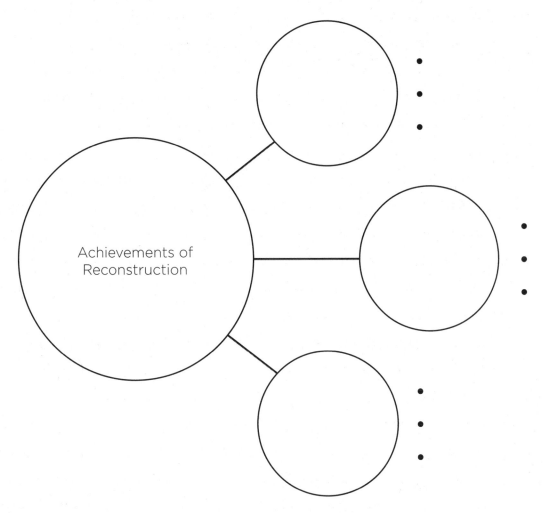

Name _____ Date _____

GRAPHIC ORGANIZER: Main Idea Web

Complete this Main Idea Web to show failures or limitations of Reconstruction. For supporting resources, go to A Nation Divided > Reconstruction > An Era Ends > Explore > The Limits of Reconstruction.

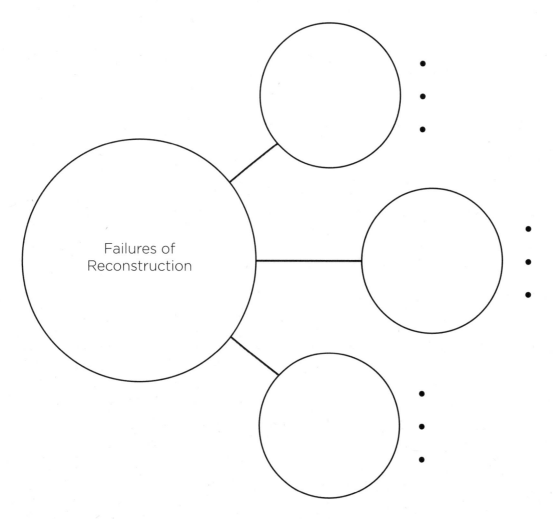

Failures of Reconstruction

Name _____ Date _____

EXPLORE: FOCUS QUESTIONS

Using what you learned from the Core Interactive Text, answer each page's focus question:

The Election of 1876

What effect did the election of 1876 have on Reconstruction?

_____

_____

_____

Achievements of Reconstruction

What were the long-lasting achievements of Reconstruction?

_____

_____

_____

The Limits of Reconstruction

In what ways did Reconstruction fail to achieve its goals?

_____

_____

_____

Political Legacies

What were the political effects of Reconstruction?

_____

_____

_____

PROJECTS AND ASSESSMENTS

Explain Activities

ACTIVITY TYPE: DIAGRAM

U.S. History, Prehistory–1877

Think about various events, trends, and patterns you've studied so far in U.S. history. Use the space to the right of the word bank to create a graphic history or mind map that you think explains U.S. history from colonial times through 1877.

ACTIVITY TYPE: DIAGRAM

An Era Ends: Comparison Chart

In this activity, you will use a Comparison Chart to make notes on the achievements and failures of Reconstruction in a number of key areas.

ACTIVITY TYPE: DIAGRAM

An Era Ends: Diagram

In what ways did Reconstruction resolve issues and conflicts that remained after the Civil War? Use the Comparison Chart to identify ways in which issues and conflicts from the Civil War were resolved and not resolved.

ACTIVITY TYPE: QUICK WRITE

An Era Ends: Quick Write

In this Quick Write activity, you will select a perspective from the 1870s. Then, from the perspective you have selected, you will write a paragraph supporting the topic sentence: "The Compromise of 1877 has changed my life forever."

ACTIVITY TYPE: SOCIAL STUDIES EXPLANATION

An Era Ends

In this activity, you will use the template to assemble evidence from the sources you have explored. Then, you will write an answer to the Essential Question and defend your answer with supporting evidence.

PROJECTS AND ASSESSMENTS *(continued)*

Elaborate Activities

photo: Harpweek

INVESTIGATION TYPE: DATA ANALYSIS

The Compromise of 1877

The Compromise of 1877 settled a split presidential election without resorting to constitutional law or the courts. How did this split election lead to the end of Reconstruction? Your mission is to analyze the factors that led to the Compromise of 1877.

photo: Library of Congress

ACTIVITY TYPE: ROLE PLAY

An Era Ends

In this activity, you will take on the role of an African American living in the South and write a journal entry comparing what your life was like during Reconstruction and what your life is like now that the era has ended.

photo: Library of Congress

ACTIVITY TYPE: YOU AS ARTIST

An Era Ends

In this activity, you will analyze a political cartoon from the post-Reconstruction era to understand its message. Then, you will use the common elements of political cartoons to draw your own cartoon that will make a point about events following the end of Reconstruction.

photo: Library of Congress

ACTIVITY TYPE: DOCUMENT-BASED INVESTIGATION

End of an Era

In this Document-Based Investigation, you will utilize primary documents to investigate the following question: When it ended in 1877, was Reconstruction a success?

PROJECTS AND ASSESSMENTS *(continued)*

Evaluate Activities

 BRIEF-CONSTRUCTED RESPONSE (BCR)

An Era Ends

 EXTENDED-CONSTRUCTED RESPONSE (ECR)

An Era Ends

photo: Library of Congress

UNIT 4: A NATION DIVIDED (1820 TO 1877)

Chapter 10: Reconstruction

10.4 African American Life After Reconstruction

LESSON OVERVIEW

Lesson Objectives:

By the end of this lesson, you should be able to:

- Evaluate practices and policies used to deny African Americans' civil rights.
- Examine African American responses to economic challenges and the denial of civil rights.

Lesson Essential Question:

After Reconstruction, how did African Americans respond to racial discrimination?

Key Vocabulary

Booker T. Washington, Fourteenth Amendment, grandfather clause, Ida B. Wells, Jim Crow laws, literacy test, lobbyists, lynching, National Association for the Advancement of Colored People (NAACP), *Plessy v. Ferguson*, poll tax, segregation, W. E. B. Du Bois

FLASHCARDS

1 Taking Back the South

After Reconstruction, whites returned to power in the South. Laws and policies were instituted to deny African Americans their civil rights and preserve white supremacy.

- Southern states (and others) passed Jim Crow laws. These laws established racial segregation of most public accommodations.

- Local and state governments adopted discriminatory policies to keep African Americans from voting.

- These policies included poll taxes, literacy tests, and the grandfather clause.

- The Supreme Court ruling in *Plessy v. Ferguson* in 1896 meant that most segregation laws were constitutional. This set the precedent that allowed for "separate but equal" legal segregation.

- White citizens and businesses used a variety of techniques to make African Americans too fearful to fight for their rights and maintain the racial status quo. These tactics included lynchings, mob violence, and intimidation.

Why Does It Matter?

Although the rights of African Americans were protected during Reconstruction, once the era ended, white Southerners did everything in their power to reverse this newfound equality. Laws and policies denied the civil rights of African Americans for many decades.

photo: Library of Congress

Legal segregation of blacks and whites lasted for several decades.

2 Facing the Challenges of Segregation

The African American community responded to the economic and social challenges of segregation in many ways. There were competing philosophies on how to best restore civil rights and cope with discrimination.

- Black churches, colleges, and newspapers helped hold together the African American community and enabled African Americans to cope with a segregated society.

- Churches provided social support and education.

- African American newspapers provided a source of information and editorial articles designed for primarily African American readers.

- Activist journalists such as Ida B. Wells shed light on important issues and educated both blacks and whites.

- African American leader Booker T. Washington believed blacks should tolerate discrimination. He advocated education in industrial and business skills to help African Americans find work.

- W. E. B. Du Bois believed blacks should educate themselves in all areas and fight for their civil rights. Du Bois's philosophy was later adopted and carried out by the civil rights movement.

- African Americans established organizations such as the NAACP (1909) to advocate for their economic, political, and social advancement.

- Entrepreneurs and scholars such as George Washington Carver, Garrett Morgan, and Madam C. J. Walker overcame their circumstances and rose to prominence in the late 1800s and early 1900s. Such leaders contributed money and resources to advance African American causes.

- Many African Americans moved west or to Northern cities to escape Jim Crow laws. However, they were still met with discrimination and prejudice.

Why Does It Matter?

African Americans worked hard to overcome the injustices and prejudices of segregation. Community resources such as churches and newspapers proved invaluable. African American leaders and role models urged education and helped mobilize some in the African American community to fight for their civil rights.

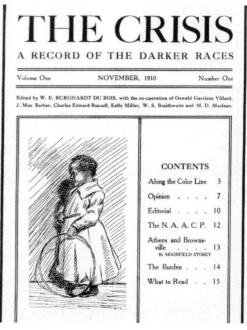

photo: Getty Images

African Americans established churches, schools, newspapers, and magazines to provide support, education, and information for the African American community.

Name _____ Date _____

GRAPHIC ORGANIZER: Cause/Event/Effect Chart

Use this Cause/Event/Effect Chart to identify the causes and outcomes of three major trends in racial discrimination against African Americans. For supporting resources, go to A Nation Divided > Reconstruction > African American Life After Reconstruction > Explore > Jim Crow Laws and Voting Barriers.

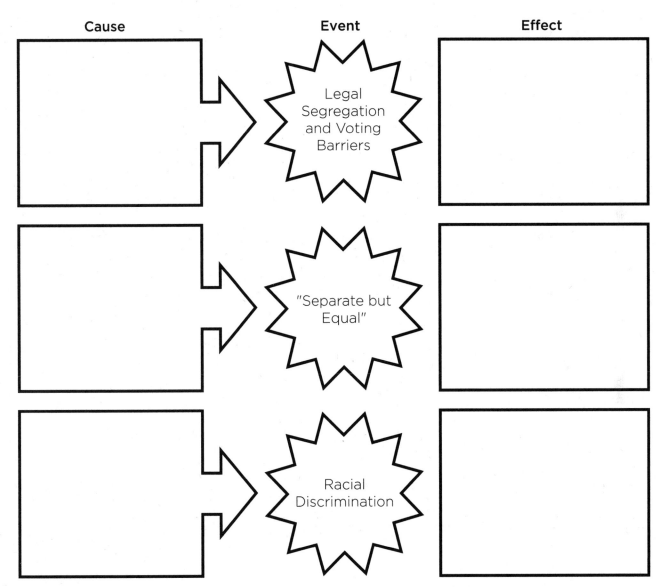

Cause   **Event**   **Effect**

Legal Segregation and Voting Barriers

"Separate but Equal"

Racial Discrimination

Name _____ **Date** _____

GRAPHIC ORGANIZER: Main Idea Web

Use this Main Idea Web to record details identifying how African American churches, schools, and newspapers responded to segregation and racial discrimination. For supporting resources, go to A Nation Divided > Reconstruction > African American Life After Reconstruction > Explore > Finding Hope in the Church.

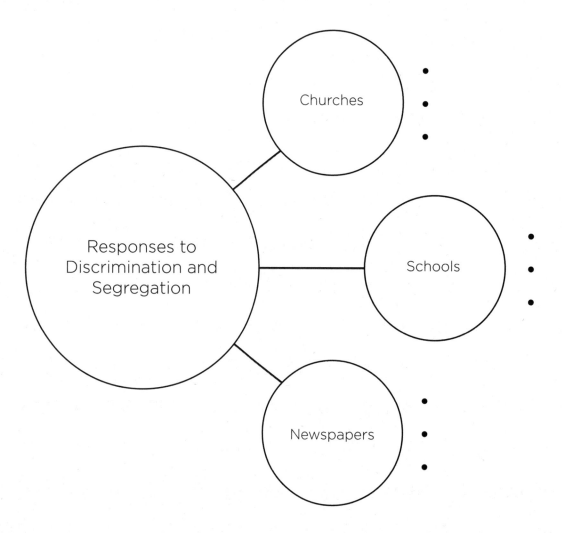

Name _____ Date _____

GRAPHIC ORGANIZER: Venn Diagram

Use this Venn Diagram to compare and contrast the views and approaches of Booker T. Washington and W. E. B. Du Bois with regard to gaining civil rights for African Americans. For supporting resources, go to A Nation Divided > Reconstruction > African American Life After Reconstruction > Explore > Booker T. Washington.

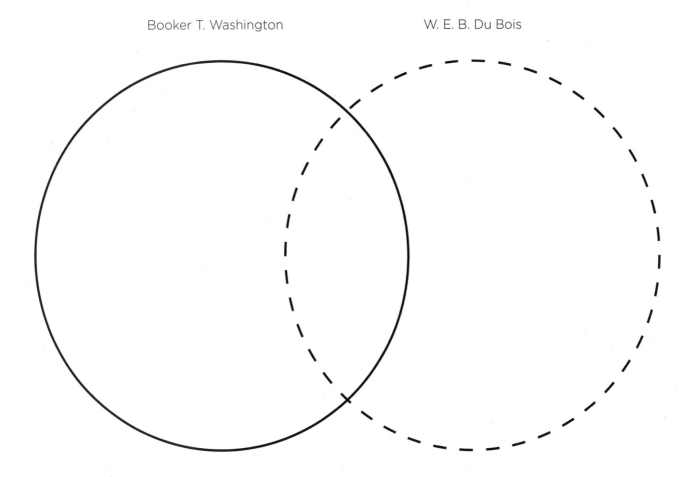

Booker T. Washington   W. E. B. Du Bois

Name _____ Date _____

 GRAPHIC ORGANIZER: Problem/Solution Chart

Use this Problem/Solution Chart to identify the problems and solutions addressed by national civil rights organizations, migration, and influential African Americans. For supporting resources, go to A Nation Divided > Reconstruction > African American Life After Reconstruction > Explore > Forming National Civil Rights Organizations.

Problem   **Solution**

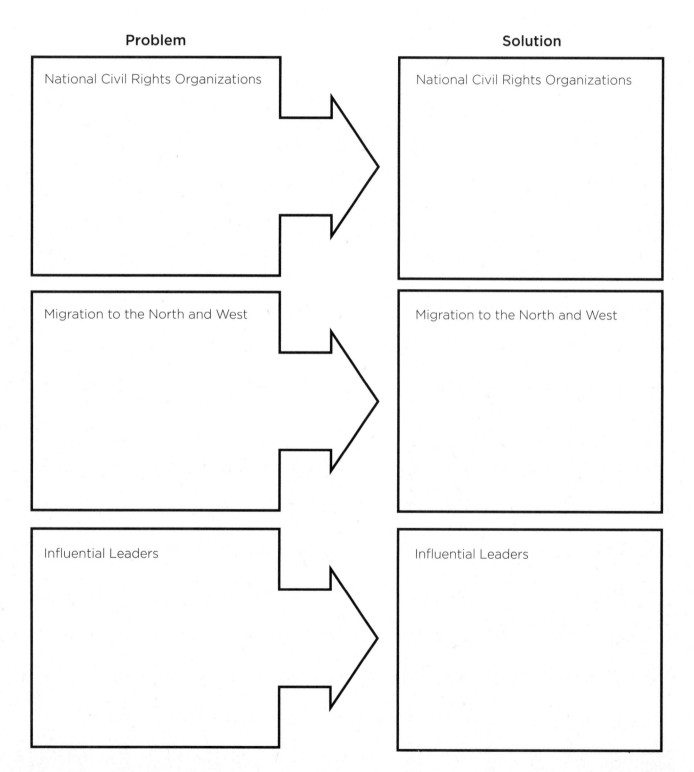

National Civil Rights Organizations

National Civil Rights Organizations

Migration to the North and West

Migration to the North and West

Influential Leaders

Influential Leaders

Name _____ Date _____

EXPLORE: FOCUS QUESTIONS

Using what you learned from the Core Interactive Text, answer each page's focus question:

Jim Crow Laws and Voting Barriers

How did state and local governments promote racial segregation?

_____

_____

_____

"Separate but Equal"

How did *Plessy v. Ferguson* solidify segregation policies?

_____

_____

_____

White Supremacy

How was racial discrimination practiced by private citizens after Reconstruction?

_____

_____

_____

Finding Hope in the Church

How did churches help African Americans cope with segregation?

_____

_____

_____

A College Education

How did African Americans use education to increase their opportunities?

_____

_____

_____

Spreading the News

How did African Americans use newspapers to give themselves a voice in society?

_____

_____

_____

Name _____ Date _____

EXPLORE: FOCUS QUESTIONS *(continued)*

Booker T. Washington

How did African American leaders promote equality and social justice?

_____
_____
_____
_____

W. E. B. Du Bois

How did Booker T. Washington and W. E. B. Du Bois differ in their philosophies?

_____
_____

Forming National Civil Rights Organizations

What is the NAACP? Why were organizations like this established?

_____
_____
_____

Making the Move

Where did many African Americans move after Reconstruction?

_____
_____
_____

Influential African Americans

Who were some prominent African Americans of the late 1800s and early 1900s?

_____
_____
_____

PROJECTS AND ASSESSMENTS

Explain Activities

ACTIVITY TYPE: DIAGRAM

Discrimination and Responses

Use the Comparison Chart to make notes on various methods white citizens in the South used to establish and enforce discrimination and segregation and the ways in which the African American community responded.

ACTIVITY TYPE: QUICK WRITE

Plessy v. Ferguson

Write a paragraph that completes the following topic sentence: The U.S. Supreme Court's decision in *Plessy v. Ferguson* was important because . . .

ACTIVITY TYPE: SOCIAL STUDIES EXPLANATION

African American Life After Reconstruction

In this activity, you will use the template to assemble evidence from the sources you have explored. Then, you will write an answer to the Essential Question and defend your answer with supporting evidence.

Elaborate Activities

photo: Library of Congress

INVESTIGATION TYPE: ENDURING DEBATE

Washington vs. Du Bois

In what ways can African Americans respond to racial discrimination? In this investigation, you will use the interactive Enduring Debate tool to analyze the perspectives of two African American civil rights activists from the post-Reconstruction era. Then, you will decide whose ideas you most agree with.

PROJECTS AND ASSESSMENTS *(continued)*

photo: Library of Congress

ACTIVITY TYPE: ROLE PLAY

Compromise or Demand?

You will take on the role of an African American writing an editorial for an African American newspaper that supports the approach of either Booker T. Washington or W. E. B. Du Bois.

photo: Library of Congress

ACTIVITY TYPE: SAY WHAT?

Opposing Legal Segregation in 1896

You will read excerpts from Justice Harlan's dissenting opinion and "translate" it for modern readers. Then, you will respond to the analysis questions to explain why Harlan's opinion in *Plessy v. Ferguson* was historically important.

photo: Library of Congress

ACTIVITY TYPE: DOCUMENT-BASED INVESTIGATION

Years of Segregation

In this Document-Based Investigation, you will analyze source materials and investigate this question: Why did racial segregation persist for so long, despite the passage of the Fourteenth Amendment?

Evaluate Activities

BRIEF-CONSTRUCTED RESPONSE (BCR)

African American Life After Reconstruction

EXTENDED-CONSTRUCTED RESPONSE (ECR)

African American Life After Reconstruction

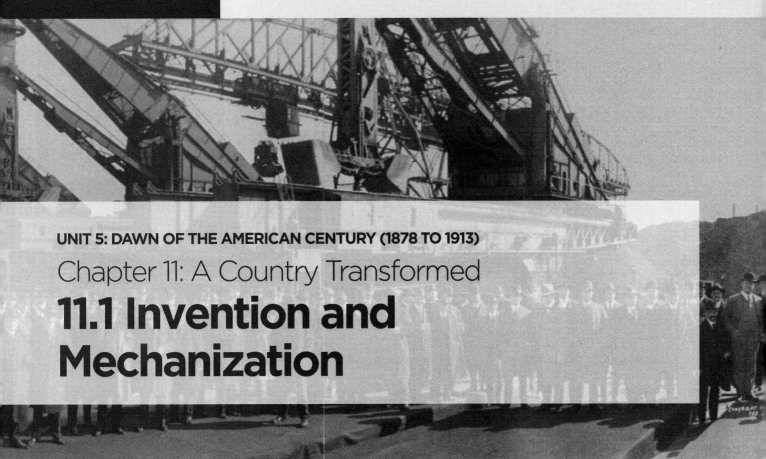

SOCIAL STUDIES
TECHBOOK

UNIT 5: DAWN OF THE AMERICAN CENTURY (1878 TO 1913)

Chapter 11: A Country Transformed

11.1 Invention and Mechanization

photo: Library of Congress

LESSON OVERVIEW

Lesson Objectives:

By the end of this lesson, you should be able to:

- Explain how industrialization changed the production of goods and services and transformed American society.

- Identify and explain the most important causes of industrialization.

- Describe and explain the impact of new technologies and innovations in various areas of American life.

Lesson Essential Question:

How did the development of new technologies change life in the United States?

Key Vocabulary

Alexander Graham Bell, assembly line, corporation, horizontal integration, Industrial Revolution, Thomas Edison, transcontinental railroad, vertical integration, Scientific Management, transcontinental railroad

FLASHCARDS

1 The Production of Goods and Services

As industrialization progressed, the methods used to produce goods and retrieve raw materials changed.

- Companies improved methods of removing raw materials from underground.
- Companies began to use the Bessemer process to produce steel, which made the mass production of steel cheaper.
- Companies replaced the Bessemer process with the open-hearth method, which improved the production of steel even more.
- Companies began to use division of labor to organize workers.
- Companies began to use the assembly line, which made mass production quicker.
- Companies replaced steam-powered machines with gas-powered machines. Later, electricity-powered machines became popular. This made machines more efficient and more powerful.

Why Does It Matter?

Many of the methods that industries developed after the Civil War, such as the assembly line, are still used by industries today. Also, gasoline and electricity remain a common way to power machines.

photo: Library of Congress
This image shows the making of steel using the Bessemer process.

2 Causes of Industrialization

Steam power, new methods of production, inventions, and immigration all caused industrialization to expand.

- The development of steam power spurred industrialization.
- The development of new methods of retrieving raw materials and producing goods increased industrialization.
- The expansion and improvement of railroads drove industrialization.
- The natural birth rate, migration from farms to cites, and immigration provided the necessary workforce for industrialization.
- New business methods supported industrialization. These innovative models included the corporation, vertical integration, investment through stocks and bonds, and bureaucracy.
- Advertisements increased the sale of products, which allowed industries to grow.
- New forms of communication, such as the telegraph and telephone, increased the speed of communication between businesses.

Why Does It Matter?

New technologies and methods of production continue to enhance business operations. For example, the development of the telephone connected companies and private citizens around the country, forming a national communication network.

photo: Library of Congress
In Montana, a worker loads freight from a train onto a wagon.

FLASHCARDS *(continued)*

3 New Technologies and American Innovation

New technologies and innovations shaped industrial development, agriculture, communications, the environment, and society.

- Because of new technologies, industries grew and had a greater impact on the environment, such as water and air pollution.
- As industries increased in cities, more people moved from rural areas to urban areas, and the population of cities soared.
- The development of industry led to the formation of a large middle class, but it also led to a large number of unemployed people who lived in poverty.
- New technologies, such as the steel plow and the combine, increased agricultural production.
- New technologies, such as the telegraph and telephone, made communication over long distances much faster.
- Industries developed a way of organizing work called a bureaucracy. This led to the separation of white-collar workers and blue-collar workers.

Why Does It Matter?

The emergence of new technologies and innovations, brought many benefits to American life but also had negative consequences. The environmental damage industries caused led to the passage of laws that restricted pollution. Balancing industrial development and the protection of the environment remains a serious concern today.

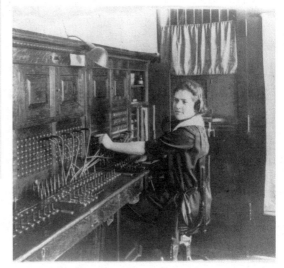

photo: Library of Congress
A woman works at a telephone switchboard in 1922.

Name _____ **Date** _____

GRAPHIC ORGANIZER: Main Idea Web

Use this Main Idea Web to record information about industrialization in the United States, better production methods, and the driving force of transportation. For supporting resources, go to Dawn of the American Century (1878 to 1913) > A Country Transformed > Invention and Mechanization > Explore > Industrialization in the United States.

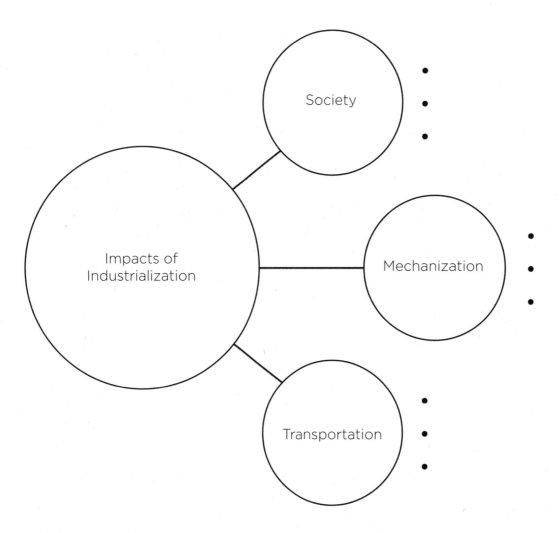

Name _____ Date _____

GRAPHIC ORGANIZER: Comparison Chart

Use this Comparison Chart to compare the effects of changes in the workplace, business organizations, and advertising and sales. For supporting resources, go to Dawn of the American Century (1878 to 1913) > A Country Transformed > Invention and Mechanization > Explore > A New Workforce.

Criteria	What Changes Occurred?	Whom Did the Changes Affect?	What Were the Effects of the Changes?
Workforce			
Business Organizations			
Advertising and Sales			

SOCIAL STUDIES TECHBOOK

Name _____ Date _____

GRAPHIC ORGANIZER: Cause/Event/Effect Chart

Use this Cause/Event/Effect chart to organize details related to the causes and effects of agricultural mechanization, inventions in communication, the use of electricity, and environmental pollution from industrialization. For supporting resources, go to Dawn of the American Century (1878 to 1913) > A Country Transformed > Invention and Mechanization > Explore > Inventions for the Field.

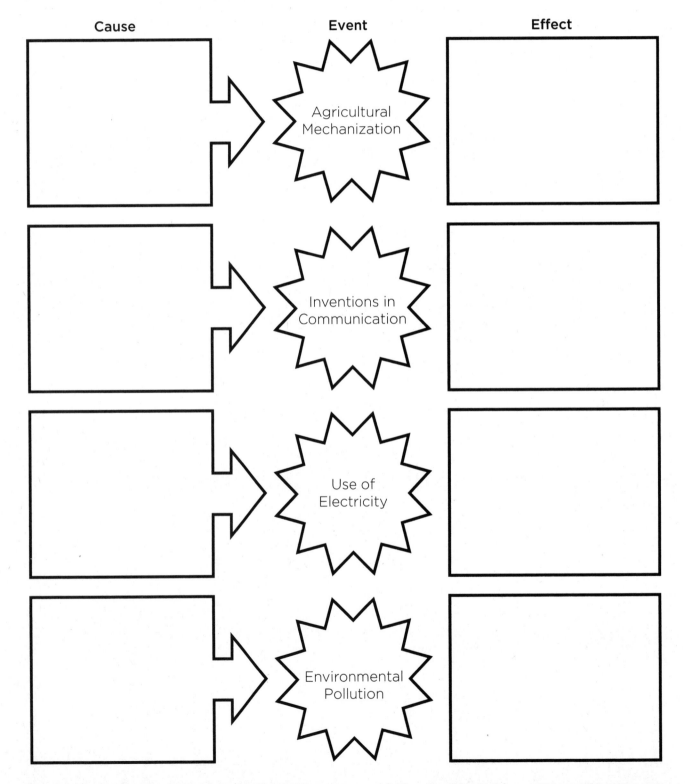

Cause · Event · Effect

- Agricultural Mechanization
- Inventions in Communication
- Use of Electricity
- Environmental Pollution

Name _____ Date _____

EXPLORE: FOCUS QUESTIONS

Using what you learned from the Core Interactive Text, answer each page's focus question:

Industrialization in the United States

How did industrialization in the United States contribute to rapid change?

_____

_____

_____

Better Production Methods

How were production methods mechanized?

_____

_____

_____

The Driving Force of Transportation

What inventions helped expand the railroad system?

_____

_____

_____

A New Workforce

How did the workforce expand in the United States?

_____

_____

_____

A Corporate World

What new business methods shaped industrialization?

_____

_____

_____

Advertising and Sales

How were people lured into purchasing new goods?

_____

_____

_____

Name _____ Date _____

EXPLORE: FOCUS QUESTIONS *(continued)*

Inventions for the Field

What inventions helped improve agriculture?

_____
_____
_____
_____

Everybody's Talking

How did communication methods improve due to American inventions?

_____
_____
_____
_____

The Wizard of Menlo Park

How did electricity transform American society?

_____
_____
_____
_____

Polluting the Environment

How did industrialization impact the environment and society?

_____
_____
_____
_____

PROJECTS AND ASSESSMENTS

Explain Activities

ACTIVITY TYPE: DIAGRAM

Before and After Industrialization

Use a Change Over Time Chart to describe the United States before and after industrialization, analyzing what caused the changes.

ACTIVITY TYPE: ENCYCLOPEDIA ENTRY

Inventions

In this activity, you will create an encyclopedia entry describing an invention that helped change life in the United States. Identify the inventor, the year it was invented, and its development and use. Conclude your entry with a short description of the way in which the invention changed life in the United States in the 1800s.

ACTIVITY TYPE: SOCIAL STUDIES EXPLANATION

Invention and Mechanization

In this activity, you will use the template to assemble evidence from the sources you have explored. Then, you will write an answer to the Essential Question and defend your answer with supporting evidence.

Elaborate Activities

photo: Library of Congress

INVESTIGATION: DATA ANALYSIS

Industrialization and Society

Industrialization had an enormous impact on the United States in the late 1800s and early 1900s. What was life like for the people who lived during this time? In this investigation, you will use the interactive Data Analysis tool to determine how industrial innovations affected life in the United States.

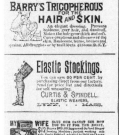

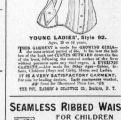

photo: Library of Congress

ACTIVITY: DOCUMENT-BASED INVESTIGATION

Benefits and Costs of Industrialization

In this Document-Based Investigation, you will analyze source materials and investigate this question: Were the benefits of new technologies from industrialization worth the costs?

PROJECTS AND ASSESSMENTS *(continued)*

photo: Library of Congress

ACTIVITY: CURRENT EVENTS CONNECTION

Early and Modern Telephones

Today, people take for granted their ability to speak to anyone in any part of the world at any time. In this activity, you will review some of the ways that the telephone has changed since Bell's first efforts and write a report on how the telephone has evolved since 1876.

photo: Library of Congress

ACTIVITY: ROLE PLAY

Inventions Change Lives

In this activity, you will take on the role of someone whose life has changed due to inventions and mechanization. You will select one of the following people and write a journal entry describing some of the effects of inventions and mechanization on your life at work or outside work: a man or woman working in a factory that has been affected by inventions or mechanization or a man or woman farmer whose life has been affected by inventions or mechanization.

Evaluate Activities

BRIEF-CONSTRUCTED RESPONSE (BCR)

Invention and Mechanization

EXTENDED-CONSTRUCTED RESPONSE (ECR)

Invention and Mechanization

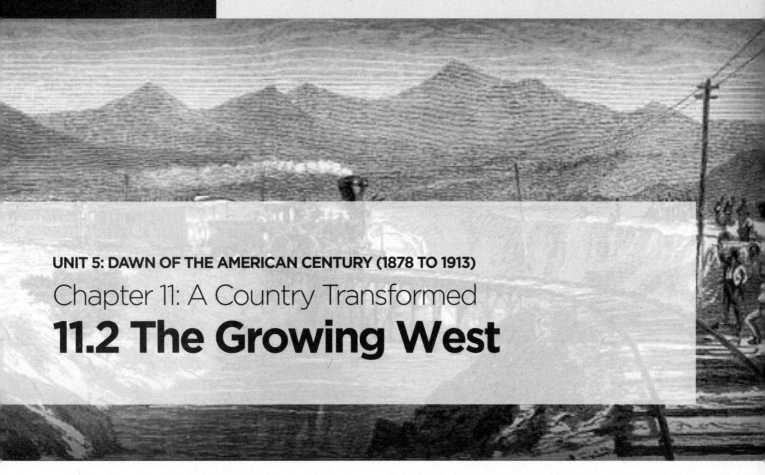

UNIT 5: DAWN OF THE AMERICAN CENTURY (1878 TO 1913)

Chapter 11: A Country Transformed

11.2 The Growing West

LESSON OVERVIEW

Lesson Objectives:

By the end of this lesson, you should be able to:

- Explain factors that led to westward expansion after the Civil War.
- Evaluate consequences and impacts of westward expansion.
- Evaluate the impact of westward expansion on Native Americans.
- Describe the experiences of women, immigrants, African Americans, and other minority groups in the West.

Key Vocabulary

Californios, assimilation, Chief Joseph, Dawes Severalty Act of 1887, Geronimo, Homestead Act of 1862, Plains Indians, reservation, Sand Creek Massacre, Sikhism, Sitting Bull, transcontinental railroad, Wounded Knee

Lesson Essential Question:

Who benefited from the second wave of westward expansion in the United States?

1 Causes of Westward Expansion After the Civil War

Many factors led to the movement westward after the Civil War.

- The building of railroads, including the transcontinental railroad, improved transportation into the West.
- Ranchers established cattle drives to railheads, which helped ranching spread throughout the West.
- Eastern industry needed more resources, which spurred the development of mining and logging in the West.
- U.S. laws, such as the Homestead Act, encouraged farming in the West.
- Companies recruited people from Europe and China to work in the West.

Why Does It Matter?

Economic, technological, and political factors spurred the development of the West. Today, railroads remain an important form of transportation for goods and resources. U.S. laws on immigration also continue to shape American society.

photo: IRC
These workmen helped build the Central Pacific Railroad.

2 Consequences and Impacts of Westward Expansion

The expansion westward had a strong impact on U.S. society and culture.

- Many people made a fortune by investing in business ventures in the West, while others went bankrupt.
- Westward expansion spurred the growth of many cities in the West and caused the population of the United States to shift westward.
- Mining, logging, ranching, and farming encroached on the lands and lifestyle of Native Americans and often had a severe impact on the environment in the West.
- Westward expansion brought many immigrants to the West and resulted in the first U.S. legislation that restricted immigration.
- Westward expansion provided more opportunities for women.

Why Does It Matter?

Today, the population of the United States continues to shift westward, and western cities, such as Phoenix and Los Angeles, continue to grow. The damage to the environment caused by businesses in the West led to laws that protect the environment and to the development of national parks and forests.

photo: Library of Congress
Mining for gold and other minerals contributed to the establishment of cities in the West.

FLASHCARDS *(continued)*

3 The Impact of Westward Expansion on Native Americans

Westward expansion had severe consequences for the culture and way of life of Native Americans.

- The boundaries of Native American reservations were repeatedly redrawn and contracted.
- Because Native Americans often ended up living on poor land, they had trouble hunting enough wild game and their poverty increased.
- The Dawes Severalty Act forced Native Americans to give up reservation land and change their lifestyles.
- Assimilation policies, such as sending native children to boarding schools, damaged Native American culture and families.
- Some Native American nations fought the United States, which caused the loss of lives of both Native Americans and European Americans.
- The U.S. military massacred Native Americans at Sand Creek and Wounded Knee.

Why Does It Matter?

Today, about half of the Native Americans in the United States live on reservations. Many Native Americans on and outside reservations live in poverty. Native American poverty, land rights, and cultural preservation continue to be issues in the United States.

photo: Corbis

This painting by W. M. Cary of the Battle of Wounded Knee shows the bloody conflict between Native Americans and the U.S. military.

4 Minority Groups in the West

African Americans, Mexican Americans, immigrants, and women had a wide range of experiences in the West.

- Thousands of African Americans moved west and became farmers or cowboys, but they still faced discrimination.
- Many Mexican Americans lost their land to white settlers.
- Many immigrants came from northwestern Europe and China to work on railroads and in mines.
- Many Americans of European descent resented Asian American workers because they competed for work.
- The 1882 Chinese Exclusion Act stopped the immigration of Chinese people.
- The 1924 Immigration Act prohibited the immigration of Asian workers.
- Although women faced the same inequalities and traditional roles as women in the East, they also performed a greater variety of work and gained more rights, including the right to vote in several Western states.

Why Does It Matter?

The culture of minority groups remains a strong influence in the West. For example, Mexican culture has influenced food, architecture, and clothing. Conflict about immigration continues to be an important issue in the United States, and many people want to restrict immigration because they fear that immigrants will take away jobs from people born in the United States. The advances made by women in the West paved the way for the women's suffrage movement and other movements for women's rights.

photo: IRC

Chinese men (right) work as laborers for white California miners (left).

Name _____   Date _____

GRAPHIC ORGANIZER: Cause/Event/Effect Chart

Use this Cause/Event/Effect Chart to record information about how the completion of the transcontinental railroad and the industries of the West affected the geography and environment in the region. For supporting resources, go to Dawn of the American Century (1878 to 1913) > A Country Transformed > The Growing West > Explore > The Transcontinental Railroad.

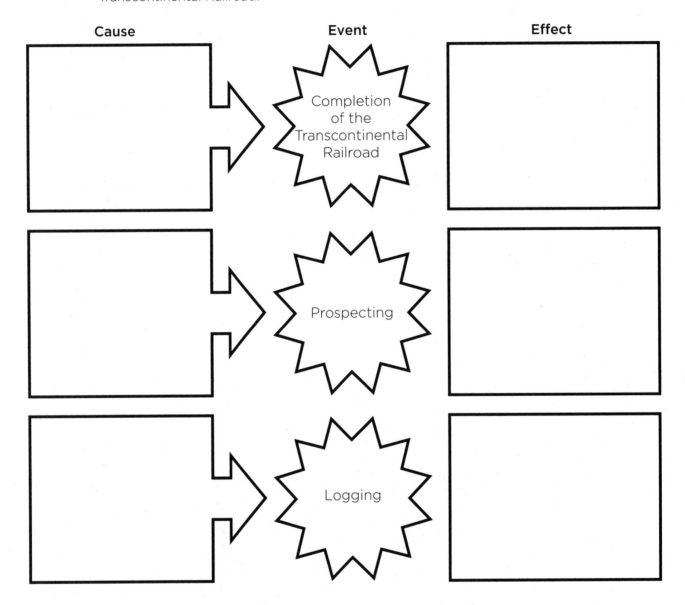

© Discovery Education | www.DiscoveryEducation.com

Name _____ Date _____

GRAPHIC ORGANIZER: Cause/Event/Effect Chart *(continued)*

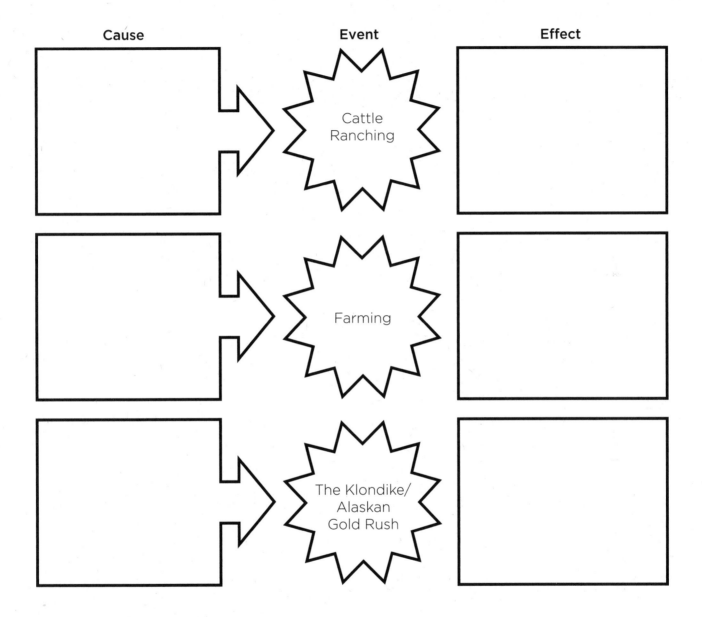

Cause	Event	Effect
	Cattle Ranching	
	Farming	
	The Klondike/Alaskan Gold Rush	

Name _____ **Date** _____

GRAPHIC ORGANIZER: Change Over Time Chart

Use this Change Over Time Chart to show how the population of the West changed between the 1870s and 1900. For supporting resources, go to Dawn of the American Century (1878 to 1913) > A Country Transformed > The Growing West > Explore > Economic and Demographic Changes.

Before:	After:

Changes:

Name _____ **Date** _____

GRAPHIC ORGANIZER: Summary Frames

Use these Summary Frames to identify, summarize, and illustrate six events that you think are most important for understanding the story of Native Americans during the westward expansion of the United States in the late 1800s and early 1900s. For supporting resources, go to Dawn of the American Century (1878 to 1913) > A Country Transformed > The Growing West > Explore > Native Americans in the West.

Name _____ **Date** _____

GRAPHIC ORGANIZER: Comparison Chart

Use this Comparison Chart to record opportunities and challenges various groups faced in the West. For supporting resources, go to Dawn of the American Century (1878 to 1913) > A Country Transformed > The Growing West > Explore > African and Mexican Americans in the West.

Criteria	Opportunities	Challenges
African Americans		
Mexican Americans		
Asian Immigrants		
Women		

Name _____ Date _____

EXPLORE: FOCUS QUESTIONS

Using what you learned from the Core Interactive Text, answer each page's focus question:

The Transcontinental Railroad
How did railroads expand across the continent?

_____

_____

_____

Mining and Logging Industries
How did the natural resources of the West feed industrialization?

_____

_____

_____

Cattle Drives
How did ranching develop in the West?

_____

_____

_____

Homesteaders
How did the U.S. government support the development of farming in the West?

_____

_____

_____

Life on Farms
How did families on farms in the West survive?

_____

_____

_____

Looking North
What role did physical geography play in the settlement of Alaska during the Klondike Gold Rush?

_____

_____

_____

Name _____   Date _____

EXPLORE: FOCUS QUESTIONS *(continued)*

Economic and Demographic Changes
How did the growing West impact U.S. investment and population trends?

_____
_____
_____
_____

Native Americans in the West
How did the U.S. government respond to Native American populations in the West?

_____
_____
_____
_____

Native Americans Fight Back
How did Native Americans come into conflict with the U.S. military?

_____
_____
_____
_____

African and Mexican Americans in the West
What was life like for African Americans and Mexican Americans in the West?

_____
_____
_____
_____

Immigrants in the West
Why did immigrants come to the West?

_____
_____
_____
_____

Women in the West
What was life like for women in the West?

_____
_____
_____
_____

PROJECTS AND ASSESSMENTS

Explain Activities

ACTIVITY TYPE: DIAGRAM

The West Expands

Design your own graphic organizer such as a pyramid or other image. Place all of the words from the word bank on your graphic organizer to show how different factors led to westward expansion and how this expansion affected the inhabitants of the West.

ACTIVITY TYPE: DIAGRAM

Growth and Change

Use the GREASES Chart to categorize changes in the United States that stemmed from westward expansion. Provide at least one specific example for each category.

ACTIVITY TYPE: QUICK WRITE

Minorities in the West

You will select a perspective of a minority in the West. Then, from the perspective you have selected, you will write a paragraph supporting the topic sentence: "For members of this group, the American West (circle one) was/was not a land of opportunity."

ACTIVITY TYPE: QUICK WRITE

Settling the Frontier

In this activity, you will describe several economic factors that affected the frontier in the late 1800s. First, complete the chart based on information from the Core Interactive Text.

ACTIVITY TYPE: SOCIAL STUDIES EXPLANATION

The Growing West

In this activity, you will use the template to assemble evidence from the sources you have explored. Then, you will write an answer to the Essential Question and defend your answer with supporting evidence.

PROJECTS AND ASSESSMENTS *(continued)*

Elaborate Activities

photo: National Archives

INVESTIGATION: MAP-GUIDED INQUIRY

The Second Wave of Westward Expansion

Which people most benefited from U.S. expansion across the West? In this investigation, you will use the interactive Map-Guided Inquiry tool to study facts about this time period to determine which groups of people benefited most.

photo: IRC

ACTIVITY: EXPRESS YOUR OPINION

A Fair Policy for Native Americans

Given what we now know about the disastrous consequences of expansion for Native Americans, would there have been a better solution than breaking Native American lands into smaller parcels and forcing assimilation? It is your job to study the issue and write a proposal for an alternative to the Dawes Act and other Native American policies of the time. How could the demands of westward expansion have been balanced better with the rights of Native Americans?

photo: Library of Congress

ACTIVITY: CHANGING VIEWPOINTS

Then and Now

In this activity, you will review sources that describe the Battle of Little Bighorn.

PROJECTS AND ASSESSMENTS *(continued)*

photo: Library of Congress

ACTIVITY: PITCH YOUR IDEA

Diverse Experiences

Work in a small group to design a plan for a museum exhibit showcasing the American West. Each member of your team will be charged with choosing artifacts for a particular group of people. Then, you will prepare a speech for the museum curator justifying the artifacts that were chosen and the overall theme of the exhibit.

photo: Library of Congress

ACTIVITY: DOCUMENT-BASED INVESTIGATION

The Romantic West

Analyze the source materials to investigate this question: How accurate is the portrayal of the American West in the song "A Home on the Range"?

Evaluate Activities

BRIEF-CONSTRUCTED RESPONSE (BCR)

The Growing West

EXTENDED-CONSTRUCTED RESPONSE (ECR)

The Growing West

UNIT 5: DAWN OF THE AMERICAN CENTURY (1878 TO 1913)

Chapter 11: A Country Transformed

11.3 Coming to America

LESSON OVERVIEW

Lesson Objectives:

By the end of this lesson, you should be able to:

- Describe trends of and explain factors leading to increased immigration during the late 1800s and early 1900s.

- Evaluate governmental and public responses to the "new" immigration of the late 1800s and early 1900s.

Key Vocabulary

anarchism, Angel Island, Chinese Exclusion Act, Ellis Island, ethnic enclave, nativism, nativist, pull factor, push factor

Lesson Essential Question:

In what ways did the American Dream become a reality for immigrants to the United States?

FLASHCARDS

1 Immigrants Contribute to Growth

From the mid-1800s to the early 1900s, European and Asian immigration to the United States increased.

- Irish immigrants mostly came to the United States to escape famine.
- Germans, Italians, and Slavs mostly came to the United States for economic opportunities.
- Russian and Eastern European Jews mostly came to the United States fleeing religious persecution.
- Chinese immigrants arrived during and after the California gold rush.
- The mid-1800s immigrants were mostly from northern and western Europe, particularly Ireland and Germany. Starting in the late 1800s, more eastern and southern European immigrants arrived.
- Immigrants in urban areas lived in tenement apartments with unsanitary conditions. They often worked long hours in unsafe factories.
- The government opened new immigration processing stations at Ellis Island in New York and Angel Island in San Francisco.
- Immigrant processing included a medical exam and a legal exam and was sometimes influenced by stereotypes and personal feelings.

Why Does It Matter?

Rapid population growth enabled U.S. businesses and industries to become world leaders. The United States remained the most prosperous nation in the world through the 1900s.

photo: IRC

Immigrants often lived in cramped, dirty conditions.

2 Fitting In

The "new" immigrants of the late 1800s lived in ethnic enclaves, or areas, often in cities, in which a culturally distinct group of people live separately from people of other groups. These immigrant groups often faced hostility and prejudice in American society.

- New immigrants tended to live and work together in ethnic neighborhoods, or enclaves, in large cities, such as Little Italy in New York City and the Jewish neighborhoods of New York's Lower East Side.
- Ethnic groups had their own banks, stores, places of worship, and newspapers and formed their own mutual aid societies.
- Italians, Jews, and other "new" immigrants were frequently resented by "old" immigrants.
- Nativists pushed for restrictions on immigration.
- The Chinese Exclusion Act limited the number of Chinese immigrants who could enter the United States.
- By 1920, the federal government passed stricter naturalization laws to prevent some immigrants from becoming citizens.

Why Does It Matter?

Immigrants brought their cultures— including arts, languages, foods, and clothing—that blended to make contemporary U.S. culture as rich as it is.

photo: Library of Congress

An aerial view of Ellis Island is shown in this photograph.

Name _____ Date _____

GRAPHIC ORGANIZER: Push/Pull Chart

Use this Push/Pull Chart to identify and categorize the factors that brought immigrants to the United States. For supporting resources, go to Dawn of the American Century (1878 to 1913) > A Country Transformed > Coming to America > Explore > Waves of Immigration.

Push Factors	Pull Factors

© Discovery Education | www.DiscoveryEducation.com

Name _____ **Date** _____

GRAPHIC ORGANIZER: Main Idea Web

Use this Main Idea Web to analyze the various ways that immigrants adapted to life in the United States. For supporting resources, go to Dawn of the American Century (1878 to 1913) > A Country Transformed > Coming to America > Explore > Getting Along.

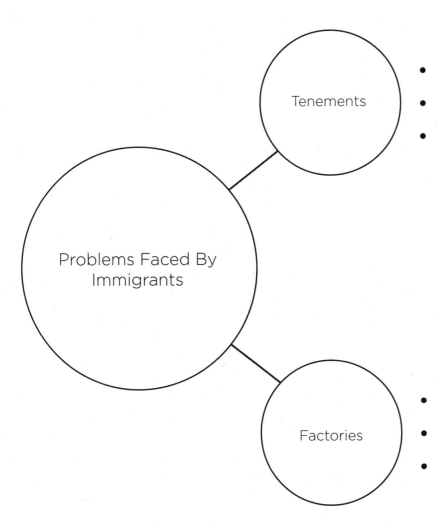

Tenements

Problems Faced By Immigrants

Factories

Name _____ **Date** _____

GRAPHIC ORGANIZER: Main Idea Web *(continued)*

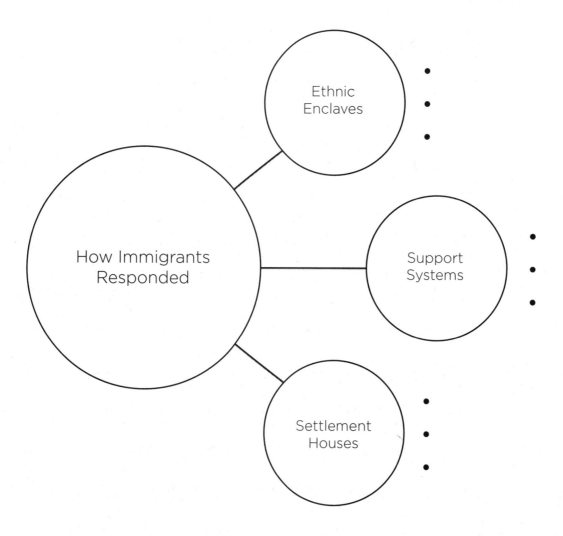

Name _____ Date _____

GRAPHIC ORGANIZER: Attitudes and Legislation Chart

Use this Attitudes and Legislation Chart to analyze the attitudes of natives toward immigrants, who held these attitudes, and how the U.S. government responded to them. For supporting resources, go to Dawn of the American Century (1878 to 1913) > A Country Transformed > Coming to America > Explore > Attitudes Toward Immigrants.

Attitudes

Attitude:

Who Held This View?

Attitude:

Who Held This View?

Attitude:

Who Held This View?

Legislation

Name _____ **Date** _____

GRAPHIC ORGANIZER: Attitudes and Legislation Chart
(continued)

Attitudes	Legislation
Attitude: **Who Held This View?**	
Attitude: **Who Held This View?**	
Attitude: **Who Held This View?**	

Name _____ Date _____

GRAPHIC ORGANIZER: Sequencing Chart

Use this Sequencing Chart to trace the steps for immigrants arriving in the United States and working toward citizenship. For supporting resources, go to Dawn of the American Century (1878 to 1913) > A Country Transformed > Coming to America > Explore > Welcome to the United States!

Event	Date	Summary

Name _____ Date _____

GRAPHIC ORGANIZER: Sequencing Chart *(continued)*

Event	Date	Summary

Name _____ Date _____

EXPLORE: FOCUS QUESTIONS

Using what you learned from the Core Interactive Text, answer each page's focus question:

Waves of Immigration

Why did immigrants come to the United States?

_____

_____

_____

Getting Along

How did immigrant groups adapt to life in the United States?

_____

_____

_____

Difficult Living and Working Conditions

What were living conditions like for immigrants?

_____

_____

_____

Immigrants at Work

What working conditions did immigrants face?

_____

_____

_____

Attitudes Toward Immigrants

How were immigrants treated?

_____

_____

_____

Name _____ Date _____

EXPLORE: FOCUS QUESTIONS *(continued)*

Closing the Doors on Immigration
How did nativists seek to restrict immigration in the late 1800s?

_____
_____
_____
_____

Welcome to the United States!
How did the immigration process work?

_____
_____
_____
_____

Becoming Citizens
How did the government increase regulation of immigration?

_____
_____
_____

PROJECTS AND ASSESSMENTS

Explain Activities

ACTIVITY TYPE: VISUALIZATION

Immigration Processing Centers

You will illustrate the experience of immigrants who entered the United States and became citizens. Use the spaces provided to create a slide show of illustrations or photographs showing the process immigrants had to go through at these immigration centers.

ACTIVITY TYPE: QUICK WRITE

A Letter Home

Writing from the perspective of an immigrant to the United States during the late 1800s, you will write a letter home explaining why you immigrated to the United States and reflecting on how you felt when you arrived.

ACTIVITY TYPE: DIAGRAM

Immigrants to the United States

In this activity, you will use a Comparison Chart to compile information about immigrant groups that came to the United States in the late 1800s and early 1900s. You will develop a system of symbols that indicate reasons for immigrating.

ACTIVITY TYPE: SOCIAL STUDIES EXPLANATION

Coming to America

In this activity, you will use the template to assemble evidence from the sources you have explored. Then, you will write an answer to the Essential Question and defend your answer with supporting evidence.

Elaborate Activities

photo: Getty Images

INVESTIGATION: DATA ANALYSIS

A Nation of Immigrants

Except for Native Americans, all Americans have ancestors who came to the United States from other places within the last 500 years. In this activity, you will use the Data Analysis interactive tool to investigate the question: Why is the United States often called "a nation of immigrants"?

PROJECTS AND ASSESSMENTS *(continued)*

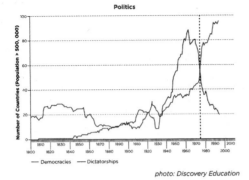

photo: Discovery Education

ACTIVITY: CURRENT EVENTS CONNECTION

Immigration Trends

You have been assigned to research the trends in immigration to the United States from the late 1800s to the present day. For this research, you will analyze various graphs and determine what effects (if any) economics, politics, and warfare has had on immigration to the United States. After analyzing the data, you will create a research report for the head of your department answering the question: Based on immigration patterns from 1890 to the present, how will immigration change in the next 10 years?

photo: Library of Congresss

ACTIVITY: DOCUMENT-BASED INVESTIGATION

The "American Dream"

In this Document-Based Investigation, you will analyze source materials detailing the immigrant experience in the United States during the late 1800s and early 1900s to investigate these questions: In what ways did the "American Dream" become a reality for immigrants to the United States? In what ways did it not become a reality?

photo: Library of Congress

ACTIVITY: YOU AS ARTIST

Welcome to the United States

In this activity, you will analyze Lazarus's poem "The New Colossus" and compare the ideal Lazarus describes to the realities immigrants faced. Then, you will write your own poem that responds to Lazarus about the realities of the immigrant experience.

PROJECTS AND ASSESSMENTS *(continued)*

Evaluate Activities

BRIEF-CONSTRUCTED RESPONSE (BCR)

Coming to America

EXTENDED-CONSTRUCTED RESPONSE (ECR)

Coming to America

photo: Library of Congress

UNIT 5: DAWN OF THE AMERICAN CENTURY (1878 TO 1913)

Chapter 11: A Country Transformed

11.4 City Life

LESSON OVERVIEW

Lesson Objectives:

By the end of this lesson, you should be able to:

- **Describe trends and explain factors leading to urbanization of the United States during the late 1800s and early 1900s.**

- **Describe how American cities and American society as a whole changed as a result of industrialization.**

- **Describe the influence of urbanization on American politics**

Lesson Essential Question:

How did industrialization drive American urbanization in the late 1800s and 1900s?

Key Vocabulary

Chester Arthur, Grover Cleveland, James Garfield, lobbyists, political machine, spoils system, suburb, Tammany Hall, tenement

FLASHCARDS

1 ▸ Causes of Urbanization

Urbanization resulted from many factors relating to industrialization.

- Industrialization created factory jobs in cities. People migrated to cities from foreign countries and rural areas seeking jobs.
- The increased productivity from industrialization enabled the economy to support more people. This, in turn, drove factories to make more goods and employ more workers.
- Railroad development eased migration and encouraged the growth of shipping hubs such as Chicago.
- Farm mechanization reduced the need for rural workers.
- Racial discrimination in the South encouraged some African Americans to seek better opportunities in cities.

Why Does It Matter?

Industrialization, urbanization, and immigration all fed one another as they reshaped the United States.

photo: Library of Congress
Waves of immigration spurred the growth of U.S. cities during the late 1800s and early 1900s.

2 ▸ Effects of Urbanization

Industrialization and urbanization dramatically changed how Americans lived, worked, and played.

- City dwellers had employment opportunities in fields such as finance, office work, retail, warehousing, and manufacturing.
- Retail department stores encouraged the growth of consumerism and changed how people bought goods.
- Cities built new public transportation systems. Public transportation allowed workers to live away from factories in new streetcar suburbs.
- New immigrants and low-wage workers often lived in tenements in dirty, unhealthy neighborhoods.
- Cities had to find new ways to deliver public services and manage health, sanitation, and fire protection.
- Cities became centers of learning, culture, and entertainment, and literacy levels increased.

Why Does It Matter?

Urbanization created new elements of American culture.

Urbanization greatly impacted all areas of U.S. life.

FLASHCARDS *(continued)*

3 ▶ **Using Public Policy**

The challenges of urbanization contributed to the rise of corrupt political institutions.

- Political machines rose to power in many cities. Corruption stretched through all levels of government, due in part to the spoils system.
- Immigrants who received help from political machines opposed political reforms.
- The growth of immigrant communities contributed to a rise in nativism among some native-born Americans.
- Nativists favored English-only education and opposed funding for Catholic schools.
- Reformers worked to lessen the power of the spoils system with some success. The assassination of President James A. Garfield in 1881 led to the passage of civil service reform under his successor in 1883.

Why Does It Matter?

Urbanization influenced the distribution of political power at all levels of government.

THE "BRAINS"

photo: Library of Congress

Political machines led by corrupt politicians such "Boss" Tweed came to dominate urban politics.

Name _____ Date _____

GRAPHIC ORGANIZER: Vocabulary Chart

Use this Vocabulary Chart to define the word *urbanization* in the context of the late 1800s and early 1900s. For supporting resources, go to Dawn of the American Century (1878 to 1913) > A Country Transformed > City Life > Explore > The Rise of Cities.

DEFINITION:

Personal:

Dictionary:

EXAMPLES (drawn or written):

TERM:
urbanization

SENTENCES:

Teacher/Book:

Personal:

RELATED:

WORD PARTS:

Outside of School (Who would use the word? How would he or she use it?)

Name _____ Date _____

GRAPHIC ORGANIZER: Cause/Event/Effect Chart

Use this Cause/Event/Effect Chart to list details about the causes and effects of trends or events during the late 1800s and early 1900s. For supporting resources, go to Dawn of the American Century (1878 to 1913) > A Country Transformed > City Life > Explore > New Technology and Social Issues Fuel Urban Growth.

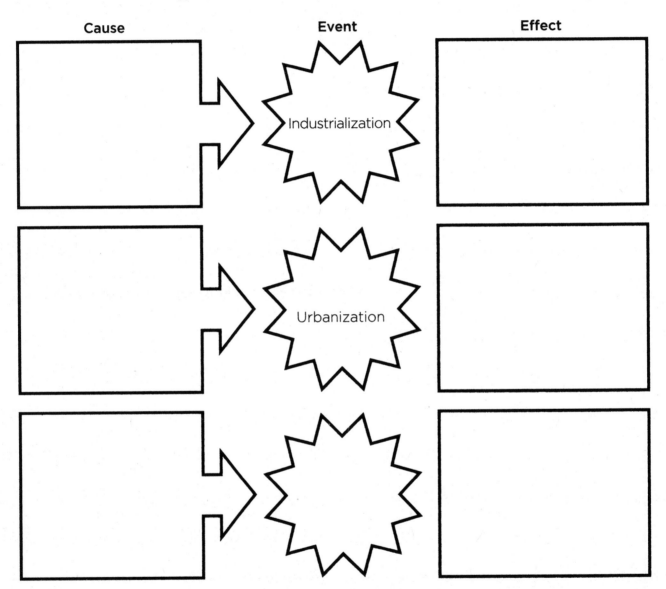

Cause   **Event**   **Effect**

Industrialization

Urbanization

Name _____ Date _____

GRAPHIC ORGANIZER: Problem/Solution Chart

Use this Problem/Solution Chart to note problems people living in cities faced and the government's attempts to solve those issues. For supporting resources, go to Dawn of the American Century (1878 to 1913) > A Country Transformed > City Life > Explore > Urban Living Leads to Problems.

Problem   **Solution**

A.   A.

B.   B.

C.   C.

Name _____ **Date** _____

GRAPHIC ORGANIZER: Main Idea Web

Use this Main Idea Web to record changes in the arts, entertainment, and urban landscape in cities. For supporting resources, go to Dawn of the American Century (1878 to 1913) > A Country Transformed > City Life > Explore > The New Leisure.

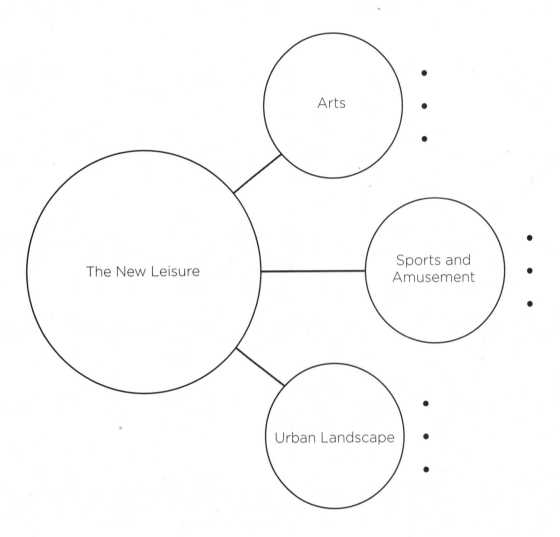

© Discovery Education | www.DiscoveryEducation.com

SOCIAL STUDIES
TECHBOOK

Name _____ Date _____

GRAPHIC ORGANIZER: Modified Problem/Solution Chart

Use this Modified Problem/Solution Chart to identify and evaluate how different groups responded to the problems of city life. For supporting resources, go to Dawn of the American Century (1878 to 1913) > A Country Transformed > City Life > Explore > Rise of the Political Machine.

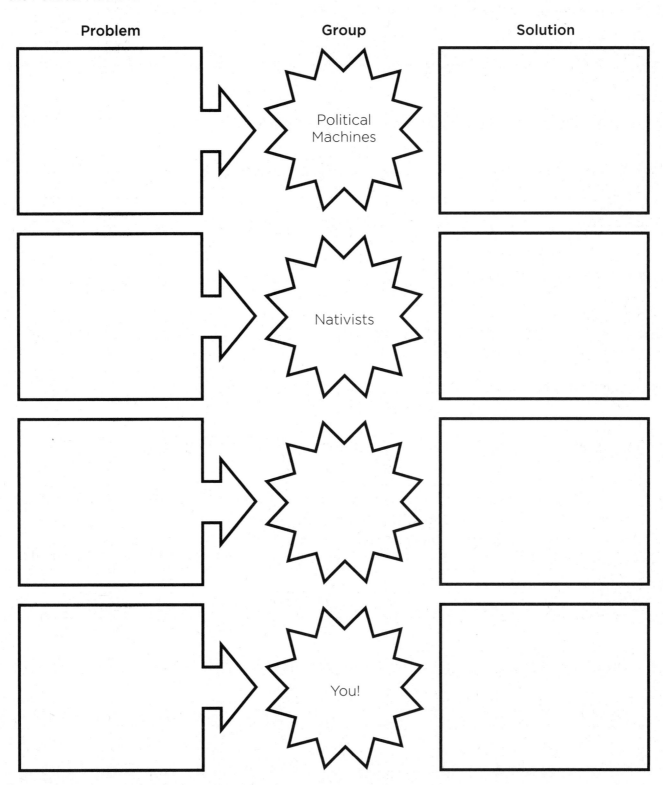

Problem	Group	Solution
	Political Machines	
	Nativists	
	You!	

Name _____ Date _____

EXPLORE: FOCUS QUESTIONS

Using what you learned from the Core Interactive Text, answer each page's focus question:

The Rise of Cities
Why did U.S. cities grow?

_____
_____
_____
_____

New Technology and Social Issues Fuel Urban Growth
What other factors contributed to urbanization?

_____
_____
_____
_____

Widespread Urbanization
Where did urbanization occur?

_____
_____
_____
_____

Urban Economic Hubs
What economic activities flourished in U.S. cities?

_____
_____
_____
_____

Upscale Suburbs and Working-Class Tenements
How did the lives of well-off and poor city dwellers differ?

_____
_____
_____
_____

Urban Living Leads to Problems
What problems arose in U.S. cities?

_____
_____
_____
_____

Name _____ Date _____

EXPLORE: FOCUS QUESTIONS *(continued)*

City Government
How did cities respond to the problems of growth?

_____

_____

_____

The New Leisure
How did urbanization lead to new cultural and leisure activities?

_____

_____

_____

Sports and Amusement
What sports and amusement activities arose in urban areas?

_____

_____

_____

The Sky's the Limit
How did city landscapes change?

_____

_____

_____

The Rise of the Political Machine
How did the social changes of urbanization lead to a transformation of city governments?

_____

_____

_____

Nativism and Cultural Conflict
How did urbanization and immigration shape politics at the local and national levels?

_____

_____

_____

Name _____ Date _____

EXPLORE: FOCUS QUESTIONS *(continued)*

Political Divisions
What competing political viewpoints emerged during the late 1800s?

_____
_____
_____

Efforts to Reform Government
How did civil service reform take place?

_____
_____
_____

PROJECTS AND ASSESSMENTS

Explain Activities

ACTIVITY TYPE: ADVERTISEMENT

A Life of Leisure

In this activity, you will create an advertisement designed to persuade citizens to spend some of their income on activities such as visiting the zoo with their children or attending a baseball game.

ACTIVITY TYPE: DIAGRAM

Categorizing Change

In this activity, you will use a GREASES Chart to analyze changes in the United States that resulted from urbanization and industrialization. For each category, provide at least one specific example and analysis of the overall changes.

ACTIVITY TYPE: QUICK WRITE

Rural-to-Urban Migration

In this Quick Write, you will write a letter from the perspective of a rural farmworker who has moved to the city to work in a factory during the late 1800s. You have received a letter from your family who is still on the farm. They have asked if you are glad you have moved. In your letter, you will describe what you hoped life would be like in the city and what it is actually like. Your letter will answer your family's question: Are you glad you have moved to the city, or do you regret your decision?

ACTIVITY TYPE: SOCIAL STUDIES EXPLANATION

City Life

In this activity, you will use the template to assemble evidence from the sources you have explored. Then, you will write an answer to the Essential Question and defend your answer with supporting evidence.

Elaborate Activities

photo: Library of Congress

INVESTIGATION: TIMELINE MAP

The Growth of Chicago over Time

How did industrialization and immigration change life in U.S. cities? Use the interactive Timeline Map tool to explore the fast-growing city of Chicago between 1835 and 1921, and then analyze how those changes reshaped daily life for the city's residents.

PROJECTS AND ASSESSMENTS *(continued)*

photo: Library of Congress

ACTIVITY: YOU AS ARTIST

A Corrupt Government

In this activity, you will analyze a political cartoon illustrating government corruption during the late 1800s and 1900s to understand its message. Then, you will use the common elements of political cartoons to draw your own cartoon that will make a point about government corruption during the late 1800s and early 1900s.

photo: Library of Congress

ACTIVITY: EXPRESS YOUR OPINION

Investigating Life in Cities

In this activity, you will take on the role of a muckraker in the early 1900s. You will explore resources that provide more information about the living conditions in U.S. cities. Then, you will use your research to write your own muckraking piece to raise public attention about the plight of the poor in U.S. cities.

photo: Library of Congress

ACTIVITY: DOCUMENT-BASED INVESTIGATION

Were Political Machines Needed?

In this Document-Based Investigation, you will analyze source materials describing the actions of political machines during the late 1800s and early 1900s to investigate this question: Did political machines do more harm than good?

Evaluate Activities

BRIEF-CONSTRUCTED RESPONSE (BCR)

City Life

EXTENDED-CONSTRUCTED RESPONSE (ECR)

City Life

UNIT 5: DAWN OF THE AMERICAN CENTURY (1878 TO 1913)

Chapter 12: Conflict in the Gilded Age

12.1 Rise of the Millionaires

LESSON OVERVIEW

Lesson Objectives:

By the end of this lesson, you should be able to:

- Define basic economic concepts and explain the role of economic systems in addressing the fundamental questions of economics.
- Explain how industrialization changed American business practices and organization.
- Evaluate governmental responses to economic problems created by industrialization and the emergence of big business.

Lesson Essential Question:

Were America's great industrial giants champions of free enterprise?

Key Vocabulary

Andrew Carnegie, capitalism, command economy, Cornelius Vanderbilt, economy, entrepreneur, Gilded Age, Interstate Commerce Act of 1887, John D. Rockefeller, laissez-faire, market economy, mixed economy, monopoly, private enterprise, robber barons, scarcity, Social Darwinism, supply and demand, trust

FLASHCARDS

1 ▸ The U.S. Free Market System

Economic systems address the problems of what to produce, how to produce it, and how to distribute it.

- Scarcity is the problem that there can never be enough goods or resources to meet every human want. Scarcity is the fundamental problem of economics.

- Because resources are scarce and wants are unlimited, people have to make choices.

- An economic system is a society's framework of formal and informal rules for addressing the fundamental questions of economics: what to produce, how to produce it, and for whom to produce it.

- Most economic systems are primarily traditional, command, or market-based. However, all economic systems are mixed economies that feature elements of all three types.

- A traditional economy primarily relies on customs or traditions passed down from generation to generation, such as hunting and gathering.

- A command-oriented economy primarily relies on a central authority to address the fundamental questions.

- In a market-based economy, buyers and sellers come together in the marketplace to address the fundamental questions of economics. The United States has a mixed-market economy.

- A market-based economy is driven by the profit motive. Individuals and groups want to offer goods or services that consumers want and are able to buy because selling these things can earn them money.

- A market-oriented economy relies on competition to meet consumers' wants. Sellers compete with one another for the buyers' business. This forces businesses to improve their products or reduce their prices.

- Some Americans favor a laissez-faire approach to government intervention in the economy. They want the role of government in the economy to be limited to protecting the free market and preserving competition.

- Other Americans want the government to intervene to promote other goals. These goals might include regulating pollution, eliminating poverty, and reducing unemployment, for instance.

Why Does It Matter?

The United States has a market-based economy. During the 1800s, the courts, Congress, and the public contested and negotiated the proper role of government in the economy. Today, disagreements about the proper role for government in a market-based economy are at the root of many political disputes.

photo: Discovery Education

In a free enterprise, market-based economy, sellers compete with one another to offer goods that buyers want at prices they are willing to pay.

FLASHCARDS *(continued)*

2 ### Economic Power in the Late 1800s

As the United States became an industrialized nation, new models of business and a new wealthy class of industrial entrepreneurs arose.

- Industrialization required large investments. Corporations sold stock to raise capital to invest in mass production.
- Large corporations began buying stock in smaller companies. Companies merged to form trusts to work around antimonopoly laws. This decreased competition in an industry.
- Lawmakers tried to outlaw trusts, but businesses got around these laws by creating holding companies.
- The new business models and combinations made competition in the marketplace difficult and depressed wages and worker safety.
- Andrew Carnegie, John D. Rockefeller, Cornelius Vanderbilt, and J. P. Morgan were important industrialists of the 1800s.
- Some industrial tycoons donated hundreds of millions of dollars to help the public through charitable organizations, art museums, libraries, and educational institutions.

Why Does It Matter?

The United States became a world industrial, economic, and military leader in the 1800s. U.S. businesses and business leaders became examples of what people all over the globe aspired to become.

photo: Library of Congress
By the late 1800s, oil tycoon John D. Rockefeller owned most of the oil industry.

3 ### The Role of Government

The emergence of big business in the late 1800s created social problems, economic inequalities, and corruption. The government did little to address these issues.

- American novelist Horatio Alger wrote dime novels about disadvantaged children who made themselves wealthy. His stories helped sell the idea that hard work and luck were all that anyone needed to succeed in America.
- Social Darwinists believed in the "survival of the fittest" when it came to social problems and poverty. Social Darwinism was used to justify economic inequality and laissez-faire government.
- Carnegie's Gospel of Wealth preached that charity was a moral duty of the rich to help the poor.
- In the 1880s and 1890s, the Supreme Court ruled against several attempts to regulate business. The justices applied the rights of "due process" and "liberty of contract" to corporations as if they were people.
- American politics in the late 1800s were dominated by corruption when big businesses tried to influence government policy-making.
- Democrats and farmers opposed high protective tariffs. Republicans and industrialists were able to preserve the tariff.
- The Interstate Commerce Act and the Sherman Antitrust Act were early departures from laissez-faire government. These attempts to restrict the power of big business were not very successful.

Why Does It Matter?

Powerful Americans and government leaders supported laissez-faire governmental policies. While a few entrepreneurs prospered, many U.S. citizens lived in squalor, or dirty conditions, and suffered serious health issues. Americans struggled to find economic and political solutions that would bring prosperity to all while safeguarding liberty and property rights.

photo: IRC
Horatio Alger wrote novels about rags-to-riches stories in America. His stories tried to show that anyone could achieve the "American Dream."

Name _____ **Date** _____

GRAPHIC ORGANIZER: Main Idea Web

Use this Main Idea Web to record information about the types of economic systems. For supporting resources, go to Dawn of the American Century (1878 to 1913) > Conflict in the Gilded Age > Rise of the Millionaires > Explore > Fundamental Economic Questions.

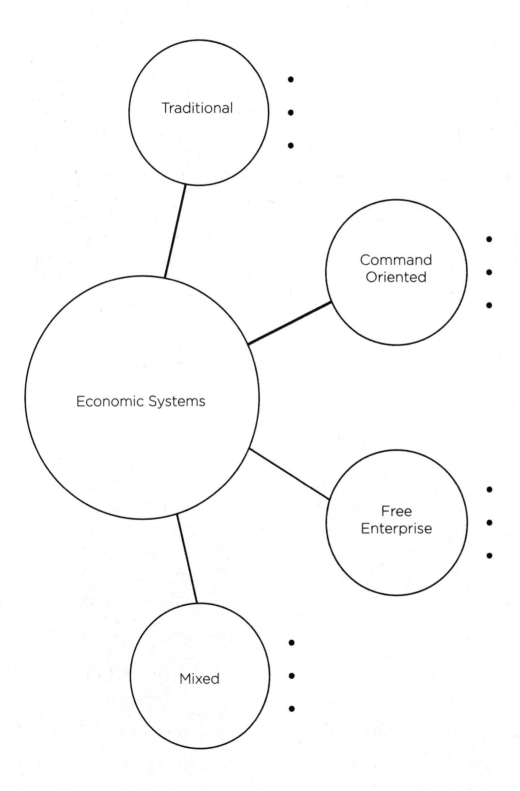

Name _____   **Date** _____

GRAPHIC ORGANIZER: Cause/Event/Effect Chart

Use this Cause/Event/Effect Chart to describe the reasons for and effects of changes to business organizations during the Gilded Age. For supporting resources, go to Dawn of the American Century (1878 to 1913) > Conflict in the Gilded Age > Rise of the Millionaires > Explore > Creating the Corporate Model.

Cause	Event	Effect
	Creation of Corporations	
	Creation of Trusts	
	Creation of Holding Companies	
	Less Competition	

Name _____ **Date** _____

GRAPHIC ORGANIZER: Comparison Chart

Use this Comparison Chart to record details about the background, industries, business methods, and philanthropic works of Cornelius Vanderbilt, John D. Rockefeller, Andrew Carnegie, and J. P. Morgan. For supporting resources, go to Dawn of the American Century (1878 to 1913) > Conflict in the Gilded Age > Rise of the Millionaires > Explore > Barons and Philanthropists: Vanderbilt and Rockefeller.

Criteria	Background	Main Industry	Business Methods	Philanthropy
Cornelius Vanderbilt				
John D. Rockefeller				
J. P. Morgan				
Andrew Carnegie				

Name _____ Date _____

GRAPHIC ORGANIZER: Change Over Time Chart

Use this Change Over Time Chart to list important characteristics of life in the United States before and after government responded to big business. For supporting resources, go to Dawn of the American Century (1878 to 1913) > Conflict in the Gilded Age > Rise of the Millionaires > Explore > Supporting a Hands-Off Approach.

Before:	After:

Changes:

Name _____ Date _____

EXPLORE: FOCUS QUESTIONS

Using what you learned from the Core Interactive Text, answer each page's focus question:

Fundamental Economic Questions

How does scarcity relate to economic production?

_____
_____
_____
_____

Types of Economic Systems

What systems do people establish to address the issue of scarcity?

_____
_____
_____
_____

Free Enterprise

How do market-based economies address the fundamental questions of economics?

_____
_____
_____
_____

Governing a Free Enterprise Economy

What is the role of government in a market-based system?

_____
_____
_____
_____

Creating the Corporate Model

How did the organization of business change in the 1800s?

_____
_____
_____
_____

Consequences of Monopolies

What were the consequences of how corporations, trusts, and holding companies were organized?

_____
_____
_____
_____

Name _____ Date _____

EXPLORE: FOCUS QUESTIONS *(continued)*

Barons and Philanthropists: Vanderbilt and Rockefeller
How did Cornelius Vanderbilt and John D. Rockefeller rise to prominence?

_____

_____

_____

Barons and Philanthropists: Carnegie and Morgan
How did Andrew Carnegie and J. P. Morgan rise to prominence?

_____

_____

_____

Supporting a Hands-Off Approach
How did Americans justify their support of a laissez-faire government?

_____

_____

_____

The Federal Government Responds
What were some early attempts to address monopolistic business practices?

_____

_____

_____

The Business of Politics
How did American politics change after Reconstruction?

_____

_____

_____

PROJECTS AND ASSESSMENTS

Explain Activities

ACTIVITY TYPE: VISUALIZATION

Barons and Philanthropists: Vanderbilt and Rockefeller

In this Visualization activity, you will illustrate and explain the social impact of the business practices of the industrialists and their philanthropic measures.

ACTIVITY TYPE: QUICK WRITE

A Champion of Free Enterprise?

Select one industrial giant from the late 1800s and early 1900s and consider whether this leader can be called a champion of free enterprise. Before writing your response, be sure to consider the principles on which the free enterprise system was founded, such as consumer choice, competition, and profit motive. Then, think about how the leader you selected changed American business. Was the industrial giant you selected a champion of free enterprise principles?

ACTIVITY TYPE: SOCIAL STUDIES EXPLANATION

Rise of the Millionaires

In this activity, you will use the template to assemble evidence from the sources you have explored. Then, you will write an answer to the Essential Question and defend your answer with supporting evidence.

ACTIVITY TYPE: DIAGRAM

Three Economic Systems

Use the Comparison Chart to compare and contrast the way that societies with different economic systems answer the three fundamental questions of economics. In each box, cite an example that illustrates how each economic system answers the three fundamental questions.

Elaborate Activities

photo: HarpWeek

INVESTIGATION TYPE: SOURCE ANALYSIS

Captains of Industry or Robber Barons?

The Industrial Revolution changed the way Americans worked, traveled, and communicated. It also made some people extremely wealthy. Were these new millionaires good for the country? Or did they prosper at the expense of ordinary Americans? In this investigation, you will use the interactive Source Analysis tool to explore these questions.

PROJECTS AND ASSESSMENTS *(continued)*

photo: Library of Congress

ACTIVITY TYPE: YOU AS ARTIST

Big Business's Influence

In this activity, you will analyze a political cartoon illustrating the artist's opinion of big business in the early 1900s. Then, you will use the common elements of political cartoons to draw your own cartoon that will make a point about big business or the rise of industrialists during the late 1800s and early 1900s.

photo: Library of Congresss

ACTIVITY TYPE: DOCUMENT-BASED INVESTIGATION

Giants of American Ideals?

During the late 1800s and early 1900s, industrial giants became the celebrities of their day. Many people admired millionaires such as Andrew Carnegie, John D. Rockefeller, and others for their success. In this Document-Based Investigation, you will analyze source materials to investigate this question: Were America's industrial giants champions of American ideals?

photo: IRC

ACTIVITY TYPE: SAY WHAT?

"Acres of Diamonds"

Read the excerpts from Reverend Conwell's "Acres of Diamonds" speech and translate the speech for modern times. Then, you will respond to the analysis questions to explain whether Conwell's message was relevant to industrial workers during the late 1800s and early 1900s.

Evaluate Activities

BRIEF-CONSTRUCTED RESPONSE (BCR)

Rise of the Millionaires

EXTENDED-CONSTRUCTED RESPONSE (ECR)

Rise of the Millionaires

UNIT 5: DAWN OF THE AMERICAN CENTURY (1878 TO 1913)

Chapter 12: Conflict in the Gilded Age

12.2 Labor and Populism

LESSON OVERVIEW

Lesson Objectives:

By the end of this lesson, you should be able to:

- **Explain the impact of industrialization and laissez-faire policies on American workers.**

- **Evaluate the early labor movement in addressing economic and social problems created by industrialization.**

- **Explain the impact of industrialization and laissez-faire policies on American farmers.**

- **Evaluate the effectiveness of the Populist Party and other political movements in addressing economic and social problems created by industrialization.**

Lesson Essential Questions:

How were the early labor and farmers' movements alike? How were they different?

Key Vocabulary

American Federation of Labor, collective bargaining, deflation, Eugene Debs, Farmers' Alliance, gold standard, Haymarket Riot, Homestead Strike, inflation, International Workers of the World, Knights of Labor, labor union, laissez-faire, Populist Party, Pullman Strike, Samuel Gompers, socialism, strike, The Grange, William Jennings Bryan

FLASHCARDS

1 Working for a Living

Industrialization changed the lives of workers in America. Industry and government saw regulations as "interference." Working-class people could not protect themselves.

- Because there was a constant supply of willing or desperate workers, wages stayed low and workers endured difficult and dangerous conditions.
- Factories hired many women and children because they could pay them less to perform the same jobs as adult men.
- Many working-class children did not go to school. They worked in factories and mines, sold newspapers, or shined shoes on street corners to support their families and themselves.
- Workers in factories, mines, and sweatshops endured unsafe working conditions and long workdays.
- Workers were economically dependent on their employers, especially in company towns.
- The labor of factory and industrial workers was treated as a commodity. Business owners did not focus on meeting workers' human needs but on ways to lower labor costs and increase productivity.

Why Does It Matter?

Working-class people had few rights and very little say in their lives. There were no laws preventing businesses from valuing profit over the safety of their workers. Over time, federal organizations, such as the Department of Labor, were established to protect workers, regulate workplace safety, and manage disputes between labor unions and company owners.

photo: IRC
A woman works in an American factory in the late 1800s.

2 Early Labor Organizations

Early labor movements sought different types of reforms for workers. The Knights of Labor and the American Federation of Labor were two prominent organizations.

- The earliest organized unions were trade unions intent on better working conditions for skilled workers in a single industry.
- The Knights of Labor, founded in 1869 and led by Terence Powderly, was founded to represent all workers. It sought broad societal reforms, including cooperative factories and markets.
- Samuel Gompers's American Federation of Labor was a collection of separate trade unions that concentrated on "bread-and-butter" issues such as wages and workplace safety.
- Labor organizations lost support after the 1886 Haymarket Incident where at least 11 people, including 7 police officers, died.
- Led by Eugene Debs, the American Socialist Party tried to reform American society by creating more government ownership of industries.
- The International Workers of the World (IWW) wanted government ownership and control of business and complete equality between workers and managers.
- During the Homestead Strike of 1892 and the Pullman Strike of 1894, government power was used to suppress the labor movement.

Why Does It Matter?

Early labor movements fought for better working conditions and brought attention to the problems of the working class through strikes and calls for reform. However, not all labor movements had the same goals and tactics. As time passed, the labor organizations grew more political. Labor unions for public sector employees, such as teachers and police, still play an active role in government reforms for the workplace.

photo: Library of Congress
Workers in the railroad and other industries went on strike to fight for reforms and better working conditions.

FLASHCARDS (continued)

3 ▸ Agricultural Issues

In the 1800s, farmers had to deal with many issues, including a flooded grain market, uncontrollable natural factors, creditors, and railroad price gouging.

- Farming is affected by many factors outside the control of farmers. These include drought, weather, insects, and crop disease.
- Industrialization and mechanization increased the efficiency of farm labor. As a result, worldwide grain output increased and prices dropped.
- Falling prices made it more difficult for farmers to pay back bank loans they had taken out to purchase seeds and mechanical equipment.
- Many farmers supported inflationary monetary policies to increase the money supply. They believed this would increase crop prices and help them pay off debt.
- Many farmers depended on railroads to transport their crops. Railroads were unregulated monopolies whose high rates threatened to put farmers out of business.

Why Does It Matter?

Industrialized farming created more efficient output, but it also affected the prices of crops. Farmers faced a dilemma in which they made less money and owed more to banks. They were also dependent on the railroads to bring their goods to market and thus had to be willing to pay whatever the railroad companies wanted to charge. These factors made making a living as a farmer very difficult. The farming population in the United States gradually decreased throughout the early 1900s.

photo: IRC
Farmers in California relied on the railroads to transport their produce to the rest of the country.

4 ▸ The Farmers Unite

In the 1800s, farmers united and created organizations to protect their working conditions and interests.

- Inflationary monetary policies that farmers favored included increasing the amount of silver dollars and creating paper money that was not backed by silver or gold.
- Sound money advocates opposed farmers and favored a gold standard.
- Farmers created their own labor organizations such as the Grange, established in 1867.
- Grangers bought cooperative factories and grain storage facilities and pushed for restrictions on railroad fees. The Grange declined in the 1880s.
- The Populist Party (formed in 1892) favored inflationary monetary policies, a graduated income tax, government control (and sometimes ownership) of railroad companies, low-interest government loans, and direct election of U.S. senators.
- Many farmers in the South did not support the Populists out of fear that a break from the Democratic Party would help the Republicans come to power in the South.
- The Populist Party did not do well in national elections. However, many of its policies were adopted by the Democrats, by William Jennings Bryan, and later by progressives.

Why Does It Matter?

The early farmers' organizations had limited success in addressing economic and social problems created by industrialization. However, the creation of the Populist Party brought public awareness to their needs. While the Populist Party did not last forever, its policies continued and were adopted by other political groups, including those during the Progressive Era.

photo: Library of Congress
The Grangers tried to help farmers create cooperative markets and resources.

Discovery | SOCIAL STUDIES **TECHBOOK**

Name _____ Date _____

GRAPHIC ORGANIZER: Main Idea Web

Use this Main Idea Web to record information about life in industrial America. For supporting resources, go to Dawn of the American Century (1878 to 1913) > Conflict in the Gilded Age > Labor and Populism > Explore > An Industrialized America.

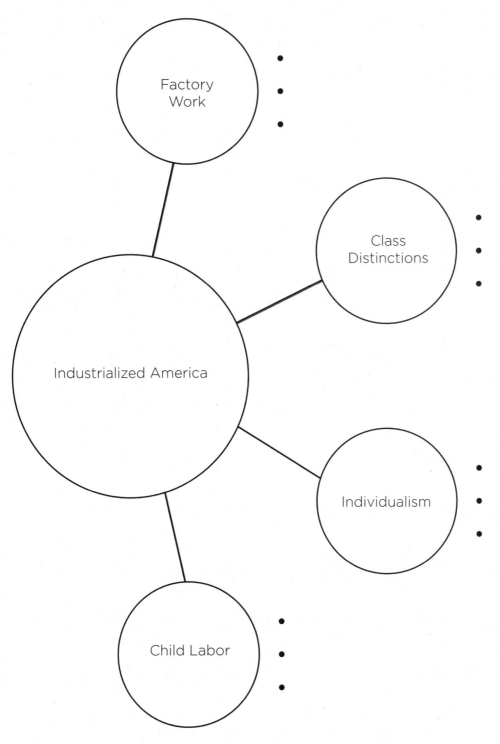

Name _____   Date _____

GRAPHIC ORGANIZER: Vocabulary Chart

Use this Vocabulary Chart to define the term *company town*. For supporting resources, go to Dawn of the American Century (1878 to 1913) > Conflict in the Gilded Age > Labor and Populism > Explore > Company Towns.

DEFINITION:	EXAMPLES (drawn or written):
Personal:	
Dictionary:	

TERM: company town

SENTENCES:		RELATED:	WORD PARTS:
Teacher/Book:			
Personal:			

Impact on Workers:

Name _____ Date _____

GRAPHIC ORGANIZER: Timeline

Use this Timeline to trace the history of the labor movement. For supporting resources, go to Dawn of the American Century (1878 to 1913) > Conflict in the Gilded Age > Labor and Populism > Explore > The Labor Movement.

1828

The Great Depression

Name _____ Date _____

GRAPHIC ORGANIZER: Problem/Solution Chart

Use this Problem/Solution Chart to list the problems farmers faced and the economic and political solutions they sought. For supporting resources, go to Dawn of the American Century (1878 to 1913) > Conflict in the Gilded Age > Labor and Populism > Explore > The Plight of Farmers.

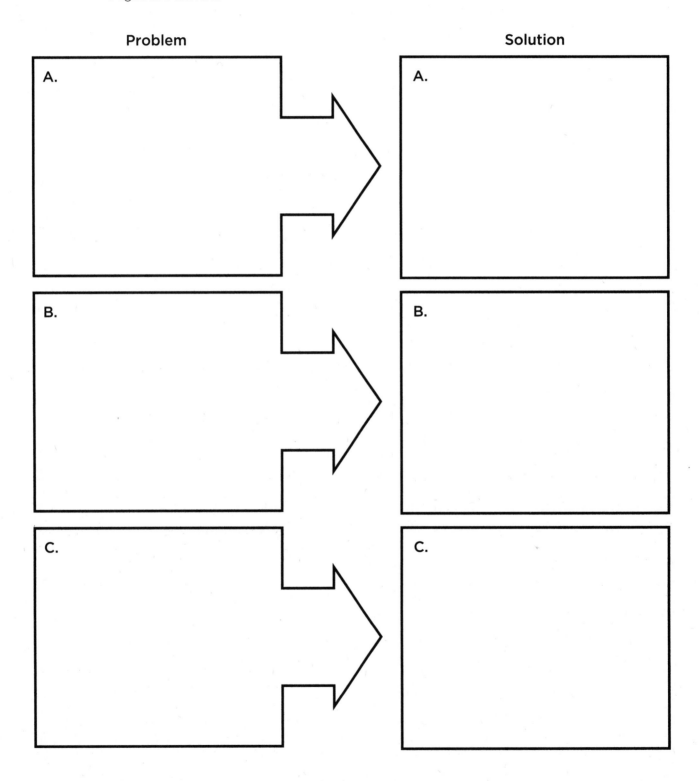

Problem

A.

B.

C.

Solution

A.

B.

C.

Name _____ Date _____

EXPLORE: FOCUS QUESTIONS

Using what you learned from the Core Interactive Text, answer each page's focus question:

An Industrialized America

How did industrialization affect employees of U.S. businesses?

_____

_____

_____

The Plight of the Working Class

What was life in the United States like for working-class families?

_____

_____

_____

Company Towns

What were company towns?

_____

_____

_____

The Labor Movement

How did workers respond to difficult conditions?

_____

_____

_____

National Labor Organizations

How did the national labor movement make progress for workers?

_____

_____

_____

Backlash Against Labor

How did incidents of violence affect the labor movement?

_____

_____

_____

Name _____ Date _____

EXPLORE: FOCUS QUESTIONS *(continued)*

Labor and Politics

What was the connection between socialism and the early labor movements?

_____
_____
_____
_____

The Plight of Farmers

What issues were affecting farmers in the late 1800s?

_____
_____
_____
_____

Free Silver vs. the Gold Standard

Why did farmers push for monetary reform?

_____
_____
_____
_____

Protecting Agricultural Interests

What early organizations represented the interests of farmers?

_____
_____
_____
_____

The Populist Party

Who supported the Populist Party? Who opposed it?

_____
_____
_____
_____

© Discovery Education | www.DiscoveryEducation.com

PROJECTS AND ASSESSMENTS

Explain Activities

ACTIVITY TYPE: DIAGRAM

Labor and Populism

Use the Modified Comparison Chart to compare and contrast the farmers' and the labor movements. Note any similarities in the circles and any differences in the spaces to the left and right of each circle.

ACTIVITY TYPE: QUICK WRITE

Dealing with Life's Problems

In this Quick Write, you will choose to take on the perspective of someone from the late 1800s to the early 1900s in American society. Then, from the perspective you have selected, you will write a paragraph in which you identify a problem that you face and propose a solution for that problem. Consider how your problems are similar to or different from the other groups. Plan who could help you solve your problem or what objections the other group might have.

ACTIVITY TYPE: SOCIAL STUDIES EXPLANATION

Labor and Populism

In this activity, you will use the template to assemble evidence from the sources you have explored. Then, you will write an answer to the Essential Questions and defend your answer with supporting evidence.

Elaborate Activities

photo: Discovery Education

INVESTIGATION TYPE: HISTORICAL PERSPECTIVES

The Drawbacks of Industrialization

How did industrialization change the lives of workers, farmers, and business owners from 1877 to 1900? In this investigation, you will use the interactive Historical Perspectives tool to explore the changes in the national economy through the perspectives of four individuals who might have lived in that time.

PROJECTS AND ASSESSMENTS *(continued)*

photo: Library of Congress

ACTIVITY TYPE: EXPRESS YOUR OPINION

Assisting the Farmers

Imagine that you are a newspaper reporter assigned to cover the organization of the Grange and the Farmers' Alliance and their demands for greater government regulation of grain elevators and railroads. You will investigate the environmental and economic challenges facing small farmers at the turn of the century, as well as the role played by commercial interests such as grain elevators, banks, and railroads.

photo: Library of Congress

ACTIVITY TYPE: CLASSROOM DEBATE

Ending the Pullman Strike

Imagine that you are a striking railroad worker or a representative of the Pullman Palace Car Company. Investigate your role in the events of the Pullman Strike to formulate an opinion on the question: Was the federal government right to intervene to end the strike? Then, use what you have learned to write an opening statement in defense of your position. Your statement should demonstrate your understanding of your assigned perspective's stance on federal intervention in the Pullman Strike. You will then use your knowledge of your perspective's stance to participate in a debate with classmates representing the other perspectives.

photo: Library of Congress

ACTIVITY TYPE: DOCUMENT-BASED INVESTIGATION

Farm and Labor, Unite?

In this Document-Based Investigation, you will analyze source materials and investigate this question: Should efforts to improve the lives of laborers and farmers be viewed as a single reform movement?

PROJECTS AND ASSESSMENTS *(continued)*

Evaluate Activities

BRIEF-CONSTRUCTED RESPONSE (BCR)

Labor and Populism

EXTENDED-CONSTRUCTED RESPONSE (ECR)

Labor and Populism

photo: Library of Congress

UNIT 5: DAWN OF THE AMERICAN CENTURY (1878 TO 1913)

Chapter 12: Conflict in the Gilded Age

12.3 The Progressive Reformers

LESSON OVERVIEW

Lesson Objectives:

By the end of this lesson, you should be able to:

- Describe the Progressive movement and explain factors leading to its emergence.
- Evaluate the Progressive Era's responses to political corruption.
- Evaluate the Progressive Era's responses to economic and social problems created by industrialization.
- Evaluate the Progressive Era's impact on women, immigrants, and African Americans.

Lesson Essential Question:

How well did the Progressive movement address the consequences of industrialization?

Key Vocabulary

initiative, Jane Addams, muckraker, National American Woman Suffrage Association, Nineteenth Amendment, nominating conventions, primary election, Progressive movement, Prohibition, recall, referendum, Robert La Follette, Scientific Management, settlement house, Social Gospel movement, suffrage, temperance, Upton Sinclair

FLASHCARDS

1 The Rise of Progressivism

Progressives sought to reform U.S. social, economic, and political institutions.

- **Progressive reformers sought to change U.S. life at the local, state, and national levels. They wanted government to directly involve itself in reform.**
- **Progressivism grew out of the earlier Social Gospel movement. This movement connected Christianity with social justice.**
- **Women, muckrakers, and politicians were all central to the Progressive movement.**
- **Muckrakers and intellectuals promoted Progressive causes through articles, books, and photography.**
- **Progressive reformers were often middle class and white. Some had little respect for African Americans or immigrants, and they ignored, or even opposed, issues important to these groups.**

Why Does It Matter?

Progressive leaders identified the ills plaguing U.S. society and sought to correct those wrongs. Progressive leaders showed their contemporaries and future generations that people can take action to reform society.

photo: IRC

Jacob Riis's photographs helped expose the difficulties of life for many immigrants and citizens living in urban areas.

2 Progressive Politics

Progressives supported measures to weaken the corrupt political system that grew during the late 1800s.

- **Progressive reformers made significant changes to politics at all levels. At the municipal level, they introduced the new city commission form of government.**
- **Progressives sought to weaken the power of political machines and party bosses. To do this, they supported campaign finance reform, the direct election of U.S. senators, the direct primary, and other measures.**
- **Progressives supported direct democracy. They worked for the creation of the initiative, referendum, and recall.**
- **Progressives expanded voter involvement by supporting the secret ballot and expanding voter registration efforts.**
- **Some Progressive reforms weakened the political rights of African Americans and immigrants.**

Why Does It Matter?

Progressive reforms changed the way Americans interacted with their government.

photo: Library of Congress

Progressives worked to enact sweeping changes to all parts of U.S. life.

FLASHCARDS *(continued)*

3 Improving Society

Progressive reforms worked to solve the problems of industrialization and urbanization.

- **Settlement houses such as Jane Addams's Hull House reached out to immigrant neighborhoods.**
- **Many Progressive women supported temperance, or prohibition. These policies aimed to reduce or eliminate alcohol consumption.**
- **The Women's Christian Temperance Union, formed in 1874, was a major organization working for temperance.**

Why Does It Matter?

Industrialization and urbanization helped build the country's wealth and provided opportunities for laborers. However, these trends brought increased poverty and crime. Progressive reformers provided a new vision for U.S. cities and life.

photo: IRC

Members of the Women's Christian Temperance Union unite to protest the use of alcohol.

4 Progressives and the Struggle for Rights

Progressives sought to expand social, political, and economic power for some Americans.

- **Women's suffrage was a key Progressive goal. Supporters argued that granting women the vote was both just and beneficial for the country.**
- **The National American Women's Suffrage Association campaigned for suffrage for many decades.**
- **Early suffrage successes saw women in certain states win the right to vote.**
- **The Nineteenth Amendment extended women's suffrage in 1920.**
- **African Americans were largely left out of Progressive reforms. Some formed organizations, including the Niagara Movement and the NAACP, to seek equality.**
- **Immigrants sometimes viewed Progressive reforms as working against their rights, political influence, and cultural practices.**

Why Does It Matter?

Many historians question the success of Progressivism in addressing the struggles of all Americans. Even though Progressive reforms did not eliminate all social problems, they inspired groups that did not benefit from Progressive reforms to seek increased opportunities and rights.

photo: Library of Congress

Progressives sought to reform corrupt government practices at the local, state, and national levels.

Name _____ **Date** _____

GRAPHIC ORGANIZER: Main Idea Web

Use this Main Idea Web to identify the key groups of the Progressive movement, why they formed, and how they approached Progressive policies. For supporting resources, go to Dawn of the American Century (1878 to 1913) > Conflict in the Gilded Age > The Progressive Reformers > Explore > The Rise of the Progressive Movement.

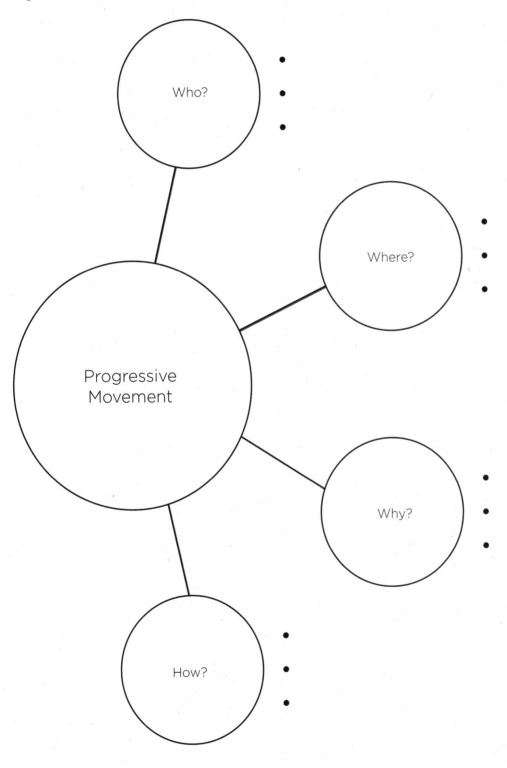

Name _____ **Date** _____

GRAPHIC ORGANIZER: Three-Way Venn Diagram

Use this Three-Way Venn Diagram to compare and contrast the cultural, political, and social reforms of the Progressive Era. For supporting resources, go to Dawn of the American Century (1878 to 1913) > Conflict in the Gilded Age > The Progressive Reformers > Explore > Muckrakers.

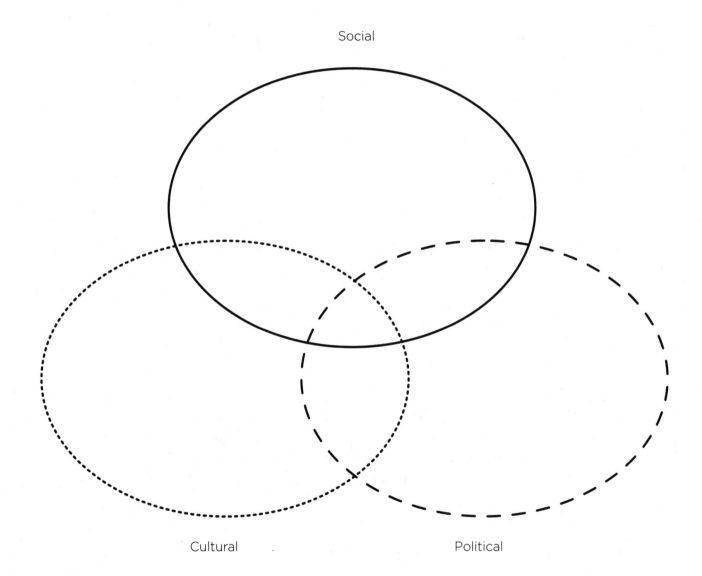

Social

Cultural

Political

Name _____ **Date** _____

GRAPHIC ORGANIZER: Problem/Solution Chart

Use this Problem/Solution Chart to identify Progressive solutions to the economic and social problems caused by industrialization. For supporting resources, go to Dawn of the American Century (1878 to 1913) > Conflict in the Gilded Age > The Progressive Reformers > Explore > Progressive Social Reform.

Problem	Solution
A.	A.
B.	B.
C.	C.

Name _____ **Date** _____

GRAPHIC ORGANIZER: Comparison Chart

Use this Comparison Chart to record information about the roles various groups played in the Progressive movement. For supporting resources, go to Dawn of the American Century (1878 to 1913) > Conflict in the Gilded Age > The Progressive Reformers > Explore > Votes for Women.

Criteria	Goals	Important Groups	Accomplishments	Setbacks
Women				
Socialists				
African Americans				
Immigrants				

Name _____ Date _____

EXPLORE: FOCUS QUESTIONS

Using what you learned from the Core Interactive Text, answer each page's focus question:

The Rise of the Progressive Movement

How did the Progressive movement form?

_____

_____

_____

A Nation of Reformers

Who were the Progressives?

_____

_____

_____

Muckrakers

How did journalists strengthen the Progressive movement?

_____

_____

_____

Rise of Realism

How did the Progressive movement lead to the rise of realism?

_____

_____

_____

Progressive Political Reform

How did Progressives work to end the power of political machines?

_____

_____

_____

Increased Reforms and Limitations

How did Progressive reforms serve to both advance and limit the rights of citizens?

_____

_____

_____

Name _____ Date _____

EXPLORE: FOCUS QUESTIONS *(continued)*

Progressive Social Reform
How did Progressives seek to reform U.S. society and morals?

_____
_____
_____
_____

Votes for Women
How did Progressives work to gain the vote for women?

_____
_____
_____
_____

Socialism and Radicalism
Why did socialism gain support during the Progressive Era?

_____
_____
_____
_____

Progressivism and African Americans
How did African Americans seek change during the Progressive Era?

_____
_____
_____
_____

Progressivism and Immigration
How did immigrants respond to the Progressive movement?

_____
_____
_____

© Discovery Education | www.DiscoveryEducation.com

PROJECTS AND ASSESSMENTS

Explain Activities

ACTIVITY TYPE: QUICK WRITE

Progressive Muckrakers

In this activity, you will take on the role of a Progressive Era muckraker. Then, you will write a newspaper article like a muckraker would have written in the early 1900s calling for a needed reform. Be sure to support your ideas with facts and details.

ACTIVITY TYPE: SOCIAL STUDIES EXPLANATION

The Progressive Reformers

In this activity, you will use the template to assemble evidence from the sources you have explored. Then, you will write an answer to the Essential Question and defend your answer with supporting evidence.

ACTIVITY TYPE: ENCYCLOPEDIA ENTRY

The Progressive Era

In this activity, you will create an encyclopedia entry describing a topic from the Progressive Era. Then, you will write an entry that clearly describes the topic you have selected.

Elaborate Activities

photo: Library of Congress

INVESTIGATION TYPE: KEY DECISION

Mayor for a Day

Imagine that it is 1901 and you are the new mayor of Cleveland, Ohio. In this activity, you will use the interactive Key Decision tool to examine the problems facing your city and evaluate some strategies for solving them. At the end of the exercise, you will learn which strategies Mayor Tom Johnson actually used and compare his choices to the ones you made.

photo: National Archives

ACTIVITY TYPE: DOCUMENT-BASED INVESTIGATION

Different Movements, Common Goals

In this Document-Based Investigation, you will analyze source materials and investigate this question: Did the Progressive movement seek to support or control working-class Americans?

PROJECTS AND ASSESSMENTS *(continued)*

photo: Library of Congress

ACTIVITY TYPE: CLASSROOM DEBATE

Evaluating Progressive Reforms

In this activity, you will investigate and evaluate some Progressive responses to the consequences of industrialization. Then, you will participate in a debate with classmates over whether these responses were mostly successes or failures.

ACTIVITY TYPE: ACT LOCALLY

Lobby for Change

How much change can people create in the world around them? The answer depends on you! The more citizens that actively support a specific idea or cause, the better chance they have that their initiative or change will be adopted. Lobbying is the act of attempting to influence the decisions made by government officials or those in an authoritative position. It can happen at the school, local, state, national, or even international level.

photo: Library of Congress

ACTIVITY TYPE: YOU AS ARTIST

Realism

In this activity, you will analyze a series of artworks to determine what makes them Realistic. You will compare them to photographs of the time. Then, you will use these elements to create your own Realistic artwork or to design a museum exhibit about Realism.

Evaluate Activities

BRIEF-CONSTRUCTED RESPONSE (BCR)

The Progressive Reformers

EXTENDED-CONSTRUCTED RESPONSE (ECR)

The Progressive Reformers

photo: Library of Congress

UNIT 5: DAWN OF THE AMERICAN CENTURY (1878 TO 1913)

Chapter 12: Conflict in the Gilded Age

12.4 Progressivism in the White House

LESSON OVERVIEW

Lesson Objectives:

By the end of this lesson, you should be able to:

- Evaluate major Progressive Era policies enacted on a national scale by the federal government.
- Analyze the emergence of governmental efforts to conserve and protect the environment.

Lesson Essential Question:

How did the Progressive Era change the role of the federal government?

Key Vocabulary

Benjamin Harrison, Eighteenth Amendment, Federal Reserve System, Federal Trade Commission, National Park Service, Seventeenth Amendment, Sixteenth Amendment, Square Deal, Theodore Roosevelt, William Howard Taft, William McKinley, Woodrow Wilson

FLASHCARDS

1 ▶ Progressive-Era Policies of Theodore Roosevelt

President Theodore Roosevelt supported the federal enactment of Progressive reforms in many areas, including trusts, labor, railroads, foods, and banking. Here are key accomplishments during President Roosevelt's terms in office.

- The U.S. government won a lawsuit against the Northern Securities Company, breaking up this monopoly. Backed by Roosevelt, the federal government broke up more than 40 other monopolies.

- Roosevelt supported striking coal miners and helped settle the strike through arbitration.

- The Hepburn Railway Act prohibited railroad companies from raising rates without the approval of the government.

- The Food and Drug Acts and the Meat Inspection Act helped ensure sanitary conditions in meatpacking and other food industries.

- Roosevelt advocated a policy called New Nationalism, which involved the president acting as a steward, or manager, for public welfare.

Why Does It Matter?

President Roosevelt was a strong leader on the battlefield during the Spanish-American War, and he proved to be equally strong as he faced the ills of industry and society as president. Many of Roosevelt's initiatives, such as the Food and Drug Acts and the breakup of monopolies, are still relevant in today's society.

A Contract
With the People

PLATFORM
OF THE
Progressive Party
ADOPTED AT ITS
First National Convention

Chicago, August 7th, 1912

If you want these things done ratify this contract on November 5, by casting your vote for Roosevelt and Johnson and the Progressive Party Candidates

photo: IRC

The Progressive Party chose former President Theodore Roosevelt to be its candidate for president in 1912.

FLASHCARDS *(continued)*

2 **Progressive-Era Policies of Woodrow Wilson**

Similar to President Theodore Roosevelt, President Woodrow Wilson supported the federal enactment of Progressive reforms. Here are key accomplishments made during President Wilson's terms in office.

- The Underwood Tariff Act, supported by President Wilson, lowered tariffs.
- The Federal Reserve Act formed a more efficient banking and currency system.
- The Federal Trade Commission maintained free and fair competition between businesses and protected consumers from unfair business practices.
- The Clayton Antitrust Acts enabled better enforcement of antitrust laws.
- The Sixteenth Amendment empowered Congress to levy federal income tax.
- The Seventeenth Amendment established direct voting for U.S. senators.
- The Eighteenth Amendment banned the selling and consumption of alcoholic beverages.
- The Nineteenth Amendment gave women the right to vote.

Why Does It Matter?

Many of the reforms passed during the Progressive Era are still in effect today. For example, the Clayton Antitrust Act is still enforced, and other antitrust acts have been added. The Federal Reserve and Federal Trade Commission remain vital government institutions. The Sixteenth and Seventeenth Amendments are still in place; however, the government repealed the Eighteenth Amendment in 1933. As a result of the Nineteenth Amendment, women have become a powerful voting bloc, and many women serve as elected officials at the local, state, and national levels, representing both major political parties.

photo: Library of Congress
In this cartoon, President Wilson holds an axe labeled "Tariff Revision" and uses it to chop down vines labeled "excessive protection." This causes a giant labeled "Monopoly" to fall to the ground.

3 **Federal Conservation of the Environment**

President Theodore Roosevelt and other conservationists attempt to protect the environment and its natural resources through legislation.

- The U.S. government formed the world's first national park: Yellowstone National Park.
- Naturalist John Muir helped convince Congress to form Yosemite National Park and Sequoia National Park.
- President Theodore Roosevelt set aside millions of acres as forest reserves.
- Roosevelt formed bird reserves and national game preserves.
- Roosevelt supported government regulation of the use of land and water resources, including the Reclamation Act of 1902.
- Gifford Pinchot organized the first inventory of the natural resources in the United States.
- Pinchot convinced the government to keep sites for hydroelectric plants under federal control.

Why Does It Matter?

The U.S. government continued to establish national parks throughout the 1900s. Forest and wildlife reserves continue to protect the environment today. Conservation has become an important issue throughout the world. Today, the threats to the environment have increased, including climate change, deforestation, desertification, depletion of natural resources, and various types of pollution.

photo: Library of Congress:
Conservation efforts against deforestation and other misuses of natural resources continue to this day.

Name _____ **Date** _____

GRAPHIC ORGANIZER: Timeline

Use this Timeline to record the names and dates of President Roosevelt's reforms during his two terms in office. Provide a short description of each reform you include. For supporting resources, go to Dawn of the American Century (1878 to 1913) > Conflict in the Gilded Age > Progressivism in the White House > Explore > Steward of the People.

1901   **1909**

Name _____ Date _____

GRAPHIC ORGANIZER: Main Idea Web

Use this Main Idea Web to list the reforms of President Wilson with regard to tariffs, banking, and businesses. For supporting resources, go to Dawn of the American Century (1878 to 1913) > Conflict in the Gilded Age > Progressivism in the White House > Explore > Woodrow Wilson's Reforms.

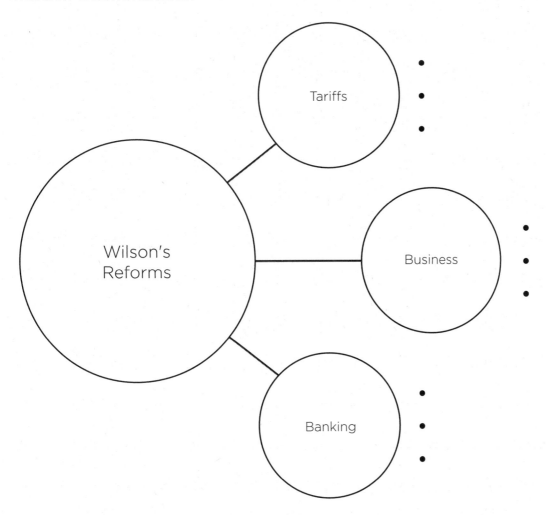

Name _____ Date _____

GRAPHIC ORGANIZER: Change Over Time Chart

Use this Change Over Time Chart to describe the changes in conservation that took place during the Progressive Era. For supporting resources, go to Dawn of the American Century (1878 to 1913) > Conflict in the Gilded Age > Progressivism in the White House > Explore > Protecting the Environment.

Before:	After:

Changes:

Name _____ Date _____

EXPLORE: FOCUS QUESTIONS

Using what you learned from the Core Interactive Text, answer each page's focus question:

Steward of the People
How did Americans perceive Theodore Roosevelt?

_____

_____

_____

Theodore Roosevelt's Reforms: First Term
What reforms did Roosevelt implement during his first term?

_____

_____

_____

Theodore Roosevelt's Reforms: Second Term
What reforms did Roosevelt implement during his second term?

_____

_____

_____

Woodrow Wilson's Reforms
What reforms did Wilson implement during his presidency?

_____

_____

_____

Progressivism and the Constitution
How did Progressivism change the U.S. Constitution?

_____

_____

_____

Name _____ Date _____

EXPLORE: FOCUS QUESTIONS *(continued)*

Protecting the Environment
How did conservation begin in the United States?

_____
_____
_____

Conservation Movement Expands
How did Theodore Roosevelt support the conservation movement?

_____
_____
_____

PROJECTS AND ASSESSMENTS

Explain Activities

ACTIVITY TYPE: DIAGRAM

Roosevelt vs. Wilson

Use the Modified Comparison Chart to compare and contrast the reforms of Presidents Theodore Roosevelt and Woodrow Wilson during the Progressive Era.

ACTIVITY TYPE: QUICK WRITE

Preservation or Conservation?

In this Quick Write, you will review the preservationist philosophy of John Muir and the conservationist philosophy of Gifford Pinchot and decide how these philosophies best serve the nation's interests. You will express your understanding of the philosophies and your opinion of each by writing a paragraph for each of the two prompts.

ACTIVITY TYPE: SOCIAL STUDIES EXPLANATION

Progressivism in the White House

In this activity, you will use the template to assemble evidence from the sources you have explored. Then, you will write an answer to the Essential Question and defend your answer with supporting evidence.

Elaborate Activities

photo: Discovery Education

INVESTIGATION TYPE: TIMELINE MAP

Conservation and National Parks

How was the conservation movement related to the creation of national parks in the United States? In this activity, you will use the interactive Timeline Map tool to examine the main events in the development of the U.S. national park system and explain what motivated those events.

ACTIVITY TYPE: PITCH YOUR IDEA

Conservation Policy

The growth of the National Park System has paralleled the nation's population growth. As a result, the number of visits to national parks has risen from 1 million in 1920 to 286 million in 2012. In this activity, you will design a proposal that you feel will enable the National Park Service to flourish in the coming decades.

photo: Library of Congress

PROJECTS AND ASSESSMENTS *(continued)*

photo: Library of Congress

ACTIVITY TYPE: DOCUMENT-BASED INVESTIGATION

Progressives in the White House

The Progressive era was a time of reform and change in the United States. In this Document-Based Investigation, you will analyze source materials and investigate this question: Which president most embodied the spirit of the Progressive movement—Theodore Roosevelt or Woodrow Wilson?

photo: Library of Congress

ACTIVITY TYPE: EXPRESS YOUR OPINION

Vote for the Best Candidate

In this activity, you will analyze political cartoons, video segments, speeches, and texts that showcase either Theodore Roosevelt or Woodrow Wilson. You will decide which person would make the best candidate for a third term in office. Then, you will write an editorial and create a campaign poster in support of either Roosevelt or Wilson.

Evaluate Activities

BRIEF-CONSTRUCTED RESPONSE (BCR)

Progressivism in the White House

EXTENDED-CONSTRUCTED RESPONSE (ECR)

Progressivism in the White House

UNIT 5: DAWN OF THE AMERICAN CENTURY (1878 TO 1913)

Chapter 12: Conflict in the Gilded Age

12.5 Imperialism and the Spanish-American War

LESSON OVERVIEW

Lesson Objectives:

By the end of this lesson, you should be able to:

- Describe and explain factors that contributed to imperialism during the late 1800s and early 1900s.
- Assess the impact of the Spanish-American War on the United States and on U.S. foreign policy.
- Analyze the arguments of a variety of Americans who opposed imperialism.
- Evaluate U.S. policies in a variety of world regions during the era of imperialism.

Key Vocabulary

American Anti-Imperialist League, annex, colony, Dollar Diplomacy, imperialism, isolationism, isthmus, jingoism, Monroe Doctrine, neutrality, Open Door Policy, Panama Canal, Queen Liliuokalani, Roosevelt Corollary, Spanish-American War, yellow journalism

Lesson Essential Question:

What were the costs and benefits of the United States becoming a global power?

FLASHCARDS

1 ▶ **Imperialism Takes Off**

In the late 1800s and early 1900s, imperialism became a driving force in U.S. foreign policy.

- Since President George Washington's Neutrality Proclamation in 1793, the United States isolated itself from world affairs. By the late 1800s, the economy was growing, and the United States was looking to extend its influence abroad.

- One reason for extending the U.S. sphere of influence was to compete with the European powers, which had expanded their territory and resources by claiming more land.

- By the 1880s, European nations had colonies in Asia and were increasing their control over Africa.

- Christian missionaries wanted to spread their religious and moral ideas abroad. Some were motivated by the belief that non-Christians needed to be converted to Christianity.

- U.S. businesses wanted to continue expanding their markets and find new sources of raw materials for manufacturing.

- Frederick Jackson Turner's "frontier thesis" suggested that without the drive of expansionism, Americans could lose their individualism and passion.

- The extreme nationalists who believed fighting wars would bring glory to the United States were known as "American jingoists."

Why Does It Matter?

Imperialism was a major change from isolationism. Foreign affairs received much more attention in the late 1800s. The U.S. military and its budget greatly increased. Beginning in the 1900s, the United States would become involved militarily in conflicts around the world.

photo: IRC

European powers discussed how to colonize most of the continent of Africa at the Conference of Berlin.

FLASHCARDS (continued)

2 The United States Goes to War

The United States fought the Spanish-American War in 1898.

- In the 1890s, the United States asserted that the Americas were closed to colonization, and any European power looking to forcibly control a Latin American country was a direct threat to the United States.

- The United States used its interpretation of the Monroe Doctrine to justify support for Latin American independence movements.

- In the 1890s, the United States became involved in a conflict between Cuban rebels and their Spanish colonial rulers. This involvement resulted in the Spanish-American War.

- U.S. journalists wrote sensational, dramatized, and even false stories of the events in Cuba. This type of journalism is known as yellow journalism.

- The yellow journalism in U.S. newspapers turned public opinion in support of the Cubans.

- A letter written by Dupuy de Lôme, the Spanish ambassador to the United States, was intercepted and printed in an American newspaper. The letter contained insults about President William McKinley and intensified the calls for invading Cuba.

- The USS *Maine* exploded in Havana Harbor. Yellow journalism helped convince the American public that the Spanish had blown up the ship.

- The United States declared war on Spain in April 1898.

- The Spanish-American War ended in August 1898. The results included relatively few U.S. casualties, and the Cubans were freed from Spanish rule. In addition, the United States acquired the Philippines, Guam, and Puerto Rico.

- Theodore Roosevelt led the Rough Riders, a volunteer cavalry, in the war. The cavalry helped the United States secure victory.

Why Does It Matter?

U.S. acquisitions from the Spanish-American War changed the Philippines, Guam, Puerto Rico, and Cuba. All four territories were key in World War II. Guam remains an important U.S. military outpost in the Pacific Ocean. The Philippines became a lasting source of conflict. Immigrants from Puerto Rico and Cuba have contributed to American culture.

photo: Library of Congress

The destruction of the USS Maine *and the loss of life of those onboard led to the onset of the Spanish-American War.*

FLASHCARDS *(continued)*

3 ▶ Americans Against Imperialism

The acquisition of the Philippines made clear to the world the new imperialistic policies of the United States. Some Americans disagreed with these changes to foreign policy.

- **The Spanish-American War had been fought to free Cuba. However, after the war, U.S. President McKinley wanted to occupy the Philippines as an annexed territory.**
- **Some powerful Americans, such as Andrew Carnegie, joined the American Anti-Imperialist League.**
- **Some anti-imperialists thought that claiming and controlling lands such as the Philippines violated principles on which the United States was founded. These principles included limited government, individual rights, and self-determination.**
- **Some anti-imperialists opposed annexation of the Philippines due to racism, while others opposed it due to concern for labor interests.**

Why Does It Matter?

The controversy over the annexation of the Philippines highlighted the balance that the United States, as a new global power, had to strike in its policies. The desire to increase markets and protect U.S. interests abroad came with a price that the anti-imperialists voiced. The arguments that the anti-imperialists raised are still central to debates on immigration and foreign policy today.

photo: IRC

U.S. forces stationed in the Philippines captured locals who rose up against U.S. rule.

FLASHCARDS *(continued)*

4 Gaining Control, Maintaining Interests

During the Age of Imperialism, the United States acquired Hawaii, Puerto Rico, and Guam. It also became more involved in Latin American affairs and worked to support U.S. economic and political interests.

- American sugar and pineapple growers helped stage a coup d'état against the Hawaiian queen in 1893. This enabled the United States to acquire Hawaii as a territory in 1898.
- The acquisition of Hawaii gave the United States the strategic Pacific Ocean port of Pearl Harbor.
- When the United States attempted to annex the Philippines, Filipinos rebelled. A nearly four-year civil war ensued, followed by years of unrest and resistance to U.S. occupation.
- As governor of the Philippines, William Howard Taft (later president of the United States) helped bring the Philippine-American War to an end by offering more self-government and sponsoring economic development projects.
- In 1900, upon Cuban independence, the United States established guidelines for the Cuban constitution and outlined them in the Platt Amendment. The Platt Amendment limited Cuba's national sovereignty and maintained U.S. influence in the country.
- After the Spanish-American War, the United States annexed Puerto Rico. It became a U.S. territory.
- The United States maintained economic interests in China through its Open Door Policy, which was shaped by Secretary of State John Hay in 1899.
- The Boxer Rebellion was an uprising by Chinese peasants in 1900. The purpose of the rebellion was to rid China of foreign influence. The United States joined a multinational effort to suppress the Boxer Rebellion and was able to maintain its influence in the region.
- In 1904, President Roosevelt announced the Roosevelt Corollary, which described a more aggressive approach to foreign policy and led to increased U.S. involvement in Latin American affairs.
- After the United States supported a Panamanian revolution against Colombia, the new Republic of Panama sold the land for the Panama Canal to the United States. The Panama Canal drastically shortened the trip between the Pacific and Atlantic Oceans and was important for U.S. economic and military interests.
- In 1905, President Roosevelt helped negotiate a peace treaty to end the Russo-Japanese War in East Asia while preserving a balance of power.
- Roosevelt's successor, William Howard Taft, implemented "Dollar Diplomacy," which was intended to promote U.S. business interests abroad.

Why Does It Matter?

In the late 1800s and early 1900s, the imperial actions of the United States led to an expanded international role and greater global influence for the nation.

photo: Library of Congress
The United States contributed more than 2,000 troops to the relief effort in Beijing during the Boxer Rebellion.

Name _____ Date _____

GRAPHIC ORGANIZER: Vocabulary Chart

Use this Vocabulary Chart to define the term *imperialism* in the context of U.S. actions during the late 1800s and early 1900s. For supporting resources, go to Dawn of the American Century (1878 to 1913) > Conflict in the Gilded Age > Imperialism and the Spanish-American War > Explore > Roots of Imperialism.

DEFINITION:	EXAMPLES (drawn or written):
Personal:	
Dictionary:	

TERM:
Imperialism

SENTENCES:		RELATED:	WORD PARTS:
Teacher/Book:			
Personal:			

Outside of School (Who would use the word? How would he or she use it?)

Name _____ **Date** _____

GRAPHIC ORGANIZER: Main Idea Web

Use this Main Idea Web to organize details related to five motives for U.S. imperialism during this period. For supporting resources, go to Dawn of the Dawn of the American Century (1878 to 1913) > Conflict in the Gilded Age > Imperialism and the Spanish-American War > Explore > The Age of Imperialism Begins.

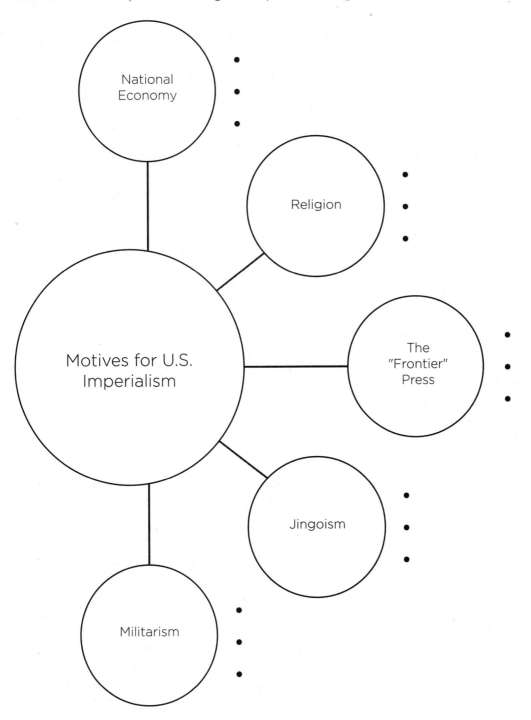

National Economy

Religion

Motives for U.S. Imperialism

The "Frontier" Press

Jingoism

Militarism

Name _____ Date _____

GRAPHIC ORGANIZER: Timeline

Use this Timeline to record the major events of the Spanish-American War, including when they happened and what happened. For supporting resources, go to Dawn of the American Century (1878 to 1913) > Conflict in the Gilded Age > Imperialism and the Spanish-American War > Going to War with Spain.

April 1898   **August 1898**

◆━━◆

Name _____ Date _____

GRAPHIC ORGANIZER: Comparison Chart

Use this Comparison Chart to organize details related to the causes of U.S. actions. Write brief descriptions of the actions and the effects of each. For supporting resources, go to Dawn of the American Century (1878 to 1913) > Conflict in the Gilded Age > Imperialism and the Spanish-American War > War in the Philippines.

Criteria	Causes	Description of Action	Effects
The Philippine-American War			
Open Door Policy			
Annexation of Hawaii			
The Platt Amendment			
The Roosevelt Corollary			
The Panama Canal			

Name _____ Date _____

EXPLORE: FOCUS QUESTIONS

Using what you learned from the Core Interactive Text, answer each page's focus question:

Roots of Imperialism
What is imperialism?

_____
_____
_____
_____

The Age of Imperialism Begins
Why did the United States look to extend its influence abroad during the Age of Imperialism?

_____
_____
_____
_____

Going to War with Spain
What led to the Spanish-American War?

_____
_____
_____
_____

Spoils of War
What was the outcome of the Spanish-American War?

_____
_____
_____
_____

Taking the Philippines
Why did anti-imperialists question annexation of the Philippines?

_____
_____
_____
_____

War in the Philippines
How did Filipinos respond to the annexation of the Philippines?

_____
_____
_____
_____

Name _____ Date _____

EXPLORE: FOCUS QUESTIONS *(continued)*

Keeping the Door Open
How did the United States maintain its economic interests in China?

_____

_____

_____

Aloha, Hawaii
How did the United States gain the Hawaiian Islands?

_____

_____

_____

Cuba After Platt
What was the significance of the Platt Amendment?

_____

_____

_____

Policing the Western Hemisphere
How did the Roosevelt Corollary change U.S. foreign policy?

_____

_____

_____

Building the Panama Canal
Why did the United States take sides in the Panamanian revolt against Colombia?

_____

_____

_____

Preserving and Promoting U.S. Interests
How did Roosevelt and Taft preserve and promote U.S. interests abroad?

_____

_____

_____

PROJECTS AND ASSESSMENTS

Explain Activities

ACTIVITY TYPE: DIAGRAM

Costs and Benefits of Imperialism

Think about how these terms are important to understanding the concept's Essential Question: What were the costs and benefits of the United States becoming a global power? Next, consider how these terms relate to one another. Then, design your diagram.

ACTIVITY TYPE: MOVIE TRAILER

The Rising Power

The Rising Power will soon be in theaters nationwide! You must develop a movie trailer that will make people want to see this documentary film. Use the frames to sketch out the trailer.

ACTIVITY TYPE: QUICK WRITE

Anti-Imperialists and Their Ideas

In this Quick Write, you will take the perspective of an imperialist or anti-imperialist from the early 1900s. From this perspective, you will write a short profile and support your beliefs.

ACTIVITY TYPE: SOCIAL STUDIES EXPLANATION

Imperialism and the Spanish-American War

In this activity, you will use the template to assemble evidence from the sources you have explored. Then, you will write an answer to the Essential Question and defend your answer with supporting evidence.

Elaborate Activities

photo: Library of Congress

INVESTIGATION TYPE: TIMELINE MAP

The United States Becomes an Imperial Power

Between the late 1800s and the beginning of World War I, the United States began to focus more on imperialism. In this investigation, you will use the interactive Timeline Map tool to analyze the interactions of the United States with other nations in the late 1800s.

PROJECTS AND ASSESSMENTS *(continued)*

photo: IRC

ACTIVITY TYPE: DOCUMENT-BASED INVESTIGATION

Benefits and Costs of Imperialism

In this Document-Based Investigation, you will analyze source materials and investigate this question: Did the costs of U.S. imperialism and involvement in foreign affairs outweigh the benefits?

photo: Library of Congress

ACTIVITY TYPE: CLASSROOM DEBATE

Debating Imperialism

Imagine you are a U.S. citizen at the time involved in the public debate over American imperialism. Write an argumentative speech that supports or opposes U.S. actions. You will then use your knowledge to participate in a debate with classmates representing different opinions.

photo: Library of Congress

ACTIVITY TYPE: YOU AS ARTIST

Imperialism and Cuba

In this activity, you will analyze a political cartoon from the Era of Imperialism to understand its message. Then, you will use the common elements of political cartoons to draw your own cartoon that will make a point about events related to another region affected by U.S. imperialism or a different aspect of imperialism.

Evaluate Activities

BRIEF-CONSTRUCTED RESPONSE (BCR)

Imperialism and the Spanish-American War

EXTENDED-CONSTRUCTED RESPONSE (ECR)

Imperialism and the Spanish-American War